Government Alive!®
Power, Politics, and You

NATIONAL CONSTITUTION CENTER

Acknowledgements

Director of Product Development: Liz Russell

Managing Editor: Laura Alavosus

Project Editor: Mali Apple

Copyeditor: Tara Joffe

Editorial Associates: Anna Embree, Sarah Sudano

Production Manager: Lynn Sanchez

Art Director: John F. Kelly

Senior Graphic Designer: Christy Uyeno

Graphic Designers: Paul Rebello, Sarah Wildfang, Don Taka

Photo Editor: Margee Robinson

Art Editor: Eric Houts

Audio Director: Katy Haun

TCi™

Teachers' Curriculum Institute
P.O. Box 50996
Palo Alto, CA 94303

ISBN 978-1-934534-08-3

1 2 3 4 5 6 7 8 9 10 -MLI- 12 11 10 09 08

Program Director

Bert Bower

Program Author

Diane Hart

Senior Writer

Brent Goff

Contributing Writers

Melissa Biegert

David Fasulo

Linda Scher

Curriculum Development Manager

Kelly Shafsky

Curriculum Developers

Nicole Boylan

Julie Cremin

Erin Fry

Amy George

Steve Seely

Program Consultant

Sharon Pope
Houston, Texas

Teacher and Content Consultants

Karl Grubaugh
Granite Bay High School
Granite Bay, California

Cathy Hix
Swanson Middle School
Arlington, Virginia

Deidre Jackson
Taylor High School
Houston, Texas

Eli Lesser
National Constitution Center
Constitution High School
Philadelphia, Pennsylvania

Greg Nakata
Glendora High School
Glendora, California

Ron Pike
Lincoln High School
San Jose, California

Ken Shears
Ponderosa High School
Shingle Springs, California

Steve Watts
Davidson High School
Hilliard, Ohio

Nathan Welbourne
Taylor High School
Houston, Texas

Scholars

Dr. Paul Barressi
Southern New Hampshire University

Dr. Dave Campbell
Notre Dame University, Indiana

Dr. Jim Gimpel
University of Maryland

Dr. George Gordon
Illinois State University
Illinois Wesleyan University

Dr. Darla Mallein
Emporia State University, Kansas

Dr. Patrice McMahon
University of Nebraska

Dr. Richard Niemi
University of Rochester, New York

Dr. Tari Renner
Illinois Wesleyan University

Dr. Michael Smith
Emporia State University, Kansas

Dr. Beth Theiss-Morse
University of Nebraska

Music Consultant

Melanie Pinkert
Music Faculty
Montgomery College, Maryland

Cartographer

Mapping Specialists
Madison, Wisconsin

Internet Consultant

Clinton Couse
Cedar Valley Community School
Edmonds School District
Edmonds, Washington

Researcher

Carla Valetich
Pittsboro, North Carolina

Contents

Contents

Contents

Unit 7   The United States and the World

The Nature of Power, Politics, and Government

Why should you care about power, politics, and government?

Speaking of Politics

As you complete the Reading Notes, use these terms in your answers:

authority	nation-state
government	sovereignty
power	politics
legitimacy	institution
public good	

PREVIEW

To evaluate power in your own life, complete a "personal power assessment."

1. In your notebook, make a list of all the individuals, institutions, and circumstances that have power over you. For each item, write a brief description of how it has power over you.

2. Now make a list of all of the individuals, institutions, and circumstances in which you have power. For each one, briefly describe how you have power.

3. Create a simple illustration that represents you and how you feel about power in your life.

4. Below your illustration, summarize in two or three sentences how you feel about power in your life.

READING NOTES

Sections 1.2 to 1.4

Create an illustrated dictionary entry for each term listed below. For each dictionary entry,

- create a symbol or an icon to represent the term.
- write a definition of the term in your own words.
- write a sentence using the term.

Section 1.2

power
authority
legitimacy
mandate of heaven
divine right of kings
social-contract theory

Section 1.3

government
public good
coercion
revenue
polity
nation-state
sovereignty

Section 1.4

politics
institution

Section 1.5

Create the table below in your notebook. In the first column of your table, enter the names of the five political games discussed in Section 1.5. Describe each game in the second column, mentioning at least two important details. Finally, list and briefly explain one historical example of each game.

Five Political Games		
Game	Description	Example

Read the quotations on Notebook Handout 1. Assign each quotation a "truth ranking" from 1 to 5 (1 = never true, 5 = always true). Then write a brief response to each of the following questions in your notebook. Support your answers with evidence from your own experience and your knowledge of historic and current events.

1. Which of the quotations do you think is the most true about power?

2. Which of the quotations do you think is the most true about politics?

3. Which of the quotations do you think is the most true about your own life?

Quotations About Power

Our scientific power has outrun our spiritual power.
We have guided missiles and misguided men.
—Martin Luther King Jr., *Strength to Love,* 1963

Power tends to corrupt, and absolute power corrupts absolutely.
—Lord Acton, *Letter to Bishop Mandell Creighton,* 1887

It is not power that corrupts but fear. Fear of losing power
corrupts those who wield it and fear of the scourge of power
corrupts those who are subject to it.
—Aung San Suu Kyi, "Freedom from fear" speech, 1990

Political power grows out of the barrel of a gun.
—Mao Zedong

Above all, we must realize that no arsenal, or no weapon
in the arsenals of the world, is so formidable as the will and
moral courage of free men and women.
—Ronald Reagan, First Inaugural Address, 1981

When I despair, I remember that all through history the ways of truth
and love have always won. There have been tyrants, and murderers, and
for a time they can seem invincible, but in the end they always fall.
—Mohandas Gandhi

When the power of love overcomes the love of power,
the world will know peace.
—Jimi Hendrix

This country has been strip-mined by rich and powerful interests.
If you don't like what they're doing, don't just sit there.
—Ralph Nader, 1992

The men who create power make an indispensable contribution
to the Nation's greatness, but the men who question power make
a contribution just as indispensable.
—John F. Kennedy, speech at Amherst College, 1963

Hint Cards

Hint Card 1

You are in a position to continue making the rules for the rest of the game. Make a rule that guarantees that you will always have the most points after trading. Consider one of these suggestions:

- Increase the point value for the color of chip you have the most of.
- Decrease the point value for the color of chip you have the least of.
- Limit the number of chips that students can trade in one transaction.
- Require a minimum or maximum number of people that students must trade with.

You cannot make a rule that will end all trading.

Hint Card 2

You may or may not have a high point value, but you can try to build an alliance with the student who has the most points. If you help that student, he or she might help you. Consider these suggestions:

- Give your chips to that student in return for your advice on making a rule.
- Recommend a new rule for the next round of trading. For example, students cannot use the word *chips,* or students have to shake hands before trading.
- Report any suspicious trading.

You might encourage other students to join your alliance.

Hint Card 3

Most likely, the student with the most points will continue to make rules that benefit him or her. It is unlikely that you will make enough trades to get in that position. *Instead, join together with other students to pool your chips.* Work quickly and quietly to avoid the notice of the student making the rules. You don't want to reveal your plan to overthrow that student until you have enough points.

Hint Card 4

Most likely, the student with the most points will continue to make rules that benefit him or her. It is unlikely that you will make enough trades to get in that position. *Instead, join together with other students to pool your chips.* Work quickly and quietly to avoid the notice of the student making the rules. You don't want to reveal your plan to overthrow that student until you have enough points.

Hint Card 5

Most likely, the student with the most points will continue to make rules that benefit him or her. It is unlikely that you will make enough trades to get in that position. *Instead, join together with other students to pool your chips.* Work quickly and quietly to avoid the notice of the student making the rules. You don't want to reveal your plan to overthrow that student until you have enough points.

Hint Card 6

Most likely, the student with the most points will continue to make rules that benefit him or her. It is unlikely that you will make enough trades to get in that position. *Instead, join together with other students to pool your chips.* Work quickly and quietly to avoid the notice of the student making the rules. You don't want to reveal your plan to overthrow that student until you have enough points.

The *Chip* Game

Follow these rules to play *Chip*.

Rules

1. For each round of the game, you will have 2 minutes to trade your chips. All trades—including those in progress—must stop when the time is up.

2. After trading, the student with the most points will be asked to make a rule for the next round of trading. That rule will apply only to the next round.

Chip Point Values

Pink	100 points
Yellow	50 points
Blue	25 points
White	10 points

Mastering the Content

1. An independent country in which people share a common culture is called
   A. a polity.
   B. a nation-state.
   C. an aristocracy.
   D. an ethnic group.

2. Which term is defined in the box below?

   > *the right to exercise supreme power and authority over a region, a group, or oneself*

   A. tyranny
   B. legitimacy
   C. sovereignty
   D. territoriality

3. Which of these is the best example of a public good?
   A. a gas station
   B. a town library
   C. a movie theater
   D. a clothing store

4. Which of these is an essential feature of political activity?
   A. It is difficult.
   B. It is idealistic.
   C. It is individualistic.
   D. It is purposeful.

5. When people call someone Machiavellian, they usually mean that person is
   A. cunning and amoral.
   B. popular and famous.
   C. quiet and thoughtful.
   D. wealthy and powerful.

6. Which of these individuals is most likely to exercise power without authority?
   A. a traffic officer
   B. an armed robber
   C. a business owner
   D. a school principal

7. On December 1, 1955, Rosa Parks went to jail rather than give up her bus seat to a white passenger. Her action was an example of which of the following?
   A. horse trading
   B. power struggle
   C. collective action
   D. civil disobedience

8. Which of the following are considered the basic building blocks of government?
   A. revenue collection and coercion
   B. political conflict and compromise
   C. a legitimate ruler and happy subjects
   D. a stable population and fixed territory

9. A ruler's legitimacy depends mainly on which of these factors?
   A. the ruler's personal wealth
   B. the ruler's political ambition
   C. people's fear of the ruler's power
   D. people's acceptance of the ruler's authority

10. Which of these is most likely to involve horse trading?
    A. a labor strike
    B. a local election
    C. a business deal
    D. a protest march

Exploring the Essential Question

Why should you care about power, politics, and government?

Understanding the various sources of power can help you analyze uses of power that affect you. Perhaps even more important, it can help you use power constructively to influence your community and your world. Use this diagram to answer the questions that follow.

Five Sources of Power

Formal authority
Power comes from the power holder's position and duties within an organization.

Expertise
Power derives from the power holder's specific skills or expertise.

Coercion
Power springs from the power holder's ability to punish or penalize others.

Power

Persuasion
Power flows from the power holder's ability to persuade or influence others.

Rewards
Power comes from the power holder's ability to give something of value, such as money, responsibility, or praise.

1. Which of the sources of power shown on the diagram does a volunteer organization use to raise money for a cause?
2. Which source(s) of power does a state or the federal government use to collect taxes?
3. Explain how a teacher might use each of the five sources of power in the classroom.
4. Suppose you wanted your community to build a bicycle path across a city park to make it easier for students to bike to school. Describe three ways you could apply your knowledge of the sources of power to try to make the bike path a reality.

Comparing Forms of Government

How should political and economic power be distributed in a society?

Speaking of Politics

As you complete the Reading Notes, use these terms in your answers:

democracy   traditional economy

monarchy   republic

dictatorship   parliament

market economy   command economy

PREVIEW

Answer the following questions in your notebook.

In your opinion, which one of the following people or groups should have the power to make the rules at your school, and why?

• principal

• teachers

• student council

• student body

• other (specify)

Are there any people or groups above that should *not* make the rules at your school? If so, why not?

READING NOTES

Section 2.2

Create a vertical timeline down the left side of a page in your notebook. Label the top of the timeline 3000 B.C.E. and the bottom 2000 C.E. As you read the section, record the date and name of each event listed below. Some of the dates will be approximate. Also write a one-sentence explanation of the main feature of the government associated with each event. The timeline has been started for you.

3000 B.C.E. *First city-states arise in Sumer: The government settles disputes and coordinates the harvesting and trading of crops.*

2330s B.C.E. *Sargon of Akkad . . .*

Timeline Events

First city-states arise in Sumer

Sargon of Akkad formed empire

Roman Republic formed

Athens formed direct democracy

Roman Empire formed

Feudalism began in Europe

Rise of absolute monarchies

Glorious Revolution in England

American Revolution

French Revolution

Rise of totalitarian dictatorships

Sections 2.3 to 2.5

Create a table like the one below. As you read each section, record information in your table for each term listed below.

Section 2.3: monarchy, dictatorship, theocracy, single-party state, direct democracy, parliamentary democracy, presidential democracy

Section 2.4: unitary system, federal system, confederal system

Section 2.5: traditional economy, market economy, command economy

Term	Definition	Pros	Cons
Monarchy			
Dictatorship			
Theocracy			

PROCESSING

Imagine that you are advising a country that is creating a new constitution. Below are the priorities that the country might have when it comes to a government and an economic system. For each possible priority, identify the combination (*form of government + system of government + economic system*) you would recommend. Then write one or two sentences explaining why you think this combination works best for the particular priority.

	Form of government	System of government	Economic system
Efficiency =	_____ +	_____ +	_____
Freedom =	_____ +	_____ +	_____
Prosperity =	_____ +	_____ +	_____
Equality =	_____ +	_____ +	_____
Security =	_____ +	_____ +	_____

Background Information on Nucountry

Nucountry is a midsize country of approximately 50,000 square miles, with a population of just over 21 million people. It is slightly larger in size and population than the state of New York.

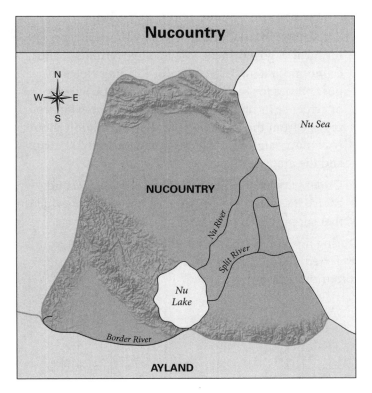

Nucountry

N
W · E
S

Nu Sea

NUCOUNTRY

Nu River

Split River

Nu Lake

Border River

AYLAND

The country is divided into three distinct geographic regions. The northern region of the country is arid and sparsely inhabited. The southeastern region is fertile, with two major rivers that flow to the ocean. The southwestern region is fertile and rich in valuable natural resources.

Nucountry has three distinct ethnic groups. The Nupeeple are the largest ethnic group, making up nearly 85% of the population. They live mostly in the southeast and tend to farm, work in the region's many cities, or own businesses.

The Apeeple are a small ethnic group, making up about 10% of the population, who speak their own language and have cultural customs different from those of the Nupeeple. They live predominantly in the southwest and control the valuable natural resources in that area.

The smallest ethnic group, the Upeeple, make up almost 5% of the population and speak the same language as the Nupeeple. However, they live a more traditional, and sometimes nomadic, lifestyle in the northern part of Nucountry. With few exceptions, they do not share in the wealth that has been enjoyed in the southern regions of the country.

Slightly more than 100 years ago, Nucountry was in a state of near chaos after the government failed. It was quickly occupied by its neighbor, Ayland, which has governed Nucountry ever since. Ayland has assisted in making Nucountry far more stable. At the end of this year, Nucountry will achieve its independence and a fresh start. A constitutional convention has been called to establish the basis of Nucountry's new government and economic systems.

Interest Groups at the Constitutional Convention

*Read the information below to become familiar with the interest group you represent.
Pay attention to what your interest group thinks is best for Nucountry and what interests
and ideas you will advocate for at the constitutional convention.*

Interest Group: Military Leaders

Your group is made up of the leaders of Nucountry's military forces and is ethnically mixed. You believe that security is the number one issue facing the country. Nucountry is about to gain its independence. Neighboring countries on all sides are more powerful and could take control if they sense weakness. The unemployment rate is high, and crime has always been a problem for Nucountry. Although crime had decreased under occupation by Ayland, you feel that it may surge again if the military is not given the power to enforce law and order appropriately. The three ethnic groups in the country have a history of conflict. You are the only group that can provide the kind of security Nucountry needs. You want to have a big say in running the government and securing the country.

List the characteristics of your group:

List your group's main concerns or issues that you feel affect Nucountry:

Constitutional Convention Preferences

Fill in the first two columns of the matrix below.

- Under "Preferred Option," record your preference for form of government, system of government, and economic system. (Consult your Reading Notes for possibilities for each of these.) Then list two pieces of evidence in support of each choice. That evidence may be from the chapter, from the information about Nucountry and your interest group, or from the maps and the graph.

- Under "Logical Compromise," record your second choice for each option. Again, list two pieces of evidence that support each choice.

During the convention, you will receive 3 points if your preferred option is chosen and 1 point if your logical compromise option is chosen.

	Preferred Option	Logical Compromise	Points
Form of Government (Round 1)			
System of Government (Round 2)			
Economic System (Round 3)			

Read the information below to become familiar with the interest group you represent.
Pay attention to what your interest group thinks is best for Nucountry and what interests
and ideas you will advocate for at the constitutional convention.

Interest Group: Working Professionals

Your group is made up of working professionals, such as doctors, lawyers, teachers, factory managers, large farm owners, small business owners, and bankers. Your group is Nucountry's middle class and is mostly made up of Nupeeple. Your primary concern is with maintaining stability and creating jobs. As Nucountry gains its independence, you want to make sure that new companies will want to open businesses in your country. However, you also want to make sure that companies are regulated to protect workers and consumers. You realize that the only way to ensure this is to make Nucountry strong, secure, and stable. You are also concerned about social problems, such as the high unemployment rate. You do not want to see power in the hands of only a few people who might not represent your interests. You personally want to have a say in the government, its leaders, and the laws that are made.

List the characteristics of your group:

List your group's main concerns or issues that you feel affect Nucountry:

Constitutional Convention Preferences

Fill in the first two columns of the matrix below.

- Under "Preferred Option," record your preference for form of government, system of government, and economic system. (Consult your Reading Notes for possibilities for each of these.) Then list two pieces of evidence in support of each choice. That evidence may be from the chapter, from the information about Nucountry and your interest group, or from the maps and the graph.

- Under "Logical Compromise," record your second choice for each option. Again, list two pieces of evidence that support each choice.

During the convention, you will receive 3 points if your preferred option is chosen and 1 point if your logical compromise option is chosen.

	Preferred Option	Logical Compromise	Points
Form of Government (Round 1)			
System of Government (Round 2)			
Economic System (Round 3)			

Read the information below to become familiar with the interest group you represent. Pay attention to what your interest group thinks is best for Nucountry and what interests and ideas you will advocate for at the constitutional convention.

Interest Group: Wealthy Business Owners

Your group, which is made up of the few elite who have owned profitable businesses and factories in Nucountry, is mostly Nupeeple. During the period of instability that preceded the occupation of your country by Ayland, most of you moved your businesses to other countries. Many of you have now returned your businesses to Nucountry and are working to expand economic opportunities. You want to make sure the new government and economic systems that are selected for Nucountry do not inhibit your ability to do business as you see fit. You see yourselves as the main engine of economic growth for Nucountry. Any regulations —taxes, minimum wage laws, required health care coverage, or mandatory vacation and overtime for workers— will cut into your ability to stimulate the economy and create jobs. They will also decrease your profits. You are also concerned about security and stability in Nucountry. You want to see power in the hands of those who can protect your business without placing regulations on it.

Constitutional Convention Preferences

Fill in the first two columns of the matrix below.

- Under "Preferred Option," record your preference for form of government, system of government, and economic system. (Consult your Reading Notes for possibilities for each of these.) Then list two pieces of evidence in support of each choice. That evidence may be from the chapter, from the information about Nucountry and your interest group, or from the maps and the graph.

- Under "Logical Compromise," record your second choice for each option. Again, list two pieces of evidence that support each choice.

During the convention, you will receive 3 points if your preferred option is chosen and 1 point if your logical compromise option is chosen.

List the characteristics of your group:

List your group's main concerns or issues that you feel affect Nucountry:

	Preferred Option	Logical Compromise	Points
Form of Government (Round 1)			
System of Government (Round 2)			
Economic System (Round 3)			

Read the information below to become familiar with the interest group you represent. Pay attention to what your interest group thinks is best for Nucountry and what interests and ideas you will advocate for at the constitutional convention.

Interest Group: Religious Leaders

Your group is made up of the leaders of Nucountry's primary religion, who are mostly Nupeeple. You are particularly concerned with social justice and feel that society—and the government in particular—needs to do more to help Nucountry's working poor. Most of these people have to move around the country looking for work, and a consistently high unemployment rate has made their situation bleak. Violence, starvation, and unrest in your country can all be at least somewhat attributed to the difficulty in finding work. You want to see the government distribute wealth more evenly so that all people can have a decent standard of living. The only way you feel confident that this will take place is if the government controls the economy. You also want to make sure the government represents and passes laws that are in accordance with your moral beliefs.

List the characteristics of your group:

List your group's main concerns or issues that you feel affect Nucountry:

Constitutional Convention Preferences

Fill in the first two columns of the matrix below.

- Under "Preferred Option," record your preference for form of government, system of government, and economic system. (Consult your Reading Notes for possibilities for each of these.) Then list two pieces of evidence in support of each choice. That evidence may be from the chapter, from the information about Nucountry and your interest group, or from the maps and the graph.

- Under "Logical Compromise," record your second choice for each option. Again, list two pieces of evidence that support each choice.

During the convention, you will receive 3 points if your preferred option is chosen and 1 point if your logical compromise option is chosen.

	Preferred Option	Logical Compromise	Points
Form of Government (Round 1)			
System of Government (Round 2)			
Economic System (Round 3)			

Read the information below to become familiar with the interest group you represent. Pay attention to what your interest group thinks is best for Nucountry and what interests and ideas you will advocate for at the constitutional convention.

Interest Group: Working Poor

Your group is made up of a large percentage of Nucountry's population and is ethnically mixed. Many people in your group have very low-paying jobs and hardly make ends meet. You live mostly in the southeast. Because of Nucountry's high unemployment, some of your people are forced to move from place to place to find work on farms, in mines, in factories, or in other unregulated industries, such as forestry or natural gas. No government in Nucountry's history has ever represented your interests. You fear that the wealthier people in Nucountry will control the government and do little to further your interests. You want a government that represents the many over the few and that allows you to participate. To change your conditions, it is crucial that an economic system that protects you is put into place. Ideally, you want wealth redistributed so that you can improve your standard of living. At the very least, you want regulations that will protect workers.

List the characteristics of your group:

List your group's main concerns or issues that you feel affect Nucountry:

Constitutional Convention Preferences

Fill in the first two columns of the matrix below.

- Under "Preferred Option," record your preference for form of government, system of government, and economic system. (Consult your Reading Notes for possibilities for each of these.) Then list two pieces of evidence in support of each choice. That evidence may be from the chapter, from the information about Nucountry and your interest group, or from the maps and the graph.

- Under "Logical Compromise," record your second choice for each option. Again, list two pieces of evidence that support each choice.

During the convention, you will receive 3 points if your preferred option is chosen and 1 point if your logical compromise option is chosen.

	Preferred Option	Logical Compromise	Points
Form of Government (Round 1)			
System of Government (Round 2)			
Economic System (Round 3)			

Read the information below to become familiar with the interest group you represent. Pay attention to what your interest group thinks is best for Nucountry and what interests and ideas you will advocate for at the constitutional convention.

Interest Group: Former Monarch's Family

Your group is made up of a large extended family that descends from Nucountry's last monarch, who ruled more than 100 years ago. Your family is ethnically Nupeeple. Most of your family members have lived in exile since the monarchy was overthrown in a civil war that sent the country into chaos and led to the occupation by Ayland. Recently, members of your family have begun moving back to Nucountry. Some of the population still views your family as the rightful heirs of the government and would like to see the monarchy reestablished. Your primary concern is seeing that this happens, or at least seeing that your family is able to play a large part in governing the country. You also feel that if your family controlled the government, you would be able to solve many of the country's economic and social problems, such as the high unemployment rate, by taking control of the economy and enacting regulations on businesses to create jobs.

List the characteristics of your group:

List your group's main concerns or issues that you feel affect Nucountry:

Constitutional Convention Preferences

Fill in the first two columns of the matrix below.

- Under "Preferred Option," record your preference for form of government, system of government, and economic system. (Consult your Reading Notes for possibilities for each of these.) Then list two pieces of evidence in support of each choice. That evidence may be from the chapter, from the information about Nucountry and your interest group, or from the maps and the graph.

- Under "Logical Compromise," record your second choice for each option. Again, list two pieces of evidence that support each choice.

During the convention, you will receive 3 points if your preferred option is chosen and 1 point if your logical compromise option is chosen.

	Preferred Option	Logical Compromise	Points
Form of Government (Round 1)			
System of Government (Round 2)			
Economic System (Round 3)			

Read the information below to become familiar with the interest group you represent. Pay attention to what your interest group thinks is best for Nucountry and what interests and ideas you will advocate for at the constitutional convention.

Interest Group: Apeeple Ethnic Group

Your group is an ethnic minority spread over a large area in the southwestern part of Nucountry. You speak a different language from the Nupeeple and Upeeple, and you have different cultural customs. The area where you live is rich in your country's most valuable natural resource: diamonds. The Apeeple own and control the diamond mines in the region and have recently built a hydroelectric plant to bring power to all of your people. You also sell this power to neighboring countries. Because of these resources, and the jobs and income they create, Apeeple tend to have higher-than-average incomes and a high standard of living. Your primary concern is that Nucountry's government does not interfere with your ability to control the natural resources in your area. Under no circumstances do you want resources and wealth redistributed. Also, because you speak a different language and have different cultural customs from the Nupeeple and Upeeple, it is crucial that you are able to participate in government to make sure the laws passed do not infringe on your rights.

List the characteristics of your group:

List your group's main concerns or issues that you feel affect Nucountry:

Constitutional Convention Preferences

Fill in the first two columns of the matrix below.

- Under "Preferred Option," record your preference for form of government, system of government, and economic system. (Consult your Reading Notes for possibilities for each of these.) Then list two pieces of evidence in support of each choice. That evidence may be from the chapter, from the information about Nucountry and your interest group, or from the maps and the graph.

- Under "Logical Compromise," record your second choice for each option. Again, list two pieces of evidence that support each choice.

During the convention, you will receive 3 points if your preferred option is chosen and 1 point if your logical compromise option is chosen.

	Preferred Option	Logical Compromise	Points
Form of Government (Round 1)			
System of Government (Round 2)			
Economic System (Round 3)			

*Read the information below to become familiar with the interest group you represent.
Pay attention to what your interest group thinks is best for Nucountry and what interests
and ideas you will advocate for at the constitutional convention.*

Interest Group: Upeeple Ethnic Group

Your group is a very small ethnic minority spread over
a large area of land in the northern part of Nucountry.
You are mostly nomadic herders and farmers and do not
control much, if any, of the nation's wealth. Because you
are geographically close to Ayland's border and were the
group most affected by the invasion decades ago, you are
concerned about the safety and security of Nucountry after
occupation by Ayland ends. You want to make sure the
country's borders are protected and that Ayland cannot
invade again. You are also concerned about the valuable
deposits of natural gas that lie within your area. These
deposits are entirely controlled by wealthy business owners
who all live in the southeastern region of your country and
are from the Nupeeple ethnic group. For this reason, you
would like to see the new government distribute resources
and wealth more equally to all people living in Nucountry.

List the characteristics of your group:

**List your group's main concerns or issues that you feel
affect Nucountry:**

Constitutional Convention Preferences

Fill in the first two columns of the matrix below.

- Under "Preferred Option," record your preference
  for form of government, system of government, and
  economic system. (Consult your Reading Notes for
  possibilities for each of these.) Then list two pieces
  of evidence in support of each choice. That evidence
  may be from the chapter, from the information about
  Nucountry and your interest group, or from the maps
  and the graph.
- Under "Logical Compromise," record your second
  choice for each option. Again, list two pieces of evidence
  that support each choice.

During the convention, you will receive 3 points if your
preferred option is chosen and 1 point if your logical
compromise option is chosen.

	Preferred Option	Logical Compromise	Points
Form of Government (Round 1)			
System of Government (Round 2)			
Economic System (Round 3)			

Comparing Forms of Government

Demographic Information on Nucountry

Economic Activity in Nucountry

Where are the country's natural resources located? Most profitable economic activities?

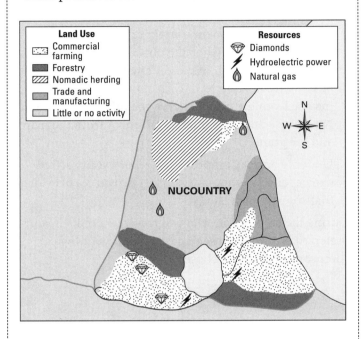

Ethnic Distribution in Nucountry

Which resources and economic activities does each ethnic group control?

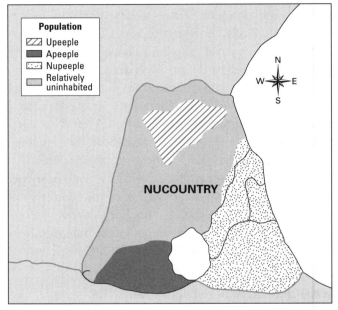

Population Density in Nucountry

Where do most people in Nucountry live? What comparisons can you draw between this map and the other two?

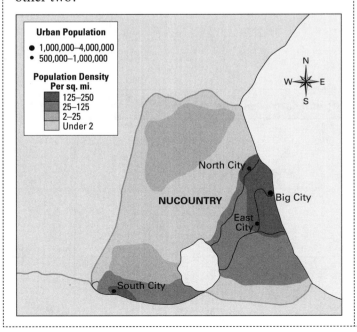

Income Distribution in Nucountry

Which groups have the highest and lowest income? Which represent the largest and smallest percent of the population?

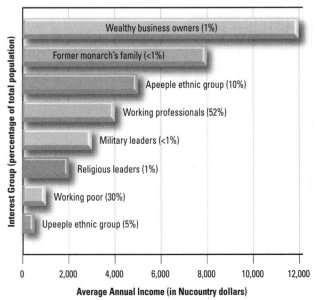

Mastering the Content

1. Which of the following is the oldest form of government still in use today?
    A. republic
    B. monarchy
    C. democracy
    D. dictatorship

2. A New England town meeting is an example of
    A. confederal democracy.
    B. direct democracy.
    C. parliamentary democracy.
    D. representative democracy.

3. Nazism is a form of fascism built on the idea of
    A. free enterprise.
    B. market socialism.
    C. racial superiority.
    D. national sovereignty.

4. Socialism began as an attempt to correct which disadvantage of capitalism?
    A. lack of motivation to work
    B. failure to reward new ideas
    C. uneven distribution of wealth
    D. inflexibility in the face of change

5. Which of these is a common feature of market economies?
    A. low living standards for most people
    B. economic stability with no recessions
    C. public ownership of farms and factories
    D. production of high-quality goods and services

6. In a command economy, who decides how much to produce?
    A. government planners
    B. individual consumers
    C. industrial labor unions
    D. corporate shareholders

7. Which of these factors most distinguishes dictators from monarchs?
    A. how they acquire and retain power
    B. how they make economic decisions
    C. how they choose their close advisers
    D. how they regard the rights of citizens

8. In a parliamentary democracy, who chooses the prime minister?
    A. the country's single party
    B. an assembly of eligible voters
    C. electors appointed by the monarch
    D. the party with a legislative majority

9. Which kind of economy is most common in the world today?
    A. command
    B. market
    C. mixed
    D. traditional

10. Which kind of country is most likely to have a federal system of government?
    A. large, with a diverse population
    B. urban, with an industrial economy
    C. poor, with an unskilled population
    D. small, with an abundance of resources

Exploring the Essential Question

How should political and economic power be distributed in a society?

Different histories and cultures have led nations to establish forms of government that distribute power in different ways. Look for patterns in this map. Then answer the questions that follow.

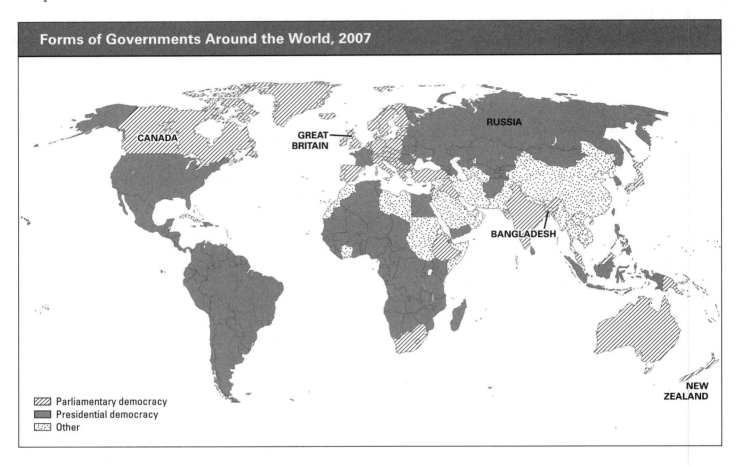

Forms of Governments Around the World, 2007

Legend:
- Parliamentary democracy
- Presidential democracy
- Other

1. Based on this map, which form of government is most common in Latin America?
2. Which form of government has developed in most countries of Central and Western Europe?
3. Bangladesh, Canada, and New Zealand were all formerly colonies of Great Britain. What can you infer about how this aspect of their history influenced the form of government they chose on gaining their independence?
4. In 1991, the Soviet Union, long a repressive single-party state, collapsed. Fifteen new nation-states, including Russia, emerged out of the old Soviet empire. Eleven of the 15 chose presidential democracy as their new form of government. Identify three factors that may have influenced their decision to choose this form of government over a dictatorship, single-party, or parliamentary democracy form.

The Roots of American Democracy

What ideas gave birth to the world's first modern democratic nation?

Speaking of Politics

As you complete the Reading Notes, use these terms in your answers:

representative government

rule of law

limited government

individual rights

separation of powers

popular sovereignty

constitutionalism

majority rule

PREVIEW

Take the Greece, Rome, or Home Challenge. Examine the photographs of buildings from ancient Greece, ancient Rome, and Washington, D.C. In your notebook, identify each as "ancient" or "United States."

Now answer these questions:

1. What do you notice about the architectural style of the buildings in Washington, D.C.? Can you think of any other buildings that reflect this style?

2. What ideas about government might the ancient Greeks and Romans have contributed to the world?

3. Why do you think so many U.S. government buildings reflect Greek and Roman architecture?

4. From where else do you think the United States got ideas about government?

READING NOTES

Section 3.2

Tape the illustration of a tree at the top of a page in your notebook. For each root on the tree, identify at least two ideas that shaped colonial views on government. Describe each idea, and explain why it is important.

Section 3.3

Create a timeline that extends from 1619 to 1776. On your timeline, plot the following events with the correct year:

- Mayflower Compact
- Virginia House of Burgesses
- French and Indian War
- Stamp Act
- Battles at Lexington and Concord
- Declaration of Independence

Write a brief description of each event. Then explain how each event influenced the development of American government.

Section 3.4

After reading the section, answer these questions:

1. How did state constitutions lay the groundwork for the U.S. Constitution?

2. What were the main weaknesses of the Articles of Confederation? What did these weaknesses mean for the national government?

3. What were three of the major challenges that the Constitutional Convention delegates faced, and how was each resolved?

Sections 3.5 and 3.6

Create a T-chart to compare the main arguments of the Federalists and the Anti-Federalists. Identify at least three arguments for each side. Then answer this question: *How was the debate over the ratification of the Constitution resolved?*

PROCESSING

Write three journal entries from the perspective of a delegate to the Constitutional Convention. Date each entry. Address each of these topics in one or more of your entries:

- Which ideas most influenced you in the development of the Constitution? Where did these ideas come from?
- What were the greatest challenges in developing the Constitution? How were these challenges resolved?
- Do you think the states should ratify the Constitution? Why or why not?

Roots of U.S. Government

Preparing for the Interview

You will bring to life a statue of a historical figure who influenced the development of democratic government in the United States.

Step 1 Read the biography of your historical figure. Then discuss these questions with your partner:

- What is the most important or interesting piece of personal information about your figure?
- What important idea did your figure have about government? Which quotation from your figure best demonstrates this idea?
- How does the time in which your figure lived help explain his idea about government?

Step 2 Prepare for your role.

- Write a brief introduction that provides important or interesting personal information.
- Prepare answers to these interview questions: *What is your most important idea about government? How does the time in which you live help explain your idea?*
- Make or find a simple prop to help explain your figure's important idea about government. For example, if the idea is separation of powers, you might use a three-legged stool to show how three branches make government more stable.
- Read the quotation in the biography, and choose one or more sentences from it to help support your answers. Use at least one of these sentences during your interview.

Step 3 Assemble your costume.

- Make or find a simple costume to wear.
- Cut out the mask from the handout, and cut holes for the mouth and eyes.
- Make a nameplate that clearly identifies who you are.

Biographies of Historical Figures

Pericles
Ancient Athenian Leader

Pericles was born about 490 B.C.E. in Athens. His father was actively involved in Athenian politics and served as a military commander during the Persian Wars. His mother was the niece of a well-known Athenian political reformer. Being from a wealthy family, Pericles was educated in many subjects, including music, logic, and philosophy. When he entered public life, he quickly rose to leadership because of his knowledge and skill.

As a leader, Pericles witnessed a golden age of peace and prosperity for Athens. To help maintain this peace, he organized neighboring Greek city-states to prepare for any future threat from the nearby Persian Empire. He also encouraged the buildup of the Athenian military. Pericles worked to beautify the city by promoting the creation of many public and religious buildings. The most famous of these buildings is the Parthenon, the temple to the ancient Greek goddess of wisdom, Athena. Industry and commerce also flourished under Pericles's leadership.

Pericles believed that Athens should lead the Greeks not just in culture and trade but also in government. Athens was the first Greek city-state to introduce the idea of democracy, or rule by the people, in which all citizens (native Athenian men over age 18) shared in the ruling of the city-state. Democracy was an unusual choice for governing. Most of the governments in other Greek city-states placed power in the hands of one person or a select few. Pericles, however, was a strong supporter of Athenian democracy. In a speech honoring soldiers who died in battle, Pericles praised this form of government.

[Our government] does not copy the laws of neighboring states; we are rather a pattern to others than imitators ourselves. Its administration favors the many instead of the few; this is why it is called a democracy. If we look to the laws, they afford equal justice to all in their private differences [based on social class] . . . The freedom which we enjoy in our government extends also to our ordinary life . . . But all this ease [freedom] . . . does not make us lawless as citizens. [We are taught] to obey the magistrates and the laws . . . whether they are actually on the statute [law] book, or belong to [an unwritten moral code].

Pericles also made reforms to advance democracy. He believed that all citizens, rich or poor, had an equal right to participate in government. Under his leadership, Athens paid the salaries of men who held public office. This reform allowed poor men, who otherwise would not be able to afford to leave their jobs and farms, to serve in public office.

Cicero
Ancient Roman Senator

Marcus Tullius Cicero was born in 106 B.C.E. in a town outside of Rome. His family was part of the local nobility but not of the wealthy Roman elite. One of the few career options open to someone of his social standing was law. Cicero quickly became known for his excellence in oration and built a successful law practice. When he turned his attention to politics, he enjoyed similar success. After serving in four elected offices, Cicero became a member of the Roman Senate.

The Senate was the main governing body of the Roman Republic, a representative form of government established by the ancient Romans. In this form of government, elected officials, called senators, hold power. This is in contrast to a direct democracy, in which decisions are made by all citizens. The senators of the Roman Republic served for life.

During Cicero's time in the Senate, political power became concentrated in the hands of fewer and fewer people. Cicero believed that Roman politicians had become corrupt, because they took rights away from the people. When Julius Caesar, Pompey, and Crassus took control of Roman politics, Cicero did not support them. As a result, he lost his property and was exiled.

Throughout his life, Cicero wrote many letters, speeches, and essays in support of the Roman Republic. He wrote about civic virtue, or the idea that people had a duty to participate in government and to be morally responsible while in office. In particular, the elite had a special duty as role models for Roman citizens. Cicero believed that senators and other members of the elite needed to commit to pursuing the republic's well-being over their own fame, wealth, and power. In his book *Des Officiis* (On Duties), Cicero described two types of injustices he saw committed by politicians.

There are . . . two kinds of injustice—the one, on the part of those who inflict wrong, the other on the part of those who, when they can, do not shield from wrong those upon whom it is being inflicted . . . He who does not prevent or oppose wrong, if he can, is just as guilty of wrong as if he deserted his parents or his friends or his country.

Cicero was eventually allowed to return from exile, only to witness Julius Caesar become dictator of Rome. With the consolidation of power in the hands of one individual, the Roman Republic would never reflect Cicero's ideal vision again.

Archbishop Stephen Langton
Witness to the Sealing of the Magna Carta

Stephen Langton was born around the year 1150 in England. Though his father was a landowner, Langton decided to pursue a religious career. After entering the clergy, he studied in Paris and wrote several works on theological topics. When the archbishop of Canterbury died, Langton was elected to that position, with strong support from the pope. However, King John of England refused to recognize Langton as archbishop due to a long-standing feud with the church.

Langton's election as archbishop of Canterbury in 1207 came at a tumultuous time in English politics. King John was not only quarreling with the church, he was also struggling to hold on to English lands in France. To finance his wars, he levied heavy taxes. Under England's feudal government, barons and other nobles had to pay taxes to the king for the privilege of land and protection. King John's punishments for those who did not pay were arbitrary and severe. As a result, the barons felt that their traditional rights were being ignored. Archbishop Langton supported the barons. In 1212, for example, he forced the king to give a fair trial to some barons accused of treason.

Eventually, the angry barons took up arms and captured London. Soon thereafter, they forced the king to put his seal on a document that later became the Magna Carta, or great charter. Archbishop Langton was one of the witnesses at this event. The Magna Carta was an agreement between the barons and the king. In return for keeping his rule, King John agreed to uphold the traditional rights of the barons. The Magna Carta limited the king's power by reminding him that he did not have absolute power—even the king had to follow the law. The charter included protection against the type of arbitrary punishment that King John had forced upon the barons.

> *No constable or other royal official shall take corn [grain] or other movable goods from any man without immediate payment, unless the seller voluntarily offers postponement of this [payment] . . .*

> *No official shall place a man on trial upon his own unsupported statement, without producing credible witnesses to the truth of it . . .*

> *No free man shall be seized or imprisoned, or stripped of his rights or possessions, or outlawed or exiled, or deprived of his standing in any other way, nor will we proceed with force against him, or send others to do so, except by the lawful judgement of his equals or by the law of the land . . .*

> *To no one will we sell, to no one deny or delay right or justice.*

Originally, the Magna Carta was intended only to protect the rights and property of the barons—the wealthy elite of England. Eventually, however, its protections were extended to all the British people. The Magna Carta became one of the cornerstones of constitutional rights in Britain.

John Somers
Member of the 1689 English Parliament

John Somers was born in 1651 near Worcester, England. His father was a successful lawyer. After an education at Trinity College in Oxford, Somers followed in his father's career. Although his interests included a wide range of law, he was especially knowledgeable in constitutional law. As a junior counsel, for example, he helped his team win a case by citing precedents stating that a law could not be suspended without Parliament's consent. In 1689, Somers became a member of the English Parliament.

Somers entered Parliament during an unsettled time in English history known as the Glorious Revolution. When King Charles II died in 1685, he left no eligible heirs. Instead, his brother, James II, peacefully ascended to the throne. Over the next several years, however, the king showed more and more favoritism toward Catholics, angering Protestant members of Parliament. In 1688, King James fled from England amid increasing opposition over his Catholic religion and his abuse of power. Parliament invited a Dutch prince, William of Orange, and Mary, the Protestant daughter of James, to rule England together. In 1689, the members of Parliament drafted a Declaration of Rights that outlined the conditions under which the two monarchs would rule. Somers headed the committee that created this document, which became known as the English Bill of Rights.

The English Bill of Rights outlawed certain acts that had been committed by James II and stated that he had given up the throne. By accepting the Bill of Rights, William III and Mary II were recognized as the lawful rulers of England. Most important, the English Bill of Rights declared that all Englishmen had certain civil and political rights that could not be violated. Such rights included the right to free elections and freedom of speech in Parliament.

That the raising or keeping a Standing Army within the Kingdome in time of Peace unless it be with Consent of Parliament is against Law . . .

That Election of Members of Parliament ought to be free

That the Freedome of Speech and Debates or Proceedings in Parliament ought not to be impeached [put on trial] or questioned in any Court or Place out of Parliament

That excessive Bayle ought not to be required nor excessive Fines imposed nor cruell and unusuall Punishments inflicted.

The English Bill of Rights limited the power of the ruler by acknowledging these rights. It also strengthened the power of Parliament to govern the people.

John Locke
English Philosopher

John Locke was born in 1632 in England. His father was a lawyer who had served in the military. Locke studied at Christ Church in Oxford, and it seemed likely that he would become a minister. Instead, he became a doctor. In 1667, he became the personal physician for a wealthy politician and moved to London.

In London, Locke pursued his interest in philosophy, which had begun during his medical studies. He was particularly interested in issues of religious freedom and the rights of citizens. He continued to read, write, and discuss political philosophy. In 1683, Locke fled to Holland when his ideas were seen by the English government as a challenge to the king's authority. In 1689, he returned to England after a series of events in Great Britain known as the Glorious Revolution. As a result of the revolution, Parliament forced the new rulers to respect its authority by accepting a Bill of Rights, which limited the monarch's power.

Locke supported the changes brought about by the Glorious Revolution. In 1689, he published *Two Treatises of Government,* which outlined his view of government. Locke did not believe in the divine right of monarchs to rule. Instead, he supported a government in which the monarch's power was limited in order to respect the rights of the people. He also believed there were certain natural rights that belonged to all people.

Man [who is] born . . . with a title to . . . all the rights and privileges of the law of nature, equally with any other man, or number of men in the world, hath [have] by nature a power, not only to preserve his property, that is, his life, liberty and estate, against the injuries and attempts of other men; but to judge of, and punish the breaches [violations] of that law . . . as he is persuaded the offence deserves.

In exchange for protection of these natural rights, the people gave power to government to make and enforce laws. Locke argued that government's authority existed only by a social contract, or agreement, among free people to let it exist. Therefore, if the government failed to respect the natural rights of the people, it could be overthrown.

Baron de Montesquieu
French Philosopher

Charles-Louis de Secondat was born in 1689 outside of Bordeaux, France, to a wealthy family. After studying science and history, he became a lawyer. After his uncle's death in 1716, he inherited his title and became Baron de Montesquieu. He became a member of the Bordeaux and French Academies of Science, where he studied the customs and government of European countries.

In France, the king and nobility lived extravagantly. King Louis XIV, for example, renovated and expanded his royal palace, Chateau de Versailles, at great expense. Visitors were awestruck by its luxurious grandeur and were entertained with lavish balls, dinners, performances, and celebrations. Montesquieu disapproved of the lifestyle and freedoms of the wealthy French elite. In 1721, he published his first major work, *The Persian Letters,* in which he wrote about the people of Europe from the perspective of foreign visitors. This book was a criticism of several French institutions, such as the king's court and the Catholic church.

Published in 1748, *The Spirit of the Laws* was Montesquieu's most famous work. In it, he discussed three types of government. In describing the pros and cons of each type, he stated that the success of a democracy depends on keeping an appropriate balance of power within the government. Montesquieu proposed that power be divided among three groups of officials, or branches, of government. This idea became known as "separation of powers." Each branch would be separate and equal, but with different powers to avoid placing too much power in the hands of one individual or one group of individuals.

When the legislative and executive powers are united in the same person, or in the same body of magistrates [public officials], there can be no liberty . . .

Again, there is no liberty, if the power of judging be not separated from the legislative and executive powers. Were it joined with the legislative, the life and liberty of the subject would be exposed to arbitrary control, for the judge would then be the legislator. Were it joined to the executive power, the judge might behave with all the violence of an oppressor.

In looking at the countries of Europe, Montesquieu thought England provided a good model of government. In England, power was divided among the Parliament (which made laws), the king (who enforced laws), and the courts (which interpreted laws).

John Adams
American Founding Father

John Adams was born in 1735 in Braintree, Massachusetts. His father was active in the local church and in local politics. After graduating from Harvard College in 1755, Adams taught school in Worcester, Massachusetts. He then decided to pursue a career in law and studied under attorney James Putnam. Over the next several years, Adams became one of Boston's most successful lawyers.

Adams firmly believed in the traditions of English law. For example, he defended the British soldiers charged in the Boston Massacre in 1770. After 1770, Adams became an outspoken critic of the way the British government treated its subjects in the American colonies. He increasingly supported a fight for independence against British rule. In 1774, he was elected as a delegate from Massachusetts to the First Continental Congress in Philadelphia. This congress met to discuss colonial opposition to England. Adams actively participated in this congress and in the Second Continental Congress in 1775. He nominated George Washington to serve as commander in chief of the Continental Army. He also spoke strongly in favor of drafting a declaration of independence from England. He suggested that Thomas Jefferson be one of the writers of this declaration.

In 1776, Adams wrote *Thoughts on Government*. In this book, he provided an outline for government if the colonies were to declare independence from England. He believed that history was providing the colonies with a unique opportunity to form their own independent, free governments. Adams's vision reflected the influence of ancient and modern philosophy. He wrote about a democratic form of government in which a small group of people represented the society as a whole and made the laws.

How shall your laws be made? In a large society, inhabiting an extensive country, it is impossible that the whole should assemble, to make laws: The first necessary step then, is, to depute [give] power from the many, to a few of the most wise and good . . .

The greatest care should be employed in constituting this Representative Assembly. It should be in miniature, an exact portrait of the people at large. It should think, feel, reason, and act like them. That it may be the interest of this Assembly to do strict justice at all times, it should be an equal representation, or in other words equal interest among the people should have equal interest in it.

Thoughts on Government was circulated throughout the colonies and became a framework for several state constitutions. Adams was also a principal drafter of the Massachusetts Constitution, which was ratified and went into effect in 1780.

Thomas Jefferson
American Founding Father

Thomas Jefferson was born in 1743 in Shadwell, Virginia. His father was a successful planter, and his mother was a member of one of the most distinguished families in Virginia. After studying at the College of William and Mary, Jefferson became a lawyer. Although he earned a reputation of being extremely knowledgeable, he was also seen as shy and reserved. Nonetheless, in 1768, he was elected to Virginia's House of Burgesses.

As a legislator, Jefferson was strongly opposed to Britain's authority over the American colonies. In 1774, he wrote *A Summary View of the Rights of British America*. In it, he encouraged the growing sentiment for the colonies to declare independence. In 1775, he was appointed a delegate to the Second Continental Congress in Philadelphia. The purpose of this congress was to organize the colonial war effort in rebellion against England. In 1776, he was appointed to a five-man committee to draft a formal declaration of independence from England. Because he was a gifted writer and scholar of philosophy, Jefferson was nominated to write the first draft of the declaration.

In the Declaration of Independence, Jefferson outlined the grievances that the colonies had against King George III. Most important, Jefferson expressed his belief that all men have certain natural rights. Because these rights exist with or without a government, a government cannot take them away. Thus, if a government failed to respect these natural rights, the citizens of that government had a right to overthrow it.

We hold these truths to be self-evident, that all men are created equal, that they are endowed by their Creator with certain unalienable Rights, that among these are Life, Liberty and the pursuit of Happiness. —That to secure these rights, Governments are instituted among Men, deriving their just powers from the consent of the governed.

Many changes were made to Jefferson's draft. In fact, an entire one-fifth of the draft was either revised or deleted. This excerpt, however, remained untouched.

Masks of Historical Figures

Pericles

Cicero

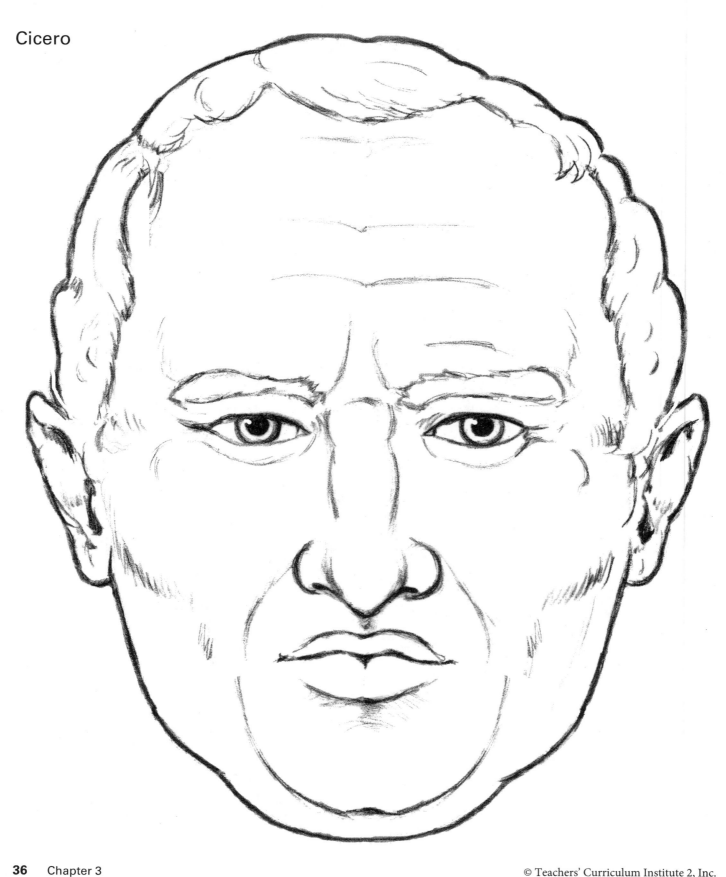

Archbishop Stephen Langton

John Somers

John Locke

Baron de Montesquieu

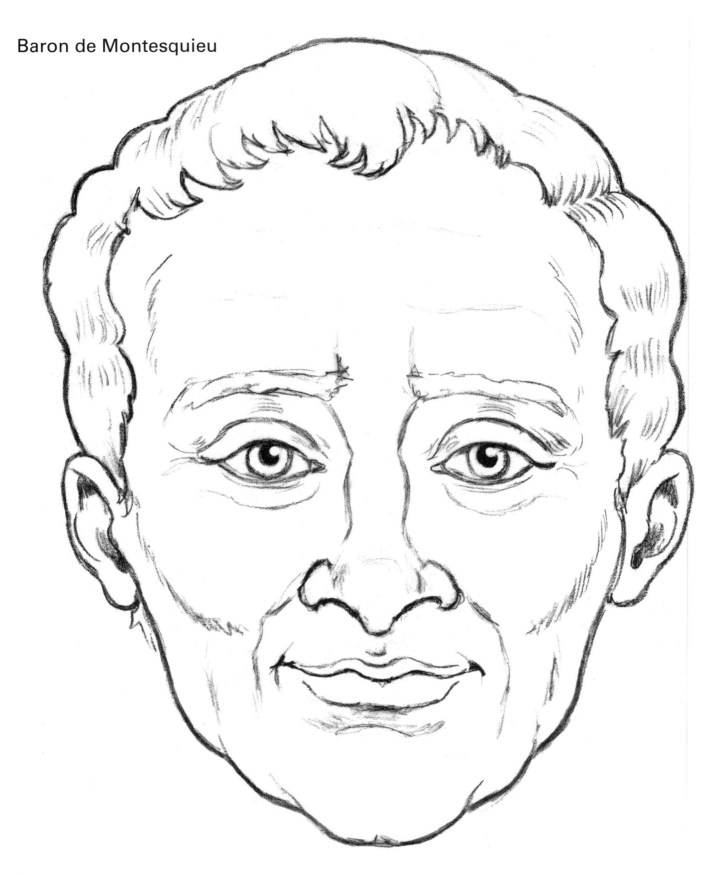

John Adams

Thomas Jefferson

Interviews of Historical Figures

Complete this matrix as you interview each statue in the National Statuary Hall. In the last column, draw a simple illustration representing the figure's main idea about government, and include a caption to explain your drawing.

Historical Figure	Important or Interesting Personal Information	What important ideas does this figure have about government?	How does the time in which this figure lived help to explain this idea?	Illustration and Brief Caption
Pericles				
Cicero				
Archbishop Stephen Langton				
John Somers				

Historical Figure	Important or Interesting Personal Information	What important ideas does this figure have about government?	How does the time in which this figure lived help to explain this idea?	Illustration and Brief Caption	
John Locke					
Baron de Montesquieu					
John Adams					
Thomas Jefferson					

Mastering the Content

1. Which of the following best defines the principle of popular sovereignty?
   A. The powers of a government are limited by the people.
   B. Government is based on laws that apply to all the people.
   C. The ultimate source of governmental authority is the people.
   D. Elected leaders work through government to serve the people.

2. The idea of representative government first developed in ancient
   A. Egypt.
   B. Greece.
   C. Israel.
   D. Rome.

3. Who is known as the Father of the Constitution and as the principal author of the Bill of Rights?
   A. Benjamin Franklin
   B. Thomas Jefferson
   C. James Madison
   D. George Washington

4. Which of these historic documents first established the principle of the rule of law?
   A. Magna Carta
   B. Mayflower Compact
   C. English Bill of Rights
   D. Second Treatise on Government

5. Which complaint was the greatest barrier to ratifying the Constitution?
   A. It did not include a bill of rights.
   B. It had to be approved by all 13 states.
   C. It allowed too many people to vote.
   D. It created a weak central government.

6. Consider the quotations below.

   > *"Life, liberty, and property . . ."* —John Locke
   >
   > *"Life, Liberty and the pursuit of Happiness . . ."*
   > —Declaration of Independence

   Both quotations list what our nation's founders believed to be
   A. civil virtues.
   B. natural rights.
   C. the general will.
   D. the rights of Englishmen.

7. Which of these issues at the Constitutional Convention was resolved by what is known as the Great Compromise?
   A. the representation of the states in Congress
   B. the eventual abolition of slavery in the South
   C. the power of Congress to regulate foreign trade
   D. the method for choosing the president of the United States

8. The Articles of Confederation reflected Americans' fear of
   A. a permanent standing army.
   B. a strong central government.
   C. a threatened foreign invasion.
   D. a breakdown in law and order.

9. Which political philosopher favored separate legislative, executive, and judicial branches?
   A. Thomas Hobbes
   B. John Locke
   C. Baron de Montesquieu
   D. Jean-Jacques Rousseau

10. Thomas Paine, author of *Common Sense,* was influenced by Rousseau's argument that a government should be dissolved if it
    A. was too weak to be effective.
    B. acted contrary to the general will.
    C. depended on inherited leadership.
    D. could not keep the economy stable.

Exploring the Essential Question

What ideas gave birth to the world's first modern democratic nation?

Use the information in the timeline, and what you already know about the ideas and events that influenced the U.S. Constitution, to answer the questions below.

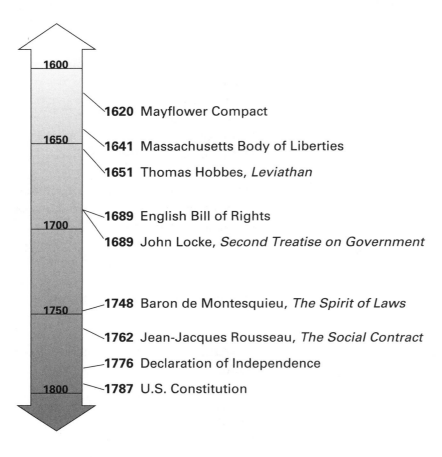

1600

1620 Mayflower Compact

1650

1641 Massachusetts Body of Liberties

1651 Thomas Hobbes, *Leviathan*

1689 English Bill of Rights

1700

1689 John Locke, *Second Treatise on Government*

1748 Baron de Montesquieu, *The Spirit of Laws*

1750

1762 Jean-Jacques Rousseau, *The Social Contract*

1776 Declaration of Independence

1787 U.S. Constitution

1800

1. Explain what Hobbes and Locke meant by a social contract. Why did Hobbes think people would choose to enter into such a contract? Why did Locke think people would enter into a social contract?
2. Identify the documents on this timeline that you consider to be examples of a social contract. Explain your choices.
3. What key idea from Locke's *Second Treatise on Government* and Rousseau's *The Social Contract* appear in the Declaration of Independence?
4. What key idea from Montesquieu's *The Spirit of Laws* helped to shape the U.S. Constitution?

The United States Constitution

How and why did the framers distribute power in the Constitution?

Speaking of Politics

As you complete the Reading Notes, use these terms in your answers:

due process	independent judiciary
republican government	strict construction
checks and balances	loose construction
federalism	judicial review

PREVIEW

Examine the outline of the Constitution on Notebook Handout 4. Then answer these questions in your notebook:

1. What observations can you make about the way the framers organized the Constitution?

2. Which branch of government did the framers give the greatest number of specific (expressed) powers to? What might be some reasons for that?

3. What inferences can you make about how the framers intended to distribute power within the federal government?

READING NOTES

Sections 4.2 and 4.3

Read Sections 4.2 and 4.3. Then do the following:

1. Create this diagram in your notebook. In your diagram, clearly explain the purpose of each of the three main parts of the Constitution. Then list an example from the Constitution that illustrates the purpose of each part.

┌─────────── **Constitution** ───────────┐

Preamble	**Articles**	**Amendments**
Purpose:	*Purpose:*	*Purpose:*
Example:	*Example:*	*Example:*

2. Explain the difference between enumerated and implied powers and describe how the Constitution establishes both.

3. Discuss why each branch of government has a different set of responsibilities and powers. List at least two powers of each branch.

4. Create a simple flowchart that illustrates the most common method of amending the Constitution.

Section 4.4

1. Create the following table in your notebook. Complete the first three columns by listing each guiding principle, creating a simple illustration to represent it, and briefly explaining it in your own words.

Guiding Principles of the Constitution

Principle	Symbol or Simple Illustration	Brief Explanation	Example from the Constitution

2. Read Section 4.4, and identify at least one place in the Constitution that illustrates each principle. In the fourth column of your table, give the exact location in the Constitution as well as the exact text that exemplifies each principle.

Section 4.5

Read Section 4.5, and then do the following:

1. Explain the difference between strict and loose construction of the Constitution.

2. On a page in your notebook, complete the table below for the three landmark cases discussed in the section.

   • Enter the case's name and the year it was decided.

   • List two or three main facts of the case.

   • Write a short summary of the Supreme Court's decision.

   • Describe the significance of the decision in terms of its effects on the government and on the interpretation of the Constitution.

Three Landmark Court Cases

Name and Date of the Case	Facts of the Case	Summary of the Decision	Significance of the Decision

PROCESSING

The framers developed the U.S. Constitution more than 200 years ago with the hope that it would remain relevant and effective for future generations. One way they sought to accomplish that was through the provisions of Article V, which spell out how the Constitution can be changed.

In recent years, Congress has fielded many proposals for changes to the Constitution, including the following:

• Requiring the federal government to balance the national budget

• Restricting the amount of money that can be spent during national electoral campaigns

• Abolishing the Electoral College and having the president and vice president elected by popular vote

• Lowering the age restriction for public offices such as senator and representative

• Repealing the Twenty-second Amendment, which sets presidential term limits

• Guaranteeing all citizens access to quality health care

If you had the opportunity to change the Constitution in one way in order to improve it, what would you propose? In a short paragraph, explain your proposal and discuss why you think the Constitution will be a stronger, better document with this change.

Outline of the U.S. Constitution

_____: We the People of the United States, in Order to form a more perfect Union, establish Justice, insure domestic Tranquility, provide for the common defence, promote the general Welfare, and secure the Blessings of Liberty to ourselves and our Posterity, do ordain and establish this Constitution for the United States of America.

Article I: _____
Section 1   Congress
Section 2   House of Representatives
Section 3   Senate
Section 4   Elections and meetings
Section 5   Legislative proceedings
Section 6   Compensation, immunities, and disabilities of members
Section 7   Revenue bills, presidential veto
Section 8   Powers of Congress
Section 9   Powers denied to Congress
Section 10   Powers denied to the states

Article II: _____
Section 1   President: term, election, qualifications, compensation, oath of office
Section 2   President's powers and duties
Section 3   President's powers and duties
Section 4   Impeachment

Article III: _____
Section 1   Courts, terms of office
Section 2   Jurisdiction
Section 3   Treason

Article IV: _____
Section 1   Full faith and credit
Section 2   Privileges and immunities of citizens
Section 3   New states, territories
Section 4   Protection afforded to states by the nation

Article V: _____

Article VI: _____
Section 1   Validity of debts
Section 2   Supremacy of national law
Section 3   Oaths of office

Article VII: _____

_____: Protection of individual rights

_____: Formal changes to the Constitution

Use these terms to fill in the blanks on the outline of the Constitution above.

Judicial branch	Provisions for amendment	Relations among states	Amendments
Legislative branch	Ratification of the Constitution	Preamble	Bill of Rights
Executive branch	Public debts, supremacy of national law, oaths		

Outline of the U.S. Constitution

Preamble: We the People of the United States, in Order to form a more perfect Union, establish Justice, insure domestic Tranquility, provide for the common defence, promote the general Welfare, and secure the Blessings of Liberty to ourselves and our Posterity, do ordain and establish this Constitution for the United States of America.

Article I: **Legislative branch**	**Article III:** **Judicial branch**
Section 1 Congress	Section 1 Courts, terms of office
Section 2 House of Representatives	Section 2 Jurisdiction
Section 3 Senate	Section 3 Treason
Section 4 Elections and meetings	
Section 5 Legislative proceedings	**Article IV:** **Relations among states**
Section 6 Compensation, immunities, and disabilities of members	Section 1 Full faith and credit
	Section 2 Privileges and immunities of citizens
Section 7 Revenue bills, presidential veto	Section 3 New states, territories
Section 8 Powers of Congress	Section 4 Protection afforded to states by the nation
Section 9 Powers denied to Congress	
Section 10 Powers denied to the states	
	Article V: **Provisions for amendment**
Article II: **Executive branch**	
Section 1 President: term, election, qualifications, compensation, oath of office	**Article VI:** **Public debts, supremacy of national law, oaths**
	Section 1 Validity of debts
Section 2 President's powers and duties	Section 2 Supremacy of national law
Section 3 President's powers and duties	Section 3 Oaths of office
Section 4 Impeachment	
	Article VII: **Ratification of the Constitution**

Bill of Rights: Protection of individual rights
Amendments: Formal changes to the Constitution

Constitutional Law 1 Cards

Card 1

Your uncle just celebrated his 30th birthday. Can he run for the House of Representatives?

Card 2

A candidate you strongly support was just elected senator. How many years must pass until this candidate can be reelected?

Card 3

The media are reporting a raise in federal income tax for the coming year. Where did the proposal for this new tax originate?

Card 4

Troops from a foreign country have invaded Oregon. Which branch of government has the power to declare war against this aggressor?

Card 5

The United States and another country recently agreed to a treaty on arms reductions. Who has the power to make such a treaty with a foreign country?

Card 6

The president appointed a new ambassador to Haiti. Who must approve this appointment before it can take effect?

Card 7

A Supreme Court justice has announced her retirement. Who has the power to nominate a replacement?

Card 8

The presidential candidate you favor has been called the "youngest person ever to run for president." How old must this candidate be to qualify for the presidency?

Card 9

You are disappointed the morning after Election Day to discover that the new president was not who you voted for. In how many years can you vote again?

Card 10

If a vice president were to commit a federal offense, who has the power to impeach him or her? Who has the power to try the impeached official?

Card 11

Who has the power to regulate trade between states?

Card 12

What is the vice president's only constitutional responsibility?

Card 13

An argument has arisen between two states. Who has the power to settle this dispute?

Card 14

After law school, your hope is to some-day serve on the Supreme Court. How long would your term of service be?

Card 15

In the 2000 presidential election, George Bush won by only 5 electoral votes. Who appointed the electors who cast those votes?

Card 16

Who is the commander in chief of the U.S. military forces?

Card 17

A law in your state was recently passed that contradicts a previous law passed by Congress. Which law does the Constitution say is valid?

Card 18

A state's governor recently denounced the U.S. government publicly during a speech. Can this governor be tried for treason?

Card 19

There has been talk of a new amend-ment allowing foreign-born citizens to run for president. Who would have the power to propose this amendment?

Card 20

Who has the power to approve or veto legislation?

Constitutional Law 1 Matrix

Card	Article	Section	Answer to Question	Constitutional Provision with Key Words Underlined
1				
2				
3				
4				
5				
6				
7				
8				
9				
10				

Card	Article	Section	Answer to Question	Constitutional Provision with Key Words Underlined
11				
12				
13				
14				
15				
16				
17				
18				
19				
20				

Completed Constitutional Law 1 Matrix

Card	Article	Section	Answer to Question	Constitutional Provision with Key Words Underlined
1	I	2	Yes	"No Person shall be a Representative who shall not have attained to the Age of twenty five Years."
2	I	3	6 years	"The Senate of the United States shall be composed of two Senators from each State . . . for six Years."
3	I	7	the House of Representatives	"All Bills for raising Revenue shall originate in the House of Representatives."
4	I	8	Congress	"The Congress shall have power . . . to declare War."
5	II	2	the president, with approval of the Senate	"He shall have Power, by and with the Advice and Consent of the Senate, to make Treaties."
6	II	2	the Senate	"He shall nominate, and by and with the Advice and Consent of the Senate, shall appoint Ambassadors."
7	II	2	the president	"He shall nominate, and by and with the Advice and Consent of the Senate, shall appoint . . . Judges of the supreme Court."
8	II	1	35 years old	". . . attained to the Age of thirty five Years."
9	II	1	four years	"He shall hold his Office during the Term of four Years."
10	I	2 and 3	the House of Representatives can impeach; the Senate tries the impeachment	"The House of Representatives . . . shall have sole Power of Impeachment." "The Senate shall have sole Power to try all Impeachments."

Card	Article	Section	Answer to Question	Constitutional Provision with Key Words Underlined
11	I	8	Congress	"The <u>Congress</u> shall have Power . . . To <u>regulate Commerce</u> with foreign Nations, and <u>among the several States</u>."
12	I	3	president of the Senate	"The <u>Vice President</u> of the United States shall be <u>President of the Senate,</u> but shall have no Vote, unless they be equally divided."
13	III	2	federal courts	"The <u>judicial Power</u> shall extend to all Cases . . . arising under this Constitution . . . to <u>Controversies between two or more States</u>."
14	III	1	for life	"The judges, Both of the supreme and inferior Courts, shall <u>hold their Offices during good Behaviour</u>."
15	II	1	the states	"Each <u>State</u> shall appoint . . . a Number of Electors."
16	II	2	the president	"The <u>President shall be Commander in Chief</u> of the Army and Navy of the United States."
17	VI		the congressional law	"<u>This Constitution,</u> and the Laws of the United States . . . shall be <u>the supreme Law of the Land</u>."
18	III	3	no	"<u>Treason</u> against the United States, shall consist only in <u>levying War against them,</u> or in <u>adhering to their Enemies,</u> giving them Aid and Comfort."
19	V		Congress	"The <u>Congress,</u> whenever two-thirds of both Houses shall deem it necessary, <u>shall propose Amendments to this Constitution</u>."
20	I	7	the president	"<u>Every bill</u> which shall have passed the House of Representatives and the Senate, shall, before it becomes a Law, be <u>presented to the President</u> of the United States; <u>If he approve, he shall sign it, but if not he shall return it</u>."

Guiding Principles of the Constitution

The limited government envisioned in the Constitution is based upon six guiding principles.

Popular Sovereignty

Because the government is created by and for the people, power resides not with the government or its leaders but with the people. In a representative democracy, the people vote to elect leaders to represent their interests.

Rule of Law

The people and their government must abide by a set of laws, rather than by arbitrary rules set down by any individual or group. The Constitution sets limits to governmental power and establishes how leaders who overstep their power can be removed.

Separation of Powers and Checks and Balances

Powers and responsibilities are divided among three government branches to prevent any one person or group from having too much power. A system of checks and balances allows each branch to monitor and check the power of the others to prevent any abuse of government power.

Federalism

Power is divided between the central government and the individual state and local governments.

Independent Judiciary

The judicial branch is established as an independent entity, free of pressures and influences from the other two branches. The Supreme Court is the highest authority in the federal court system.

Individual Rights

Individual rights and liberties are protected against government encroachment.

Constitutional Law 2 Cards

Card 1

Article IV, Section 2, Clause 1

Card 2

Article II, Section 2, Clause 2

Card 3

Article I, Section 7, Clause 2

Card 4

Tenth Amendment

Card 5

Article I, Section 2, Clause 1

Card 6

Article I, Section 8, Clause 3

Card 7

Preamble

Card 8

Article VI, Section 2

Card 9

Article IV, Section 4

Card 10

Article III, Section 1

Constitutional Law 2 Matrix

Card	Principle or Principles Exemplified	Explanation of How These Principles Are Exemplified
1		
2		
3		
4		
5		
6		
7		
8		
9		
10		

Completed Constitutional Law 2 Matrix

Card	Relevant Excerpt from the Constitution	Principle or Principles Exemplified	Explanation of How These Principles Are Exemplified
1	**Article IV, Section 2, Clause 1: Privileges and immunities.** The Citizens of each State shall be entitled to all privileges and immunities of Citizens in the Several States.	Individual rights Rule of law	States cannot discriminate against citizens of other states. This limits the power of state governments and guarantees the rights of individuals.
2	**Article II, Section 2, Clause 2: The Senate checks and balances the president's power to make treaties and appointments to office.** He [the president] shall have Power, by and with the Advice and Consent of the Senate, to make Treaties, provided two thirds of the Senators present concur; and he shall nominate, and by and with the Advice and Consent of the Senate, shall appoint Ambassadors, other public Ministers and Consuls, Judges of the supreme Court, and all other Officers of the United States.	Separation of powers and checks and balances	No treaty signed by the president can go into effect unless two-thirds of the Senate approves it. This acts as a check on the president's power. The president's nominees for judges, ambassadors, and other offices must also be confirmed by the Senate.
3	**Article I, Section 7, Clause 2: The veto.** Every Bill which shall have passed the House of Representatives and the Senate, shall, before it become a Law, be presented to the President of the United States; If he approve he shall sign it, but if not he shall return it.	Separation of powers and checks and balances	The power of Congress to make laws is checked by the president, who can approve or veto them.
4	**Tenth Amendment: Powers reserved to the states.** The powers not delegated to the United States by the Constitution . . . are reserved to the States respectively, or to the people.	Federalism Individual rights	Any powers not specifically given to the federal government or denied to the states are reserved for the states and thus the people.
5	**Article I, Section 2, Clause 1: Direct election of the House of Representatives.** The House of Representatives shall be composed of Members chosen every second Year by the People of the several States, and the Electors in each State shall have the Qualifications requisite for Electors of the most numerous Branch of the State Legislature.	Popular sovereignty Federalism	Members of the House of Representatives are elected by the people every two years. The states set the qualifications for voting.

Card	Relevant Excerpt from the Constitution	Principle or Principles Exemplified	Explanation of How These Principles Are Exemplified
6	**Article I, Section 8, Clause 3: Interstate Commerce Clause.** Congress has the power to regulate Commerce with foreign Nations, and among the several States, and with the Indian Tribes.	Federalism	The power to regulate interstate commerce is given to the federal government. This is an example of a delegated power.
7	**Preamble.** We the People of the United States, in Order to form a more perfect Union, establish Justice, insure domestic Tranquility, provide for the common defence, promote the general Welfare, and secure the Blessings of Liberty to ourselves and our Posterity, do ordain and establish this Constitution for the United States of America.	Individual rights Rule of law	The opening words of the Constitution state that the Constitution is established by the people to protect the rights and well-being of all citizens. These words also suggest that the Constitution is the basis of law.
8	**Article VI, Section 2: Supremacy Clause.** This Constitution, and the Laws of the United States which shall be made in Pursuance thereof; and all Treaties made, or which shall be made, under the Authority of the United States, shall be the supreme Law of the Land; and the Judges in every State shall be bound thereby, any Thing in the Constitution or Laws of any State to the Contrary notwithstanding.	Rule of law Federalism	The Supremacy Clause establishes the Constitution as the highest authority in the country, to which all leaders must adhere. It also establishes the authority of federal law over state law.
9	**Article IV, Section 4: Republican form of government and protection against invasion.** The United States shall guarantee to every State in this Union a Republican Form of Government, and shall protect each of them against Invasion; and on Application of the Legislature, or of the Executive (when the Legislature cannot be convened), against domestic violence.	Federalism Individual rights Popular sovereignty	This provision guarantees representative government for the states, as well as federal protection from invasion. Implied within that guarantee are the protection of rights and liberties and rule by the people.
10	**Article III, Section 1: Supreme Court, lower courts, judges serve for life or good behavior.** The judicial Power of the United States, shall be vested in one supreme Court, and in such inferior Courts as the Congress may from time to time ordain and establish. The Judges, both of the supreme and inferior Courts, shall hold their Offices during good Behavior, and shall, at stated Times, receive for their Services a Compensation, which shall not be diminished during their Continuance in Office.	Checks and balances Independent judiciary	Supreme Court justices hold their terms for life (subject to good behavior). Their pay cannot be reduced while they serve. This creates a judiciary less likely to be influenced by the other branches of government—an additional check.

Background on Three Constitutional Cases

Case 1: *Youngstown Sheet and Tube Co. v. Sawyer*

In 1952, the Korean War was in full swing. The war effort demanded that more and more weapons be made, which required the production of more and more steel. President Truman worried about an imminent strike by the United Steel-workers of America and foresaw the detrimental effect this strike could have on national defense. He issued an executive order authorizing his secretary of commerce to seize control of the steel industry and keep the steel mills operating. The president immediately reported his order to Congress, which took no action in response.

The mill owners filed suit against President Truman's secretary of commerce in federal district court. They argued that the president's order was an example of lawmaking, a power granted to Congress and not to the president. In other words, they did not deny that the government could take over their property in the event of an emergency. They simply argued that another branch of government rightfully had the power to do it.

The federal government responded that the executive order was issued to prevent a national catastrophe that would have resulted if steel production had halted. They further argued that the president was acting within the boundaries of his constitutional powers as commander in chief of the armed forces of the United States.

The case was brought before the Supreme Court to decide this question:

Does the president have the power, as commander in chief of the armed forces, to seize control of an industry during wartime?

After you have reviewed the relevant parts of the Constitution, predict what the Supreme Court will decide.

❑ Yes, the president has the power to seize control of an industry during wartime.

❑ No, the president does not have the power to seize control of an industry during wartime.

Case 2: *Gonzales v. Raich*

In 1970, Congress passed the Controlled Substances Act, which categorizes certain drugs based on what Congress believes to be their medical value. Under that act, Congress asserted that marijuana has no accepted medical value. As a result, it remains an illegal substance in the United States.

Twenty-six years later, in 1996, voters in California passed Proposition 215. This state law legalized marijuana for medical purposes and allowed patients to use and grow the plant within the state. However, after the law was passed, federal law enforcement agents in California began raiding properties and seizing marijuana crops from people who were growing it for medical purposes, arguing that federal law trumped state law.

In 2002, Angel Raich and Diane Monson sued the federal government. They hoped to stop the government from interfering with their state-sanctioned right to use and grow marijuana for medical purposes. The women claimed that under California state and local law, it was legal to grow and use medicinal marijuana. Raich's physician noted that Raich would die without marijuana. Monson explained that she grew marijuana plants as part of a cooperative venture with other patients and that no money ever changed hands. Therefore, she said, her actions had no direct impact on interstate activity or commerce.

In 2003, a court of appeals found that the Controlled Substances Act was an unconstitutional exercise of Congress's Commerce Clause authority, which gives Congress the power to regulate trade between states. The court held that growing and using marijuana within a state did not substantially affect interstate commerce and therefore could not be regulated by Congress.

In 2004, the case was brought to the Supreme Court to decide this question:

Does Congress's power to make laws and regulate commerce allow the federal government to prohibit activities that are in compliance with state law?

After you have reviewed the relevant parts of the Constitution, predict what the Supreme Court will decide.

❏ Yes, the federal government has the power to prohibit activities that comply with state law.

❏ No, the federal government does not have the power to prohibit activities that comply with state law.

Case 3: *Hamdi v. Rumsfeld*

In 2001, the United States was in Afghanistan fighting against the Taliban in the war on terrorism. While there, the United States military arrested an American citizen whom they believed was fighting on behalf of the Taliban and, therefore, had "adhered to" an enemy of the United States. This citizen, Yaser Esam Hamdi, was labeled an "enemy combatant" and sent to a military prison in Virginia for an indefinite amount of time.

Hamdi declared that his Fifth Amendment rights were being violated since he was being held indefinitely and was being denied the right to a trial. His lawyer filed a petition in federal district court declaring Hamdi's imprisonment unconstitutional. The government's response was that the executive branch could, during wartime, declare anyone who took up arms against the United States to be an enemy combatant and deny that person a trial.

The court decided in favor of Hamdi, and the government was ordered to immediately release him from prison. However, a court of appeals reversed the decision, determining that the judicial branch was not equipped to consider a case involving overseas conduct. They felt it was in the nation's best interests to allow the executive branch to determine who might qualify as an enemy combatant.

The case was then brought before the Supreme Court in 2004 to decide this question:

Does the executive branch have the power to suspend a citizen's civil rights during times of war?

After you have reviewed the relevant parts of the Constitution, predict what the Supreme Court will decide.

❏ Yes, the executive branch has the power to suspend a citizen's civil rights during times of war.

❏ No, the executive branch does not have the power to suspend a citizen's civil rights during times of war.

Mastering the Content

1. Which of these terms refers to the principle that people accused of a crime must be granted certain legal rights?
   A. due process
   B. habeas corpus
   C. judicial review
   D. eminent domain

2. The Preamble to the Constitution lists which of the following?
   A. steps for amending the Constitution
   B. purpose to be served by the Constitution
   C. procedures for ratifying the Constitution
   D. guidelines for interpreting the Constitution

3. Why did the framers of the Constitution create three separate branches of government?
   A. to help people with different opinions cooperate
   B. to increase the power of the central government
   C. to keep any one group from gaining too much power
   D. to provide enough officials to handle the volume of work

4. The first words of the Constitution indicate that power and authority in our system of government come from the
   A. states.
   B. people.
   C. voters.
   D. lawmakers.

5. Which of these is the defining characteristic of a federal system of government?
   A. Elected representatives make decisions for the nation.
   B. Power is divided between central and regional bodies.
   C. Separate branches have different areas of responsibility.
   D. Legislative actions are limited by a set of written guidelines.

6. Over time, constitutional amendments have extended which right to the groups listed below?

   - African Americans
   - women
   - residents of the District of Columbia
   - 18-year-olds

   A. right to an education
   B. right to serve on a jury
   C. right to vote in elections
   D. right to federal employment

7. The Supremacy Clause of the Constitution indicates how to resolve conflicts between
   A. state and federal laws.
   B. both chambers of Congress.
   C. strict and loose constructionists.
   D. majority rule and minority rights.

8. Which of these is the best example of constitutional checks and balances?
   A. Treaties require Senate approval.
   B. The Constitution may be amended.
   C. The president is paid for his services.
   D. Courts decide conflicts between states.

9. How did the decision in *Marbury v. Madison* (1803) strengthen the power of the Supreme Court?
   A. It denied state courts the authority to override federal precedent.
   B. It asserted that the Court could order the president to carry out a law.
   C. It intervened in a conflict between the other two branches of government.
   D. It established the Court's right to declare an act of Congress unconstitutional.

10. The process of amending the Constitution involves both
    A. the Congress and the states.
    B. the president and the Congress.
    C. the states and the Supreme Court.
    D. the Supreme Court and the president.

Exploring the Essential Question

How and why did the framers distribute power in the Constitution?

James Madison, Alexander Hamilton, and John Jay wrote essays known as
The Federalist to persuade the people of New York to ratify the Constitution.
As you read the excerpt below, think about how it applies today.

James Madison, *The Federalist* No. 51

**The Structure of the Government Must Furnish the
Proper Checks and Balances Between the Different Departments**

February 8, 1788

In order to lay a due foundation for that separate and distinct exercise of the different powers of government, which . . . [is] essential to the preservation of liberty, it is evident that each department should have a will of its own . . .

It is equally evident, that the members of each department should be as little dependent as possible on those of the others . . .

Ambition must be made to counteract ambition. The interest of the man must be connected with the constitutional rights of the place. It may be a reflection on human nature, that such devices should be necessary to control the abuses of government. But what is government itself, but the greatest of all reflections on human nature? If men were angels, no government would be necessary. If angels were to govern men, neither external nor internal controls on government would be necessary. In framing a government which is to be administered by men over men, the great difficulty lies in this: you must first enable the government to control the governed; and in the next place oblige it to control itself.

---

1. List two principles of the Constitution that were the subject of *The Federalist* No. 51.

2. According to Madison, why were these principles "essential to the preservation of liberty"?

3. Discuss a specific example of how "ambition [is] made to counteract ambition" by the Constitution.

The Bill of Rights and Civil Liberties

How are your rights defined and protected under the Constitution?

Speaking of Politics

As you complete the Reading Notes, use these terms in your answers:

civil liberties	slander
civil rights	prior restraint
incorporation	self-incrimination
libel	double jeopardy

PREVIEW

A high school principal has reason to suspect some students of bringing weapons onto campus. After receiving a tip from a teacher, the principal searches the lockers of three students and finds a knife and a small handgun in one student's locker. The other two lockers turn up nothing.

1. In this situation, what rights do the students assigned to these lockers have?

2. What rights does the principal, acting on behalf of the student body, have?

3. On a high school campus, should authorities be allowed to search student lockers whenever they want?

READING NOTES

Section 5.2

After reading the section, answer these questions:

1. Explain the difference between civil liberties and civil rights. Give at least two examples of each.

2. Discuss the significance of the Fourteenth Amendment and of *Gitlow v. New York* in terms of American civil liberties and civil rights.

3. What is the role of the Supreme Court today? What happens when the Court overturns a decision made by a lower court?

Section 5.3

Read the section. Then complete the first row of the table on Notebook Handout 5 as follows:

- List the basic rights protected or guaranteed by the First Amendment.

- List and describe at least one Supreme Court case that acted as a precedent and helped further define this amendment.

- Create or find a simple symbol, illustration, or image to represent one right that this amendment guarantees.

Sections 5.4 to 5.6

For each amendment discussed in these sections, complete that row of the table on Notebook Handout 5. A shaded box indicates that no Supreme Court cases are related to that amendment.

PROCESSING

Identify a current news story or event, or a situation from your own life, in which rights are in conflict—either between two individuals, between an individual and society, or between an individual and the government. Then do the following:

1. Briefly describe the situation.

2. Identify the rights held by one of the parties.

3. Identify the rights held by the opposing party.

4. Based on what you know about the Constitution, whose rights should take priority? Why?

The Bill of Rights

Amendment	Rights Protected by This Amendment	Supreme Court Precedents That Helped Define These Rights	Illustration That Represents These Rights
1 Congress shall make no law respecting an establishment of religion, or prohibiting the free exercise thereof; or abridging the freedom of speech, or of the press; or the right of the people peaceably to assemble, and to petition the Government for a redress of grievances.			
2 A well regulated Militia, being necessary to the security of a free State, the right of the people to keep and bear Arms, shall not be infringed.			
3 No Soldier shall, in time of peace be quartered in any house, without the consent of the Owner, nor in time of war, but in a manner to be prescribed by law.			
4 The right of the people to be secure in their persons, houses, papers, and effects, against unreasonable searches and seizures, shall not be violated, and no Warrants shall issue, but upon probable cause, supported by Oath or affirmation, and particularly describing the place to be searched, and the persons or things to be seized.			
5 No person shall be held to answer for a capital, or otherwise infamous crime, unless on a presentment or indictment of a Grand Jury, except in cases arising in the land or naval forces, or in the Militia, when in actual service in time of War or public danger; nor shall any person be subject for the same offense to be twice put in jeopardy of life or limb; nor shall be compelled in any criminal case to be a witness against himself, nor be deprived of life, liberty, or property, without due process of law; nor shall private property be taken for public use, without just compensation.			

6 In all criminal prosecutions, the accused shall enjoy the right to a speedy and public trial, by an impartial jury of the State and district wherein the crime shall have been committed, which district shall have been previously ascertained by law, and to be informed of the nature and cause of the accusation; to be confronted with the witnesses against him; to have compulsory process for obtaining witnesses in his favor, and to have the Assistance of Counsel for his defence.	**7** In Suits at common law, where the value in controversy shall exceed twenty dollars, the right of trial by jury shall be preserved, and no fact tried by a jury, shall be otherwise re-examined in any Court of the United States, than according to the rules of the common law.	**8** Excessive bail shall not be required, nor excessive fines imposed, nor cruel and unusual punishments inflicted.	**9** The enumeration in the Constitution, of certain rights, shall not be construed to deny or disparage others retained by the people.	**10** The powers not delegated to the United States by the Constitution, nor prohibited by it to the States, are reserved to the States respectively, or to the people.

Case Brief: *Hazelwood v. Kuhlmeier* (1988)

Facts of the Case

Petitioner: Hazelwood School District
Respondent: Cathy Kuhlmeier

The school newspaper of Hazelwood East High School was written and edited by students and reviewed by both an adviser and Principal Robert Reynolds. As Reynolds reviewed the page proofs for the year's final edition of the *Spectrum,* he became concerned about two articles. One article focused on divorce and contained personal anecdotes from students about their families. Reynolds objected to the fact that these family members had no chance to refute or respond to the negative comments made about them. Reynolds also questioned the appropriateness of a second article about teenage pregnancy.

Fearing that changing the articles would force the students to miss their deadline for publication, Reynolds told the paper's adviser simply to delete the two pages that contained these articles, despite the fact that there were other student-written articles on these pages. District officials supported his decision.

Cathy Kuhlmeier, a student editor of the *Spectrum,* and other student journalists were outraged by what they considered censorship of their work. Believing their First Amendment rights had been violated, they took their case to the U.S. district court in Missouri.

The district court decided against the students, saying that if the school had a "substantial and reasonable basis," it could place limits on curricular activities, including the publication of the school newspaper.

The students appealed this decision to a federal court of appeals, which sided with them and agreed that their First Amendment rights had been violated. The court noted that the newspaper was a "public forum for student expression." A student publication, such as a school newspaper, is a "public forum" when students have been given the right to make their own decisions about content. As a "public forum" and a channel for "student viewpoints," the *Spectrum* could not be censored unless it was "necessary to avoid material and substantial interference with school work or discipline . . . or the rights of others."

The school appealed, and the Supreme Court agreed to hear the case. The legal issue before it was as follows: *Was the* Spectrum *a "public forum for student expression," therefore making the principal's deletions of student-written articles a violation of the students' First Amendment rights?*

Precedent: *Cantwell v. State of Connecticut* (1940)

Essential Facts: Jesse Cantwell and his son, both Jehovah's Witnesses, were distributing religious materials by ringing doorbells and by approaching people on the street in a predominantly Catholic neighborhood. Two pedestrians became angry after voluntarily listening to the Cantwells' anti-Catholic message. The Cantwells were arrested both for violating a local law that required a permit for solicitation and for inciting a breach of the peace.

Legal Issue: Did the local law requiring a permit for solicitation or the "breach of peace" ordinance violate the Cantwells' First Amendment rights to free speech?

Holding: The Court held that the local law restricting solicitation based on religious grounds violated both the First and the Fourteenth amendments. The Court also held that an interest to maintain public order could not be used to justify the suppression of "free communication of views." The Cantwells' message, though possibly offensive, did not threaten "bodily harm."

Precedent: *Epperson v. Arkansas* (1968)

Essential Facts: A high school biology teacher, Susan Epperson, filed suit in court to challenge the constitutionality of an Arkansas law banning the teaching of evolution. The law stated that to "teach the theory or doctrine that mankind ascended or descended from a lower order of animals" was a misdemeanor and would result in the teacher's dismissal.

Legal Issue: Did the state law that made the teaching of evolution illegal violate either the teacher's right to free speech or the First Amendment's Establishment Clause?

Holding: The Court decided that the Arkansas law did violate the First Amendment, as well as the Fourteenth Amendment. It reasoned that the law violated the Establishment Clause because it was not a "manifestation of religious neutrality." In addition, the Court held that a state's right to dictate the curriculum of public schools does not allow it to prohibit teaching a scientific theory. In its holding, however, the Court noted that "public education in our Nation is committed to the control of state and local authorities." It also stated that federal courts should not ordinarily "intervene in the resolution of conflicts which arise in the daily operation of school systems."

Precedent: *Tinker v. Des Moines Independent Community School District* (1969)

Essential Facts: Two high school students, John and Mary Beth Tinker, wore black armbands to school to protest the Vietnam War. They were told that they would be suspended until they agreed to return to school without the armbands.

Legal Issue: Did prohibiting students from wearing armbands in public school, as a form of symbolic protest, violate the First Amendment's freedom of speech protections?

Holding: The Court held that the school's prohibition of the armbands was a violation of the First Amendment. For school officials to justifiably prohibit some form of expression, they must "be able to show that its action was caused by something more than a mere desire to avoid the discomfort and unpleasantness that always accompany an unpopular viewpoint." Because the Tinkers' actions did not "materially and substantially interfere with the requirements of appropriate discipline in the operation of the school," disciplinary action against them could not be supported. The Tinkers were protected under the First Amendment, because students do not "shed their constitutional rights to freedom of speech or expression at the schoolhouse gate." In its opinion, however, the Court reemphasized the need to recognize the "authority of the States and of school officials . . . to prescribe and control conduct in the schools."

Case Brief: *Wallace v. Jaffree* (1985)

Facts of the Case

Petitioner: George Wallace, Governor of Alabama

Respondent: Ishmael Jaffree

In 1978, Alabama enacted a statute that allowed a one-minute period of silence in public schools for the purpose of "meditation." In 1981, the statute was rewritten to include not only meditation but also "voluntary prayer." In 1982, the statute was further amended to authorize teachers to lead "willing students" in a prescribed prayer to "Almighty God . . . the Creator and Supreme Judge of the world."

In 1982, Ishmael Jaffree, a resident of Mobile County, Alabama, filed a complaint on behalf of his three elementary-aged schoolchildren. The complaint named school board members, school officials, and the three teachers as defendants. Jaffree sought a judgment that would prevent the defendants from performing or allowing regular religious prayer services or other forms of religious observances in the Mobile County Public Schools. He stated that these prayer services, though allowed by the 1981 and 1982 state laws, violated the First Amendment.

The district court held that both the 1981 and the 1982 statutes were constitutional because Alabama had the right to establish a state religion if it chose to. The court of appeals reversed the decision and held that both statutes were unconstitutional.

The case was appealed to the Supreme Court. The Court unanimously held that the 1982 statute authorizing teachers to lead students in prayer was unconstitutional. That left it with the 1981 statute to examine and this legal issue to decide: *Did Alabama's state law authorizing a period of silence for "meditation or voluntary prayer" violate the Establishment Clause of the First Amendment?*

Precedent: *West Virginia State Board of Education v. Barnette* (1943)

Essential Facts: In West Virginia, refusing to salute the flag was considered insubordination, and students who did so were consequently expelled from school. Various civic and religious groups challenged this statute. They argued that the statute made no allowances for religious beliefs.

Legal Issue: Did the mandatory flag salute for children in public school violate the First Amendment?

Holding: The Supreme Court held in favor of the petitioners, noting that the school district had violated the First Amendment rights of students by forcing them to salute the American flag. The Court found that the salute was a means of communicating ideas. Requiring the communication of ideas went against the intent of the First Amendment. In drawing this conclusion, the Court noted that school boards may not "prescribe what shall be orthodox in politics, nationalism, religion, or other matters of opinion."

Precedent: *Engel v. Vitale* **(1962)**

Essential Facts: New York's State Board of Regents directed their schools to recite a morning nondenominational prayer as a part of their "Statement on Moral and Spiritual Training in the Schools." On the grounds that this practice was contrary to their beliefs and religious practices and that it violated the First and Fourteenth amendments, the parents of 10 students brought this action to the Supreme Court.

Legal Issue: Did the reading of a nondenominational prayer in public school violate the Establishment Clause of the First Amendment?

Holding: The Court held in favor of the parents and students, noting that despite the prayer's nondenominational character and the fact that it was voluntary, it was still constitutionally unacceptable. By providing the prayer, New York officially approved religion.

Precedent: *Lemon v. Kurtzman* **(1971)**

Essential Facts: This case involved disputes over laws in Pennsylvania and Rhode Island. The Pennsylvania law provided financial support to private schools for teacher salaries and instructional materials for nonreligious subjects. In Rhode Island, a law supplemented the salaries of teachers in nonpublic elementary schools.

Legal Issue: Did these state laws, by providing aid to "church-related educational institutions," violate the First Amendment's Establishment Clause?

Holding: The Court held that the state statutes did violate the Establishment Clause, because the First Amendment was designed to prevent the "sponsorship, financial support, and active involvement . . . in religious activity." In its holding, the Court made the following distinction regarding state statutes that might conflict with the Establishment Clause: "First, the statute must have a secular [nonreligious] legislative purpose; second, its principal or primary effect must be one that neither advances nor inhibits religion; finally, the statute must not foster an excessive government entanglement with religion." Because both states' laws included aid to nonpublic schools, the Court held that this directly benefited the churches that operated these schools, thus violating the Establishment Clause. In addition, because the laws required close supervision, there was an excessive relationship between the state and religion.

Case Brief: *Bethel School District No. 403 v. Fraser* (1986)

Facts of the Case

Petitioner: Bethel School District
Respondent: Matthew Fraser

In April 1983, Matthew Fraser, a 17-year-old student at Bethel High School, stood before 600 of his peers at a required student-body assembly to deliver a speech supporting another student's nomination for student government. His speech was full of sexual references and innuendos. Prior to his delivering the speech, two of Fraser's teachers warned him that the speech was "inappropriate" and that should he deliver it, he could face severe reprimanding.

A counselor who was present during the speech noted that some students hooted and seemed supportive, but that others, many of whom were 14-year-olds, seemed embarrassed or even confused by the speech. One teacher later stated that she found it necessary to spend class time discussing the speech with her class.

The following morning, the assistant principal called Fraser into her office and told him that he had broken a school rule that prohibited the use of obscene language. Fraser was presented with letters written by teachers who had witnessed the speech. He was then given a chance to explain his conduct, during which time he admitted to knowingly using the obscene language. Fraser was suspended from school for three days, and his name was removed from the list of candidates who would speak at the graduation ceremonies. After serving only two days of the suspension, Fraser was allowed to return to school.

Fraser's father filed suit with the district court, alleging that Fraser's suspension violated his First Amendment right to freedom of speech. The district court held in favor of Fraser, awarded him compensation for damages and court fees, and ordered the school district to reinstate Fraser as a graduation speaker.

On appeal, the judgment of the district court was upheld on the grounds that Fraser's speech was the same as the protest armbands worn by the petitioners in *Tinker v. Des Moines Independent Community School District*. The appeals court rejected the school district's argument that the speech had a disruptive effect on the educational process.

The Supreme Court agreed to hear the case to answer the following question: *Did Bethel High School authorities violate the First Amendment by disciplining a high school student for giving a lewd speech at a school assembly?*

Precedent: *Ginsberg v. New York* (1968)

Essential Facts: The owner of a stationery store in New York was arrested and convicted of selling obscene material to a 16-year-old boy. He had violated a New York law that made it unlawful to "knowingly" sell to anyone under 17 either "any picture . . . which depicts nudity . . . and which is harmful to minors" or "any . . . magazine . . . which contains [such pictures] and which, taken as a whole, is harmful to minors."

Legal Issue: Did New York's statute prohibiting the sale of obscene material to minors, but not to adults, violate the First Amendment?

Holding: The Supreme Court held that the government is entitled to restrict children's access to certain kinds of sexually explicit material, even if the material is not obscene or illegal for adults. In its opinion, the Court reasoned that "the State has an independent interest in protecting the welfare of children and safeguarding them from abuses."

Precedent: *Tinker v. Des Moines Independent Community School District* (1969)

Essential Facts: Two high school students, John and Mary Beth Tinker, wore black armbands to school to protest the Vietnam War. They were told that they would be suspended until they agreed to return to school without the armbands.

Legal Issue: Did prohibiting students from wearing armbands in public school, as a form of symbolic protest, violate the First Amendment's freedom of speech protections?

Holding: The Court held that the school's prohibition of the armbands was a violation of the First Amendment. For school officials to justifiably prohibit some form of expression, they must "be able to show that its action was caused by something more than a mere desire to avoid the discomfort and unpleasantness that always accompany an unpopular viewpoint." Because the Tinkers' actions did not "materially and substantially interfere with the requirements of appropriate discipline in the operation of the school," disciplinary action against them could not be supported. The Tinkers were protected under the First Amendment, because students do not "shed their constitutional rights to freedom of speech or expression at the schoolhouse gate." In its opinion, however, the Court reemphasized the need to recognize the "authority of the States and of school officials . . . to prescribe and control conduct in the schools."

Precedent: *FCC v. Pacifica Foundation* (1978)

Essential Facts: A Pacifica Foundation radio station broadcast comedian George Carlin's recording of "Filthy Words." The father of a young boy who happened to be listening to the broadcast complained to the Federal Communications Commissions, the government agency that regulates radio and television broadcasting. After receiving the complaint, the FCC reprimanded the radio station for violating regulations that prohibited broadcasting "indecent" material and warned that sanctions would be imposed if there were further incidents.

Legal Issue: Could the public broadcasting of indecent language be restricted by the government without violating the First Amendment?

Holding: The Court held that a radio station could be constitutionally restricted from broadcasting offensive words. However, certain factors should be considered when invoking penalties or sanctions, such as audience, medium, time of day, and method of transmission. The Court held that the Pacifica Foundation's broadcast was "indecent" and that the FCC could prohibit such broadcasts during hours when children were likely to be listening. The Court cited an interest in both shielding children from offensive material and ensuring that unwanted speech does not enter people's homes.

Case Brief: *Board of Education of Westside Community Schools v. Mergens* (1990)

Facts of the Case

Petitioner: Westside Community School Board of Education

Respondent: Bridget Mergens

Bridget Mergens, a student at Westside High School in Nebraska, asked school authorities if she could start a Christian club at the high school. When her request was denied, she filed suit. She based her claim on the Equal Access Act, a law passed by Congress in 1984. Under this act, schools that receive federal financial assistance and that have at least one student-led, noncurriculum club that meets outside of class time must allow other clubs to organize. However, these clubs must have voluntary attendance, must be student led and initiated, and cannot be promoted by a teacher or school official.

Westside High was a public high school that received federal financial assistance. It also already had a number of recognized groups and clubs—including a chess club, a scuba club, and a service club—that met after school hours on school grounds. The school district required these clubs to have faculty sponsorship, a direct violation of the Equal Access Act. The district felt that allowing Mergens to form a Christian club would violate the Establishment Clause of the First Amendment. On those grounds, the school board voted to deny Mergens's request. Shortly afterward, Mergens and several Westside students filed suit.

The district court held in favor of the school district because it examined the extracurricular clubs available to students at the school and concluded that they were all curriculum related, making the Equal Access Act null and void in this case. The court of appeals reversed the decision, holding that several existing student clubs were indeed noncurriculum related and that therefore Mergens should have been allowed to organize a Christian club and have it receive official school recognition. In addition, it rejected the claim that the formation of a Christian club—as well as the Equal Access Act that allowed its formation—violated the Establishment Clause.

The case was brought before the Supreme Court to answer the following question: *Did the Equal Access Act, which requires that schools permitting noncurriculum clubs also allow religious clubs, violate the Establishment Clause of the First Amendment?*

Precedent: *Lemon v. Kurtzman* (1971)

Essential Facts: This case involved disputes over laws in Pennsylvania and Rhode Island. The Pennsylvania law provided financial support to private schools for teacher salaries and instructional materials for nonreligious subjects. In Rhode Island, a law supplemented the salaries of teachers in nonpublic elementary schools.

Legal Issue: Did these state laws, by providing aid to "church-related educational institutions," violate the First Amendment's Establishment Clause?

Holding: The Court held that the state statutes did violate the Establishment Clause, because the First Amendment was designed to prevent the "sponsorship, financial support, and active involvement . . . in religious activity." In its holding, the Court made the following distinction regarding state statutes that might conflict with the Establishment Clause: "First, the statute must have a secular [nonreligious] legislative purpose; second, its principal or primary effect must be one that neither advances nor inhibits religion; finally, the statute must not foster an excessive government entanglement with religion." Because both states' laws included aid to nonpublic schools, the Court held that this directly benefited the churches that operated these schools, thus violating the Establishment Clause. In addition, because the laws required close supervision, there was an excessive relationship between the state and religion.

Precedent: *Widmar v. Vincent* (1981)

Essential Facts: At the University of Missouri at Kansas City, a state university, registered student groups were permitted to use school facilities to conduct meetings. A registered student religious group that had received permission to use the facilities was then informed that it could no longer do so because the university prohibited the use of university buildings or grounds "for purposes of religious worship or religious teaching." This group sued the school, asserting that their First Amendment rights to religious free exercise and free speech had been violated.

Legal Issue: Did the university violate the First Amendment by prohibiting a religious group to use its facilities?

Holding: The Supreme Court held that by excluding the religious group from using its facilities, the university violated the "fundamental principle that a state regulation of speech should be content-neutral." The Establishment Clause does not require state universities to limit the access of religious organizations to their facilities. An "equal access" policy would not offend the Establishment Clause if it could pass the following three-pronged test: (1) It has a secular legislative purpose. (2) Its principal or primary effect would be neither to advance nor to inhibit religion. (3) It does not foster "an excessive government entanglement with religion."

Supreme Court Hearing Procedures

Arranging the Classroom for the Hearing

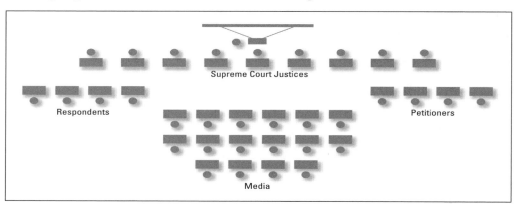

Supreme Court Justices

Respondents

Petitioners

Media

Conducting the Hearing

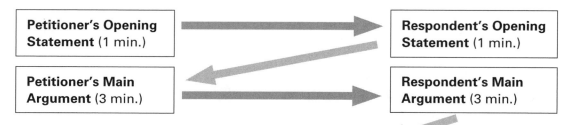

Petitioner's Opening Statement (1 min.)

Respondent's Opening Statement (1 min.)

Petitioner's Main Argument (3 min.)

Respondent's Main Argument (3 min.)

Question-and-Answer Session: During this time, the Court may address members of either team with a question or statement. Members of both teams may also ask questions of members of the opposing counsel. (4 min.)

Conference Time: Both teams will have a few minutes to confer quietly and make any revisions to their closing statements based on what they heard during the debate. (1 min.)

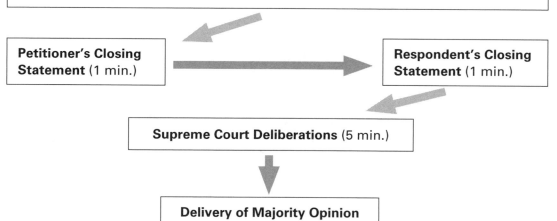

Petitioner's Closing Statement (1 min.)

Respondent's Closing Statement (1 min.)

Supreme Court Deliberations (5 min.)

Delivery of Majority Opinion

Preparing Your Case

You will work with your team to prepare a legal argument for your assigned case.

☐ **Step 1: Assign roles.** Decide with your legal team which member is best suited for each role:

Chief Counsel As the leader of your legal team, you will lead your team as it reviews the facts of the case. You will review each part of the legal arguments to ensure that all requirements are met.

Associate Counsel 1 You will lead your team as it prepares an opening statement for the Court. You will then deliver this opening statement to the Court.

Associate Counsel 2 You will lead your team as it prepares your main legal argument. You will then deliver these arguments to the Court.

Associate Counsel 3 You will lead your team as it prepares a closing statement. You will then deliver this statement to the Court.

☐ **Step 2: Review your case brief.** Your Chief Counsel will make sure everyone understands the important facts of your case. Discuss these questions with your team:

- What main arguments will your team make?

- What main arguments will the opposing team make? How will you counter them?

☐ **Step 3: Prepare your opening statement.** Under the leadership of Associate Counsel 1, decide the best way to open your argument. Your opening should be no longer than 1 minute and should contain

- a clear, concise statement of your team's opinion of this case.

- the constitutional rights pertaining to the issues of your case.

- a brief summary of the key details of the case, presented in a way that clearly favors your position. For example, in the case of *Schenck v. United States* (from Section 5.1), the petitioner's counsel might begin, *Charles Schenck acted completely within the scope of his constitutional rights when he protested the draft by mailing leaflets to young men in Philadelphia, and he should not have been arrested.* The

respondent's counsel might begin, *During wartime, the need to maintain public safety sometimes prevails over individual rights. The Espionage Act was an attempt to make sure that the war effort was not undermined, and Charles Schenck clearly violated that act by distributing antidraft leaflets.*

- what you intend to prove to the Court.

☐ **Step 4: Prepare your main legal argument.** Associate Counsel 2 will help your team formulate a strong legal argument for your case. This main argument should be roughly 3 minutes in length and

- include all the relevant facts from your case brief.

- reference any precedents that might help your argument and relate any precedents you use to your case. (You cannot simply cite a precedent. You must also clearly explain its connection to your case.)

- assert why you believe your opponent is wrong.

- strongly state your purpose and a belief that you are constitutionally right.

☐ **Step 5: Prepare your closing statement.** Associate Counsel 3 will help your team formulate a strong closing argument. It should be no more than 1 minute long and include

- a general restatement of your position.

- a quick summary of your strongest argument.

- a final rebuttal of the opposing team's argument.

- a specific recommendation to the Court as to how you believe it should decide.

☐ **Step 6: Rehearse your arguments.** As you rehearse, your Chief Counsel should listen to each team member deliver his or her portion of the legal argument and be able to identify all the specified elements of each step. The Chief Counsel should also check that each presenter

- speaks loudly and clearly, with a professional tone and without using slang.

- makes eye contact with the audience.

- stays within the given time limits.

- dresses appropriately for a member of a legal team presenting a case to the Supreme Court.

Case Summaries and Outcomes

Hazelwood v. Kuhlmeier (1988)

Case Summary: Several student writers of the Hazelwood East High School newspaper objected after their principal deleted two articles from the paper that he felt were inappropriate. The students, who felt that their paper was a "public forum" for student expression and believed that their First Amendment right to free speech had been violated, took the school to court.

Question for the Court: Was the *Spectrum* a "public forum for student expression," therefore making the principal's deletions of student-written articles a violation of the students' First Amendment rights?

Case Outcome: The Supreme Court held in favor of school officials at Hazelwood School District and found that the students' First Amendment rights had not been violated. School officials can censor speech if it conflicts with the school's basic educational mission. Because a school newspaper was involved, students could reasonably expect to have to meet the approval of the school before publication. The publication of the newspaper was also part of a journalism course, in which students received grades and academic credit and in which a teacher exercised control over the publication and the principal had to review it. There appeared to be no intent to expand this newspaper into a "public forum." The Court acknowledged that the principal's concerns—the protection of students' identities, the privacy interests of the people involved, and the fact that parents mentioned in the divorce article were not given an opportunity to defend themselves—were entirely reasonable.

However, though this decision did give public high school officials more authority to censor school-sponsored publications, it did not apply to publications that were considered "public forums for student expression." It also required school officials to demonstrate a reasonable educational justification for censoring something. In addition, since the time of this decision, six states (Arkansas, California, Colorado, Iowa, Kansas, and Massachusetts) have enacted laws that give students more press freedoms than were indicated under the *Hazelwood* decision.

Wallace v. Jaffree (1985)

Case Summary: The father of three children attending public school in Alabama challenged an Alabama law that authorized a one-minute period of silence in all public schools for meditation or voluntary prayer. He felt that this law encouraged religious activity, in violation of the First Amendment's Establishment Clause.

Question for the Court: Did Alabama's state law authorizing a period of silence for "meditation or voluntary prayer" violate the Establishment Clause of the First Amendment?

Case Outcome: The Supreme Court held in favor of the petitioners—the students and their father—and found that the Alabama law violated the Establishment Clause of the First Amendment. The intent of the First Amendment is to limit the power of the government to interfere with a person's freedom to believe, worship, and express himself or herself. Therefore, an individual has the right to his or her own beliefs without having to accept a religion established by the government. The government—even state governments—cannot endorse religion. Because the acknowledged intent of the Alabama law was "to return voluntary prayer to our public schools," the Court determined that its purpose was to endorse religion. This law was, therefore, struck down as being inconsistent with the Constitution.

Bethel School District No. 403 v. Fraser (1986)

Case Summary: Matthew Fraser, a senior at Bethel High School, gave a speech before the student body to nominate a fellow classmate for an elected school office. During this speech, Fraser made sexual innuendos and references. He was subsequently suspended for three days. Fraser sued, claiming that his rights were violated by this suspension.

Question for the Court: Did Bethel High School authorities violate the First Amendment by disciplining a high school student for giving a lewd speech at a school assembly?

Case Outcome: The Supreme Court held in favor of the school board. The Court stated that the school had every right to punish Fraser for his offensive speech. Unlike in *Tinker v. Des Moines Independent Community School District,* Fraser was not punished for expressing a political viewpoint. The sexual innuendos had no relationship to the merits of the candidate who was being nominated. The Court noted that schools are completely within their rights to "prohibit the use of vulgar and offensive terms in public discourse" as an effort to protect minors. One justice noted, "A high school assembly or classroom is no place for a sexually explicit monologue directed towards an unsuspecting audience of teenage students." The Court also stated that Fraser was given plenty of warnings that his speech might result in suspension—two teachers reacted negatively to his speech, and school policy prohibited such offensive language.

Board of Education of Westside Community Schools v. Mergens (1990)

Case Summary: Westside High School is a public school that receives federal financial assistance. It also permits students to voluntarily join a number of recognized groups and clubs, all of which meet after school hours on school premises. After one student's request to form a Christian club that would meet in a similar fashion as these other groups was denied, a group of students took the school district to court.

Question for the Court: Did the Equal Access Act, which requires that schools permitting noncurriculum clubs also allow religious clubs, violate the Establishment Clause of the First Amendment?

Case Outcome: The Supreme Court held in favor of the students. The proposed Christian club would be a non-curricular group because its subject matter would not actually be taught in classes and its members would not receive academic credit for their participation. Because other noncurricular clubs were permitted, the Court held that the Christian club should be allowed under the Equal Access Act. The Court also held the Equal Access Act to be constitutional because it served the purpose of prohibiting discrimination on the basis of philosophical, political, or other types of speech.

"State of the First Amendment" Survey Results, 2006

1. First Amendment Rights Americans are able to identify

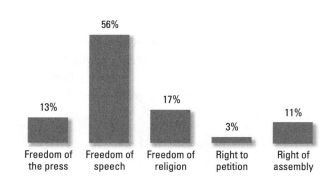

2. The First Amendment goes too far in the rights it guarantees.

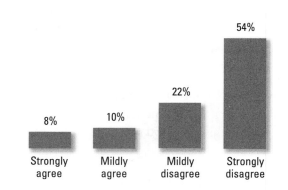

3. Amount of freedom the press has in America

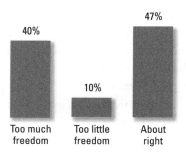

4. Newspapers should be allowed to criticize the U.S. military.

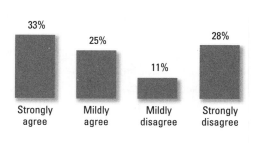

5. Musicians should be allowed to sing songs with offensive lyrics.

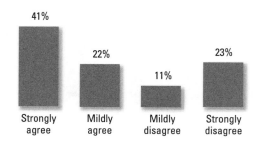

6. People should be allowed to say things that might be offensive to religious groups.

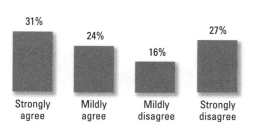

7. People should be allowed to say things that might be offensive to racial groups.

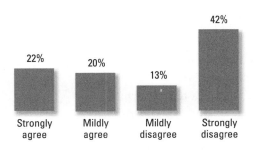

8. When should newspapers be allowed to publish sensitive or classified government information?

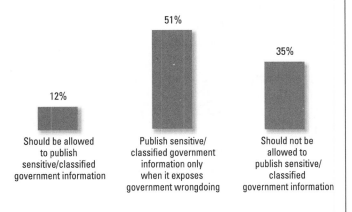

9. Newspapers should honor government requests to withhold publishing information.

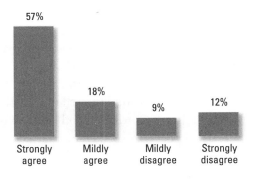

10. The press should be allowed to publish stories that criticize the government.

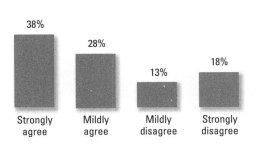

Source: First Amendment Center, firstamendmentcenter.org.

11. Political candidates should be allowed to criticize the actions of government.

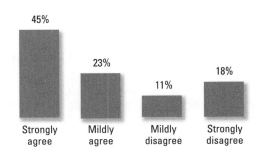

Mastering the Content

1. Which of these plays the largest role in interpreting the Bill of Rights?
   A. Congress
   B. state legislatures
   C. the Supreme Court
   D. the executive branch

2. Which of these is a civil liberty protected by the Bill of Rights?
   A. the right to work
   B. the right to marry
   C. the right to travel abroad
   D. the right to religious freedom

3. Which of these unpopular forms of expression is protected by the First Amendment?
   A. libel
   B. slander
   C. obscenity
   D. flag burning

4. Most Supreme Court decisions applying the Bill of Rights to the states are based on the
   A. Supremacy Clause.
   B. Establishment Clause.
   C. Equal Protection Clause.
   D. Necessary and Proper Clause.

5. Which of these acts is protected under the First Amendment?
   A. criticizing elected leaders
   B. selling pornography to children
   C. telling military secrets to the enemy
   D. spreading untrue rumors to harm someone

6. The Fifth, Sixth, Seventh, and Eighth amendments protect
   A. voting rights.
   B. privacy rights.
   C. rights in the legal system.
   D. rights reserved to the states.

7. Which of these rights has not been subject to incorporation?
   A. the right to bear arms
   B. the right to a fair trial
   C. the right to freedom of speech
   D. the right to petition the government

8. The phrase "You have the right to remain silent" reflects the provision in the Bill of Rights regarding
   A. double jeopardy.
   B. eminent domain.
   C. judicial review.
   D. self-incrimination.

9. The term *prior restraint* refers to which government action?
   A. deciding a law is unconstitutional
   B. preventing publication of certain material
   C. jailing individuals without bail before a trial
   D. searching people suspected of planning a crime

10. What decision did the Supreme Court make on the power of cities to regulate peaceful assembly in public places in *Hague v. CIO*?
    A. Cities may not regulate assemblies in public places in any way.
    B. Cities may set rules for the use of public places that apply equally to all.
    C. Cities may charge groups to meet in public places as long as fees are low.
    D. Cities may pick and choose which groups to allow to meet in public places.

Exploring the Essential Question

How are your rights defined and protected under the Constitution?

A high school girl was taken to the principal's office for smoking in the lavatory. She denied smoking and claimed to be a nonsmoker. A search of her purse revealed not only cigarettes but also evidence that she was selling marijuana. In juvenile court, she said that the evidence came from an illegal search. Below are parts of the Supreme Court decision in her case.

New Jersey v. T.L.O. (1985)

We are faced initially with the question whether [the Fourth] Amendment's prohibition on unreasonable searches and seizures applies to searches conducted by public school officials. We hold that it does . . .

To hold that the Fourth Amendment applies to searches conducted by school authorities is only to begin the inquiry into the standards governing such searches . . .

Students at a minimum must bring to school not only the supplies needed for their studies, but also keys, money, and the necessaries of personal hygiene and grooming. In addition, students may carry on their persons or in purses or wallets such nondisruptive yet highly personal items as photographs, letters, and diaries . . . There is no reason to conclude that they have necessarily waived all rights to privacy in such items merely by bringing them onto school grounds.

Against the child's interest in privacy must be set the substantial interest of teachers and administrators in maintaining discipline in the classroom and on school grounds. Maintaining order in the classroom has never been easy, but in recent years, school disorder has often taken particularly ugly forms: drug use and violent crime in the schools have become major social problems . . .

How, then, should we strike the balance between the schoolchild's legitimate expectations of privacy and the school's equally legitimate need to maintain an environment in which learning can take place? . . .

We join the majority of courts that have examined this issue in concluding that the accommodation of the privacy interests of schoolchildren with the substantial need of teachers and administrators for freedom to maintain order in the schools does not require . . . that searches be based on probable cause . . . Rather, the legality of a search of a student should depend simply on the reasonableness, under all the circumstances, of the search . . . Under ordinary circumstances, a search of a student by a teacher or other school official will be . . . justified . . . when there are reasonable grounds for suspecting that the search will turn up evidence that the student has violated or is violating either the law or the rules of the school.

---

1. What was the first question the Supreme Court considered in this decision? How did it answer that question?

2. Whose rights and needs did the Court seek to balance in its decision?

3. The Court set a new standard in this case in concluding that a search of students at school is allowed under the Fourth Amendment. What is that standard?

4. Based on the standard set in *New Jersey v. T.L.O.*, are random checks of school lockers constitutional? Explain your reasoning.

Federalism: National, State, and Local Powers

How does power flow through our federal system of government?

As you complete the Reading Notes, use these terms in your answers:

expressed powers   devolution

interstate commerce   apportionment

intrastate commerce   gerrymandering

unfunded mandate   redistricting

Copy the Venn diagram below into your notebook. List at least three decisions in each section, and then answer the questions.

1. What types of decisions do your parents or guardians make for you? What types of decisions do you make for yourself? What types of decisions do you make together?

2. Why are some decisions shared while others are not?

3. What are the benefits of making decisions this way? What are the drawbacks?

4 How do you think this system of making decisions is similar to the way power flows between national and state governments?

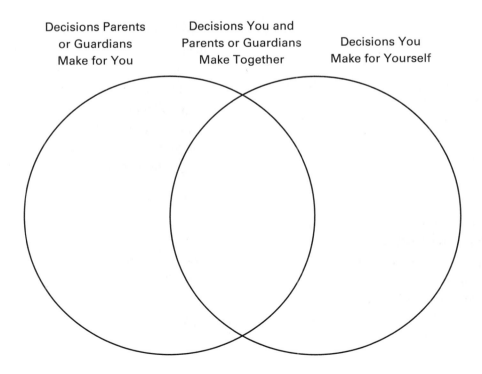

Decisions Parents or Guardians Make for You   Decisions You and Parents or Guardians Make Together   Decisions You Make for Yourself

READING NOTES

Section 6.2

Copy the Venn diagram below into your notebook. Provide a definition and at least two examples of powers for each part of the diagram. Then answer this question: *What are the benefits and drawbacks of a federal system?*

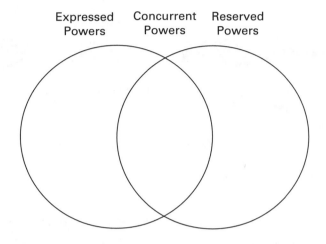

Expressed Powers Concurrent Powers Reserved Powers

Section 6.3

Create a timeline in your notebook, and place each of these terms along it:

- Dual federalism
- Cooperative federalism
- Regulated federalism
- New federalism

For each term, include the approximate dates that this type of federalism existed and a simple illustration. Also briefly explain how national and state powers were defined during each period.

Section 6.4

Answer these questions:

1. What do state constitutions show about how power is distributed in our federal system?

2. Create an illustration that will help you remember important information about the three branches of state government. On your illustration, record notes about the role of state legislatures, state governors, and state court systems.

Section 6.5

Complete the table below in your notebook by briefly describing the organization and purpose of each local government system.

Local Government System	How Is It Organized?	What Is Its Purpose?
Counties, parishes, and boroughs		
Mayor-council system		
Commission system		
Council-manager system		
Special-purpose districts		

PROCESSING

Help people your age understand more about how they can use the federal system to address issues of importance to them. Choose an issue from the list below, or come up with your own idea. Then create a public service flyer that includes

- an eye-catching title and illustration.

- a brief explanation about which level or levels of government have the power to address this issue and why.

- the names and contact information—phone numbers, mailing addresses, Web sites, e-mail addresses—of two government officials or agencies where people can get more information about this issue.

Issues of Public Concern

- Lack of a recycling and conservation program in your area

- Too strict or too lenient high school graduation requirements

- Lack of adequate health insurance coverage

- Support or protest of a U.S. foreign policy

Federalism and Gun Control Laws

In 1990, Congress passed the Gun-Free School Zones Act as part of its crime control legislation. The law made it illegal for any person to possess a firearm in a place that he or she knows is a school zone, unless that person is acting in a law enforcement capacity. Most people thought this new law, which was enacted amid increasing concerns about gun violence in schools, was a good idea.

There was soon a major challenge to the law. Early in 1992, 12th grader Alfonso Lopez Jr. brought a concealed handgun into Edison High School in San Antonio, Texas. School officials received an anonymous tip and confronted him. Lopez admitted that he was carrying a .38 caliber handgun and five bullets. He was convicted in federal district court of violating the Gun-Free School Zones Act and was sentenced to six months in prison and another two years of supervised release.

Lopez appealed his conviction, arguing that Congress did not have the constitutional power to pass the Gun-Free School Zones Act. The government, in contrast, contended that the Commerce Clause, which gives Congress the power to "regulate commerce with foreign nations, and among the several states," gave lawmakers the appropriate constitutional power. It argued that possession of a firearm in a school zone leads to violent crime, which affects the national economy (commerce) by causing insurance rates to rise and by discouraging travel through areas that are thought to be unsafe. The government also argued that allowing guns in schools undermines the goal of a safe learning environment. If students cannot learn, they become less-productive citizens.

Contrary to the government's argument, however, the power to establish and maintain schools is traditionally reserved for the states. Many states, in turn, pass this responsibility on to local governments. Although Congress has substantial experience in creating firearms legislation, it does not have knowledge about, or experience managing, any one particular school district. States also have the power to provide fire and police protection. In this capacity, many state legislatures have already passed laws similar to the Gun-Free School Zones Act.

In your group, use your Reading Notes, this handout, and the federal system diagram to answer the questions below. You must reach an agreement on Question 3 and be prepared to share your response with the class.

1. Which expressed, concurrent, and reserved powers apply to this issue?

2. What are the strongest arguments in favor of national power in this issue? Against national power?

3. Do you think the national government has the power to prohibit the possession of firearms near schools? Why or why not?

Federalism and Tobacco Advertising Laws

In November 1998, Massachusetts joined 45 other states to settle a claim against tobacco companies. Massachusetts would receive $7.6 billion over 25 years to repay money spent on treatment for sick smokers. Though he agreed to the settlement, Attorney General Scott Harshbarger believed that it did not go far enough in restricting tobacco advertising.

Two months later, the attorney general issued 11 regulations on tobacco advertising in Massachusetts, including a ban on tobacco ads within 1,000 feet of elementary and secondary schools, public playgrounds, and public parks with playgrounds. Only simple black-and-white signs saying "Tobacco products sold here" were to be allowed. In-store tobacco ads were to be placed at or above 5 feet to be out of the direct eyesight of children. In addition, new warning labels were to be included on cigar packaging. The new regulations were set to begin August 1, 1999.

Before the new regulations took effect, several tobacco companies filed lawsuits claiming that the regulations were invalid. The companies argued that a national law—the Federal Cigarette Labeling and Advertising Act—preempted any state regulations on advertising. The FCLAA required that a warning be placed on all cigarette packages and advertisements. Furthermore, the law said that states could not place restrictions or bans on the advertising of cigarettes with packaging that contained the warning. The companies also argued that Massachusetts's restrictions on advertising violated a First Amendment right to free commercial speech. Finally, they said that Massachusetts had overstepped its reserved constitutional powers. Under the Commerce Clause, only Congress has the power to regulate interstate commerce. The tobacco companies felt that the new labels on cigar packaging placed a heavy burden on interstate commerce and, therefore, only Congress could require them.

Massachusetts felt that it had a compelling state interest in preventing smoking among young people. It believed that the new regulations were a natural extension of the FCLAA, which was enacted to provide a uniform warning on all cigarette packages and advertising for all states. Massachusetts did not believe that the FCLAA intended to prevent additional state and local restrictions in places where they had jurisdiction. In addition, the location of commercial advertising was traditionally a power given to local communities. For example, a town could control whether ads were placed on its Little League field, and a state could control whether billboards overlooked its elementary schools. Massachusetts also believed that its regulations were restricting the location, not the content, of tobacco advertising. Because the state was not restricting content, it claimed that its rules did not violate a First Amendment right to free commercial speech.

In your group, use your Reading Notes, this handout, and the federal system diagram to answer the questions below. You must reach an agreement on Question 3 and be prepared to share your response with the class.

1. Which expressed, concurrent, and reserved powers apply to this issue?

2. What are the strongest arguments in favor of state power in this issue? Against state power?

3. Do you think Massachusetts has the power to regulate tobacco advertising within its borders?

Federalism and Air Pollution Laws

The Clean Air Act is a series of laws that Congress enacted to control air pollution. The most recent change to the act was passed in 1990. This addition provides guidelines on the amount of a pollutant that can be in the air. It also set deadlines for national, state, and local governments to reduce air pollution. Finally, the 1990 Clean Air Act gives the Environmental Protection Agency (EPA) power to enforce the law. Prior to 1990, state and local governments had been responsible for enforcing the Clean Air Act.

Though the 1990 Clean Air Act is a national law covering the entire country, states are expected to carry out many of its provisions. For example, states must develop implementation plans that outline their best method for controlling air pollution in areas that do not meet national air-quality standards. State standards for controlling air pollution can be stricter than those required by the Clean Air Act, but they cannot be weaker. If the EPA finds a state plan to be unacceptable, it can take over enforcement of the Clean Air Act in that state.

In 1998, the owner of a zinc mine in northwest Alaska requested a permit to build a new generator that would release more pollution into the air. The Alaska Department of Environmental Conservation approved a permit for the new generator if the company installed a technology called low NOx. The state also required the company to install low NOx on all of its existing generators. The EPA disagreed with the state of Alaska, believing that a better technology was available for the new generator. Though installing low NOx on all generators would best reduce overall pollution, the EPA said the state had to consider the best technology for each individual generator. When the EPA blocked the construction of the new generator, Alaska filed a lawsuit.

Alaska argued that the EPA did not have the power to override the state's decision. States, not the EPA, were given the power to carry out the provisions of the Clean Air Act. Alaska believed it properly followed the guidelines set forth in the law. If the EPA stepped in simply because of a disagreement, the state would have no authority to implement its plan to control air pollution. Furthermore, the technology that the EPA recommended was more expensive than the one Alaska had authorized. The state was concerned about the negative economic impact of the more expensive technology.

The national government, on the other hand, argued that Congress did give the EPA authority to enforce the Clean Air Act and ensure that states followed the guidelines of the law. Although states do have the power to make decisions about how best to control air pollution, the EPA could review those decisions. If the EPA were not allowed to do so, it would have no power to enforce the Clean Air Act. In this case, because the EPA did not think Alaska was following the guidelines, a review was required by law. When Alaska granted a permit to allow a generator to be built with low NOx technology, the EPA argued, it did not use the best technology available for controlling air pollution.

In your group, use your Reading Notes, this handout, and the federal system diagram to answer the questions below. You must reach an agreement on Question 3 and be prepared to share your response with the class.

1. Which expressed, concurrent, and reserved powers apply to this issue?

2. What are the strongest arguments in favor of state power in this issue? Against state power?

3. Which government—national or state—do you think has the power to regulate air pollution in Alaska?

Mastering the Content

1. According to the U.S. Constitution, the national government must guarantee that every state government
   A. updates its laws regularly.
   B. has a republican structure.
   C. has a bicameral legislature.
   D. limits governors to two terms.

2. Which of these officeholders is typically a county government official?
   A. delegate
   B. governor
   C. senator
   D. sheriff

3. Presidents Richard Nixon and Ronald Reagan both advocated a policy known as devolution. What was this policy aimed at?
   A. limiting taxes levied by states
   B. reducing federal grants to the states
   C. transferring power back to the states
   D. improving cooperation among the states

4. Which of these descriptions best defines *gerrymandering*?
   A. interpreting laws in a way that benefits the party in power
   B. enlarging a court by the addition of politically appointed judges
   C. drawing legislative district boundaries to give one group an advantage
   D. combining local governments into larger units to increase their influence

5. Which of these terms refers to legislation the national government requires state or local governments to implement largely at their own expense?
   A. block grants
   B. grants-in-aid
   C. federal regulations
   D. unfunded mandates

6. In which kind of court would a driver protesting a speeding ticket most likely appear?
   A. appeals court
   B. municipal court
   C. small claims court
   D. superior court

7. President Lyndon Johnson's Great Society programs began a new era of national-state relations in the 1960s. Political scientists describe this era as one of
   A. cooperative federalism.
   B. dual federalism.
   C. new federalism.
   D. regulated federalism.

8. Which of these units of government is most likely to regulate water systems, cemeteries, hospitals, sewers, fire protection services, and schools?
   A. a city council
   B. a state legislature
   C. a special-purpose district
   D. a county board of supervisors

9. Which of these is a common way to amend a state constitution?
   A. The governor drafts an amendment, and the legislature adopts it.
   B. Petitioners request an amendment, and the state courts endorse it.
   C. The legislature proposes an amendment, and the voters approve it.
   D. A constitutional convention debates an amendment, and delegates vote on it.

10. Which form of city government, combining democratic rule with professional expertise, is most common in the United States today?
    A. council-manager
    B. elected commission
    C. weak mayor-council
    D. strong mayor-council

Exploring the Essential Question

How does power flow through our federal system of government?

Concerns about air pollution, dependence on foreign oil, and climate change have motivated governments to address how we generate and use energy. Some initiatives are aimed at reducing energy consumption. Others are intended to reduce our dependence on coal and oil by promoting the use of cleaner, renewable energy sources. Such sources include wind power, solar energy, and biofuels made from crops like corn and soybeans. A few examples are shown below.

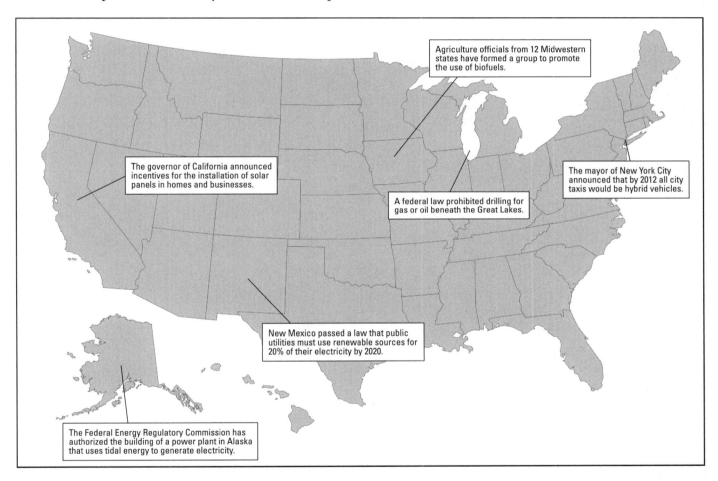

Agriculture officials from 12 Midwestern states have formed a group to promote the use of biofuels.

The governor of California announced incentives for the installation of solar panels in homes and businesses.

A federal law prohibited drilling for gas or oil beneath the Great Lakes.

The mayor of New York City announced that by 2012 all city taxis would be hybrid vehicles.

New Mexico passed a law that public utilities must use renewable sources for 20% of their electricity by 2020.

The Federal Energy Regulatory Commission has authorized the building of a power plant in Alaska that uses tidal energy to generate electricity.

1. Is policymaking in the area of energy an expressed power, a concurrent power, or a reserved power? Explain your answer.

2. Discuss why each of the different energy policy initiatives adopted in California, the Midwestern states, and New York City makes sense in terms of that region's resources, economic interests, or environmental concerns.

3. Based on the information on the map, are states living up to their potential as "laboratories for policy experiments" that may, if successful, be adopted by other states and the national government? Explain your answer.

Citizen Participation in a Democracy

How can you make a difference in a democracy?

As you complete the Reading Notes, use these terms in your answers:

citizenship

lawful permanent resident

undocumented immigrant

naturalization

ideology

liberalism

conservatism

civil society

PREVIEW

Analyze the photograph below of a lunch counter sit-in. Then answer these questions in your notebook:

1. What interesting details do you see?

2. What actions do these people appear to be taking?

3. What problem or problems do you think these people are trying to address?

4. What do you think the results of their actions were?

READING NOTES

Section 7.2

Create a T-chart with the headings "Civic Rights" and "Civic Responsibilities." As you read, record the rights and responsibilities that come with U.S. citizenship.

Section 7.3

Create a how-to flier for becoming a naturalized U.S. citizen. Your flier must include information on or an explanation of the following:

- requirements for becoming a citizen
- application for naturalization
- interview with an immigration official
- citizenship ceremony
- rights that new citizens gain

Organize the information in an attractive, easy-to-read format that would help people understand the naturalization process. Include at least one illustration.

Section 7.4

Answer these questions in your notebook:

1. Which shared political value do you feel is most important to the American way of life, and why?

2. Create a visual representation of the U.S. political landscape for each of these ideologies: liberalism, conservativism, socialism, libertarianism, environmentalism, and centrism. Follow these steps:

   - Create a simple illustration to represent the ideology.

   - Write a short definition or explanation of the ideology.

   - Rate the ideology on a scale of 1 ("I identify most closely with this ideology") to 6 ("I do not identify with this ideology").

Section 7.5

Answer these questions:

1. What is social capital, and do you think it is important? Why or why not?

2. Of the four categories of civic engagement, which best describes you (or will best describe you once you can vote), and why?

PROCESSING

Think about the problems facing your community, your country, or the world. Then choose one issue or problem that you feel strongly about. Write a short paragraph explaining why this is a problem. Back up your argument with at least one or two facts.

Now develop a plan of action to address the issue. Include in your plan of action at least two of the forms of civic participation you learned about.

Form of Civic Participation

Form of Civic Participation	How and When to Use It Effectively
1 Writing a press release	Prepare a notice about an event or issue for distribution to local newspapers, radio and television stations, or Web sites. Use to publicize an event or to make people aware of an issue.
2 Writing a letter to the editor	Draft a short letter to send to a newspaper or magazine expressing a view about a recent article or calling attention to an issue you would like to see covered. Use to express a personal view on the article or issue and to encourage others to share your point of view.
3 Communicating with a public official	Visit, call, e-mail, or write to a public official about an issue or question. Use to share ideas or concerns or to encourage a public official to take a particular action on your issue.
4 Organizing a letter-writing campaign	Convince a large number of people to write letters to their elected representatives in support of a specific action item. Use to put pressure on elected officials to pay attention to those issues.
5 Testifying before a public body	Write a short speech about your concerns and deliver it to public officials. Use to voice ideas and concerns in a public forum directly to the people elected or appointed to deal with those issues.
6 Creating an issue ad or Web site	Create an ad or Web site about an issue. Use to inform people about the issue, to gain support for your position, or to point out a problem with the way the issue is being handled.
7 Giving an interview or a speech	Write and deliver a speech to a group of people. Use to inform people about the issue, to encourage others to support your position, or to propose a method of addressing the issue.
8 Writing and circulating a petition	Create a petition that explains how you would like an issue addressed, gather signatures from supporters, and present the petition to people in a position to take action. Use to demonstrate support for your plan to address the issue and to encourage implementation of your plan.
9 Creating and conducting an opinion survey	Write a survey and collect the results in person or by phone, mail, or e-mail. Use to gather opinions or information about an issue or to raise awareness of the issue. This is a good starting point if you need to test support for your issue or want data to show that people agree with your position.
10 Joining a campaign or an interest group	Join a group of people who already support a candidate or an issue. Use when groups already exist that are effectively dealing with your issue.
11 Organizing a fundraiser	Organize a fundraising event to ask for donations, seek business sponsorships, or apply for grants from the government, corporations, or foundations to raise money for a cause you believe in. Use when your issue would benefit from additional financial support.
12 Sponsoring a ballot initiative or referendum	Collect the required number of signatures on a formal petition and submit it to the legislature for consideration or to the people for a direct vote. (Not all states offer ballot initiatives or referendums.) Use when you want to create or change a law that pertains to your issue.
13 Organizing a protest or boycott	Organize others in a collective refusal to buy certain goods or use certain services, or plan a protest to draw attention to an issue. Use as a last resort, in an effort to get others to listen to your concerns.
14 Running for public office	Gather support for your candidacy, get yourself on the ballot, and campaign for election. For most local and state offices, you must be 18 to run for office. Use if you are really committed to having an impact on your community.
15 Starting an interest group	Join with others who share your views on an issue to call attention to the issue and, possibly, to back legislation or candidates who support your position. Use when there are no other groups effectively advocating for your issue.

Civic Participation Case Studies

A School for Iqbal

Iqbal Masih was four years old when his father sold him into bonded labor with a carpet manufacturer in Pakistan for the equivalent of $12. Iqbal worked for pennies a day to repay the debt. Over the next six years, he worked 12 to 14 hours a day, 6 days a week. Sometimes he was chained to the carpet loom, and sometimes he was beaten. When he was 10, he ran away from the factory and joined an organization that fought against bonded labor and worked to educate child workers about their rights.

When Iqbal was 12, he visited the Broad Meadows Middle School in Quincy, Massachusetts, while in the United States to receive the Reebok Human Rights Youth-in-Action Award. There he met with the seventh graders of Ron Adams's language arts class. Iqbal inspired the students by telling them about his experiences speaking out against child labor and working to free other children. In his country, 7.5 million children were enslaved, and there were as many as 200 million more around the world. What Iqbal really wanted was for children to be able to attend school and learn to read and write, not to be forced into bonded labor during their childhoods.

Horrified at the idea of parents selling their young children into bonded labor, three of the students composed a letter telling Iqbal's story and asking other students to work to end child slavery. They used the Scholastic Web site to e-mail their letter to 36 other middle schools around the country.

Iqbal returned home to Pakistan, where his fame led to many death threats against him by people who stood to benefit from the current system of child labor. In the spring of 1995, four months after returning home, Iqbal was murdered in broad daylight.

When the students in Mr. Adams's class heard the news, they decided to do something to honor Iqbal's memory. What Iqbal really wanted was a school for children in Punjab province, so the students decided they would build him one. United behind their new slogan, "A bullet can't kill a dream," the students sent out an e-mail that told the story of Iqbal's short life. This e-mail asked for donations of $12, both because Iqbal was sold for $12 and because he was 12 years old when he was murdered. The students worked with volunteers from Amnesty International to create a Web site to educate people about Iqbal and the problem of child labor.

The students received more than 6,000 e-mail replies and more than 3,000 letters in response. Within one year, the students raised more than $147,000. They worked with a group in Pakistan that administered the building project. In 1996, only a year and a half after Iqbal was murdered, the school opened its doors to nearly 300 students, ages 4 to 12. Though all the students also work, their employers allow them to schedule their shifts so that they can attend school. For almost all the students, it was the first time in their lives they had attended school.

However, the students did not stop their campaign against child labor once the school for Iqbal opened. Many of them continued to speak out on the issue of child labor. They contacted and met with their elected representatives, on both the state and national levels, to fight for an international treaty to protect children from child labor. Some of the students also traveled to Washington, D.C., to testify before a congressional hearing on child labor. Another student gave a speech at the United Nations on the issue.

Every year, new Broad Meadows Middle School students become active in the cause. They continue working with other schools to establish a new school each year in a different developing country. The annual campaign is called Operation Day's Work. The American schools that sponsor the campaign are located nationwide, and the students communicate by e-mail. The story of Iqbal's impact and inspiration on students continues, and the School for Iqbal in Pakistan is thriving.

The Ryan White CARE Act

Ryan White was born on December 6, 1971, in Kokomo, Indiana. At birth, he was diagnosed with hemophilia. Hemophilia is a dangerous genetic disease that causes blood not to clot—even a small cut can lead to a life-threatening amount of blood loss. Fortunately for Ryan and his parents, a new treatment called Factor VIII had recently become available. It was a treatment made from blood and contained the clotting agent that allowed healthy people to recover quickly from cuts. As a child, Ryan went to the hospital at least twice a month to receive blood transfusions of Factor VIII. These transfusions allowed him to play sports and act like a normal child without having to worry about dying from a small cut or injury.

When Ryan was 12 years old, he began to feel more and more sick. Ryan's pediatrician said that Ryan just had a bad case of flu. A few months later, an annual checkup showed that Ryan had a disease called hepatitis. He and his family were relieved. They thought the hepatitis had caused his diarrhea, stomach cramps, and night sweats.

When he was 13, he ended up in the hospital. There Ryan learned he had AIDS, a recently discovered and deadly disease. AIDS attacks the body's ability to fight off other diseases. Ryan had gotten it through the very same blood product that had allowed him to be like other kids: Factor VIII.

Ryan's doctors told him he had only six months to live, and Ryan insisted on living a normal life. He wanted to return to school, but the administrators, teachers, students, and parents at Ryan's school were afraid that his disease would spread. In the early 1980s, little was known about how AIDS is transmitted. People were afraid that even casual contact could pass the disease from person to person.

The Indiana State Board of Health issued guidelines saying that it would be safe for Ryan to attend school, but the school still refused to allow it. His mother, Jeanne White-Ginder, took their case to court. Locally, people called his mother "unfit" because she had "allowed" her son to get AIDS. At church, people would not shake Ryan's hand.

Someone even shot a bullet through the front window of the Whites' home.

Ryan White's story was soon nationally publicized. He traveled all over the country speaking about AIDS and his fight to attend school. Many celebrities—actors, musicians, athletes, and politicians—praised Ryan for his work to educate people about AIDS. Some even became friends of the family.

Eventually the court ordered the school to admit Ryan, but he only faced more harassment. The Whites decided to move to Cicero, Indiana, using the proceeds they received from the ABC movie *The Ryan White Story*. Students at Ryan's new school, Hamilton High, went through an AIDS education program. They learned that people cannot get AIDS by touching others or sharing a bathroom. Ryan made many friends who would help and support him through his illness over the next several years.

Ryan continued to draw public attention. He felt it was important to educate people about the facts of his disease. He spoke before a presidential commission on AIDS about his experience in Kokomo. He gave interviews and spoke at public events about his disease and about AIDS education.

Just before his 18th birthday, Ryan began to feel sicker. He died on April 8, 1990. His funeral was attended by thousands of family members, friends, celebrities, and strangers, all of whom had been touched by his life.

Since Ryan's death, there has been much more education about AIDS. Shortly after his death, his mother established the Ryan White Foundation, a national organization dedicated to AIDS education for young people. She has spoken before many audiences. She worked to lobby Congress for the Ryan White Comprehensive AIDS Resources Emergency (CARE) Act, even testifying before the Senate about the bill. The bill provides funding for AIDS patients and their families to receive medical care. It has been renewed three times since it was first signed into law.

Mothers Against Drunk Driving

May 3, 1980, was a beautiful day in Fair Oaks, California. Thirteen-year-old Cari Lightner was dressed in her orange-and-white softball uniform, walking along the side of a residential street on her way to a church carnival with a friend. She was struck by a car that came out of nowhere and thrown 125 feet. The driver who killed her was a 47-year-old man who had been on a three-day drinking binge and had three prior DUIs, or citations for driving under the influence of alcohol.

After losing her daughter to such a senseless crime, Cari's mother Candy Lightner decided to do something about the problem of drunk driving. At the time, drunk driving was not a major public concern. Though alcohol was a factor in nearly 60% of fatal crashes, driving while drunk was not, in and of itself, a crime. Candy was determined to focus public attention on the issue and get laws enacted to protect people from drunk drivers.

Candy created a victims advocacy group, or interest group, called Mothers Against Drunk Driving, or MADD. Donations started pouring in, and MADD worked diligently to get then-governor of California Jerry Brown to create a task force to address the issue of drunk driving. For years, bills to help curb drunk driving had failed to become law, and MADD wanted the state of California to address the problem in a visible way.

In September 1980, a woman named Cindy Lamb started a Maryland chapter of MADD. Cindy's daughter Laura had become the nation's youngest paraplegic when she and her mother were hit head-on by a drunk driver who had five prior DUIs. In October, Candy and Cindy drew national attention to their issue when they held a press conference about drunk driving on Capitol Hill. By telling their heart-wrenching story and sharing family photographs, they brought a hidden issue to the forefront of American politics. Suddenly victims and concerned citizens were banding together to change the laws. Chapters of MADD began to spring up around the country, and stories about the organization were in newspapers and on television stations in nearly every community in the country.

As MADD continued to put a personal face on the tragedy of drunk driving, their legislative successes and fundraising ability grew. By 1982, MADD had 100 chapters nationwide and President Ronald Reagan had invited MADD to testify at a presidential commission on drunk driving. By 1983, MADD had successfully met with elected leaders to encourage the passage of 129 new anti-drunk-driving laws around the country.

Armed with loads of statistics showing that alcohol-related crashes involving teenagers occurred at higher rates in states with drinking ages below 21, MADD then pushed for a federal law raising the legal drinking age to 21 across the nation. MADD was up against the wealthy and influential alcohol industry, but in 1984 President Reagan signed the Uniform Drinking Age Act into law. MADD also held rallies to gain public support for their cause and even planned and held a 4,000-mile March Across America to publicize the problem of drunk driving.

In 1991, MADD staged press conferences and generated press releases to publicize its first "Rating the States" report, in which it evaluated each state's record at preventing drunk driving. By 1992, a poll revealed that most Americans felt that drunk driving was the number one issue on highways. By 1993, alcohol-related traffic fatalities dropped to a 30-year low.

But MADD did not rest on all it had accomplished. Instead, it used the 1990s to launch more visual appeals to discourage drunk driving and encourage tougher legislation to fight the problem. In Florida, where MADD was having a hard time getting anti-drunk-driving legislation passed, they placed a pair of shoes worn by every one of the 1,100 victims killed by a drunk driver in Florida the previous year in the rotunda of Florida's state capitol. In 2000, MADD successfully achieved another milestone, when the national legal blood alcohol concentration (BAC) level was lowered to .08. By 2004, all states and Washington, D.C., had lowered the legal BAC level to .08. MADD continues to be active in fighting to reduce drunk-driving tragedies.

Applying Forms of Civic Participation

You will now work with your class to apply the 15 forms of civic participation you learned about to a series of situations.

Step 1 You will be assigned one form of civic participation to represent in this exercise. Review Student Handout 7A to make sure you are familiar with this form of civic participation.

Step 2 As your teacher reveals each situation below, decide how effective your form of civic participation would be in addressing that situation. Then send one person from your group to stand at the appropriate place along the spectrum, holding up the form of civic participation for everyone to see.

Situations

A group of concerned citizens wants to implement a recycling policy in their town.

A group of high school students is opposed to what they consider to be an unfair dress code, and they want to make changes to that policy.

An individual is upset by her state's high taxes and wants to see a change in the state tax rates.

A group of citizens believes that the labor practices of a nationwide retailer are unfair and wants to call attention to them in order to force the company to change its policies.

A family feels that their children's school experience would be greatly enhanced by a morning moment of silence in which students and teachers could silently pray.

An individual wants to recruit others to help the victims of ethnic genocide in another country.

Mastering the Content

1. Which of these are considered the building blocks of civil society?
   A. groups that people join voluntarily
   B. media that influence public opinion
   C. patterns of generally accepted behavior
   D. agencies of local or county government

2. Which part of the U.S. Constitution defines U.S. citizenship?
   A. Preamble
   B. Article VI
   C. Bill of Rights
   D. Fourteenth Amendment

3. An immigrant who wants to become a naturalized citizen must
   A. be at least 21 years old.
   B. know how to speak some English.
   C. pass a high school equivalency test.
   D. have lived in the United States at least 8 years.

4. Which term is defined in the box below?

   > *A society's framework of shared values, beliefs, and attitudes*

   A. civic virtue
   B. public good
   C. rule of law
   D. political culture

5. In which of these areas are conservatives more likely than liberals to favor government intervention?
   A. health care
   B. moral issues
   C. business practices
   D. consumer protection

6. Someone from another country who lives in the United States illegally is called
   A. a resident alien.
   B. a naturalized citizen.
   C. a lawful permanent resident.
   D. an undocumented immigrant.

7. Which political ideology favors the least government regulation of any kind?
   A. conservatism
   B. liberalism
   C. libertarianism
   D. socialism

8. Use the quotation in the box to answer the question below.

   > *We support a sustainable society which utilizes resources in such a way that future generations will benefit and not suffer from the practices of our generation.*

   This quotation reflects the ideology of which of these groups?
   A. Green Party
   B. Libertarian Party
   C. Centrist Coalition
   D. National Urban League

9. An individual with a green card is allowed to
   A. work at a job.
   B. serve on a jury.
   C. vote in elections.
   D. run for public office.

10. Which of the following committed the United States to protecting the rights of all Americans regardless of race, sex, religion, or national origin?
    A. *Plessy v. Ferguson*
    B. Fourteenth Amendment
    C. Civil Rights Act of 1964
    D. *Brown v. Board of Education*

Exploring the Essential Question

How can you make a difference in a democracy?

This web diagram shows just a few of the many ways you can engage with others to accomplish goals for your community, the nation, or the world.

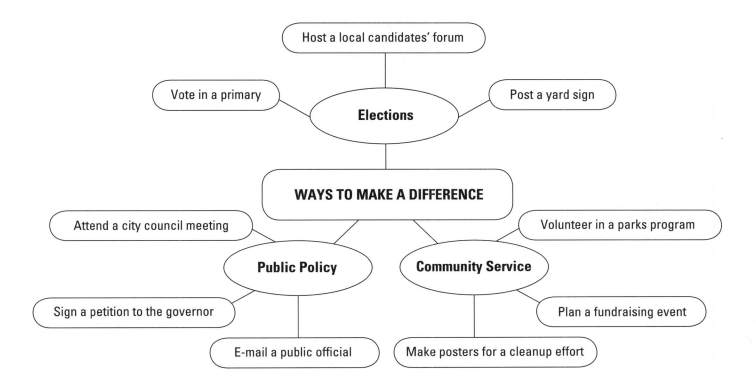

1. Which activities on the web diagram can a 14- to 17-year-old student do?

2. Some people draw a sharp distinction between political activity and community service. Do you agree? Explain your answer.

3. How might people's participation in a social or recreational club, such as a bowling league, increase their likelihood of participating in activities shown on the web diagram?

4. Suppose your community is considering imposing (or changing) a curfew on children and teenagers. State whether you support or oppose the proposed new law and explain why. List three actions you might take to convince others to support your position.

Parties, Interest Groups, and Public Policy

Political parties and interest groups: How do they influence our political decisions?

Speaking of Politics

As you complete the Reading Notes, use these terms in your answers:

political party

interest group

platform

two-party system

pluralism

political action
  committee (PAC)

lobbying

public policy

PREVIEW

If you were to register for a political party right now, which would you choose?

- Democrat

- Republican

- independent (no party affiliation)

- third party (Green Party, Libertarian, or the like)

What are some of the reasons for your choice?

READING NOTES

Section 8.2

Read the section, and then do the following:

1. Create a spoke diagram outlining what political parties do in a democracy. Off each spoke, write one function of political parties. Your diagram must have at least four spokes.

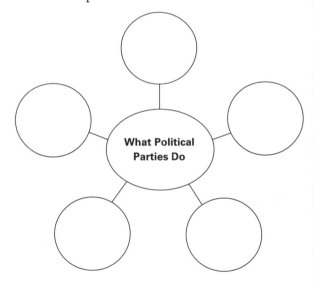

What Political Parties Do

2. What was the major dividing factor between the two first political parties, the Federalists and the Democratic-Republicans?

3. Create a T-chart with the headings "Democrats" and "Republicans." List at least four beliefs held by each party.

4. What function do third parties serve in American politics?

5. Create a simple symbol or illustration to represent independent voters. Then write one sentence describing independents.

Section 8.3

Create a T-chart titled "Opinions on Special Interests" with the headings "Good for Democracy" and "Bad for Democracy." Record at least eight examples of how interest groups are good or bad for democracy.

Section 8.4

A mnemonic is a memory device used to recall a variety of things, including a list of items or the steps required to complete a task. For example, **Please Excuse My Dear Aunt Sally** (**P**arenthesis **E**xponents **M**ultiplication **D**ivision **A**ddition **S**ubtraction) is used to help remember the order in which to complete mathematical operations.

Create a mnemonic for the six steps of the policymaking process. Then explain which step in the process you think is the most important and which is the least important.

PROCESSING

Now that you have looked more closely at political parties and their function in government, choose the political party that you would like to be affiliated with. If you haven't already registered to vote, obtain a voter registration form (or a pre-registration form, if you are not yet 18) from your local town or city hall.

Once you have selected a party or chosen to register as an independent with no party affiliation, answer these questions:

- Why did you choose your particular affiliation?
- Why are parties important in government?
- What can parties do for you? For society?

Political Issues Survey

Next to each statement, write the number that best describes how you feel about that statement.
Answer as honestly as possible. Your responses will determine where you fall along a political spectrum.

5 = Completely agree

4 = Somewhat agree

3 = Agree or disagree, depending on the situation

2 = Somewhat disagree

1 = Completely disagree

_____ The government should not enact strict laws protecting the environment.

_____ It is not the government's role to regulate businesses in order to protect consumers.

_____ Marriage should be defined as the union of one man and one woman only.

_____ Providing social welfare programs—such as Medicare, the National School Lunch Program, and Temporary Aid to Needy Families—is not the responsibility or business of the federal government.

_____ It is appropriate for the government to make laws based on moral beliefs.

_____ State governments—rather than the federal government—should make laws for their citizens, such as setting speed limits, driver's license age, and minimum drinking age.

_____ The government should not restrict the ownership of guns and other weapons by law-abiding citizens.

_____ Abortion is the equivalent of murder and should be illegal.

_____ Voluntary prayer and scripture readings should be allowed in public schools.

_____ The current level of defense spending should be increased.

_____ People who make a lot of money should not have to pay more taxes than people who make less money.

_____ It is not the government's responsibility to protect the rights of minority groups whose beliefs or actions conflict with the majority's views.

_____ Judges should apply mandatory minimum sentences for particular crimes.

_____ Capital punishment should be legal.

_____ Only heterosexual males should be allowed to serve in the U.S. military in combat.

_____ The United States should build border fences to prevent people from entering the country illegally.

_____ Convicted prisoners should not be allowed to vote while incarcerated.

_____ The United States should use force to overthrow unfriendly governments, especially if those governments have the potential to do our country harm.

_____ The United States needs to act in its own national interest, regardless of the opinion of organizations like the United Nations.

_____ When necessary, the United States should intervene in foreign nations to protect U.S. business interests there.

Total score: _____

Mark the spectrum below according to your total score.

Political Issues Spectrum

0	20	40	60	80	100
Extremely Liberal	Liberal	Moderate	Conservative	Extremely Conservative	

Campaign Team Roles

Your group will represent a political candidate. Each person in your group will take on a specific role on your campaign team.

Decide which team member will take on each role. Then read the candidate biography to learn about the candidate your group will represent. As you read, note your candidate's opinions on major issues that he or she might be asked about during the campaign.

Candidate

You are responsible for

- acting as your group's Candidate during public appearances and meetings.
- being familiar with, and able to speak intelligently about, your Candidate's views.
- approving the campaign Web site your group will create.

Research and Policy Director

You are responsible for

- making sure the Candidate is knowledgeable about the issues in the campaign.
- being familiar with the views of the opposition in order to help differentiate your Candidate from the opposition.
- ensuring that your group knows about the other candidates and the interest groups before the meet-and-greet.
- working with the Campaign Manager to ensure that the Candidate meets with interest groups that support his or her issues during the meet-and-greet you will participate in.

Campaign Manager

You are responsible for

- overseeing the crafting of the Candidate's message.
- ensuring that the issues the Candidate adopts in the campaign platform are in line with his or her beliefs and actions.
- working with the Candidate to help write his or her positions on campaign issues for the Web site your group will create.
- working with the Research and Policy Director to ensure that the Candidate meets with interest groups that support his or her issues during the meet-and-greet you will participate in.

Candidate Profiles

Pat Donnellson

Pat Donnellson graduated from one of the top law schools in the country. Donnellson then clerked for a Supreme Court justice for two years before taking a position with a nonprofit organization dedicated to protecting children. Donnellson worked diligently to get states and the federal government to pass health care and welfare laws that would help children. Donnellson then joined a prestigious law firm in Chicago, Illinois, and worked there until becoming a U.S. senator from Illinois 10 years ago. Donnellson is married with one child, an eight-year-old daughter.

Donnellson is an outspoken opponent of the death penalty and supports a federal constitutional amendment to ban its use regardless of the circumstances. Instead, Donnellson advocates investing heavily in education and community policing, which will help curb violence. Donnellson also opposes the private ownership of any type of firearm, no matter what its intended use.

The most important crisis facing our country and the world, Donnellson feels, is global warming. For this reason, the United States needs to require trucks and sport utility vehicles to meet the same emission standards as cars. In addition, the United States should set the goal of having all cars run on alternative fuels by 2025. Donnellson supports raising the gas tax to pay for research into alternative fuels and providing government subsidies for oil companies that transition into producing alternative fuels or for auto manufacturers that transition into producing vehicles that run on alternative fuels. Donnellson also wants to provide federal funding for mandated environmental education in schools.

Donnellson feels strongly that the United States is damaging its reputation around the world by not using diplomacy in actions toward other countries. The United States should not take military action without UN approval, Donnellson believes, unless directly attacked by another country. Donnellson would also like to create a U.S. Department of Peace.

At home, the lack of available health care insurance for all citizens is a vital concern. Donnellson wants to create government-sponsored health care that would be available for all. Individuals could still subscribe to private health care insurance, but those plans would be taxed to help pay for the government plan. Donnellson also wants to end private, for-profit hospitals.

To improve every person's quality of life, Donnellson wants the federal government to raise the yearly income level at which a family is considered to be in poverty. This way, more people at the lower end of the income spectrum would qualify for transitional assistance. Donnellson also wants to make housing a "right" for all Americans. In one of the most affluent countries in the world, no one should have to be homeless.

The United States is a country of immigrants, and for that reason, Donnellson strongly supports an "open borders" policy. As such, Donnellson advocates a less-restrictive immigration policy. Donnellson argues that the president should grant amnesty to all undocumented immigrants currently in the United States and then put into place an immigration policy that will allow the families of these new citizens to immigrate more easily. The United States should have no quota system for immigration—anyone who wants to come should be able to.

Terry Lankan

After college, Terry Lankan worked as an antipoverty advocate in Houston, Texas, and fought for after-school programs to keep kids out of trouble and away from gangs. Lankan then served on the Houston City Council for nearly a decade before becoming mayor. After two terms as mayor, Lankan served eight terms as a U.S. representative from Texas. Lankan has been married for 20 years and has twin sons, who are 17, and a 13-year-old daughter.

Lankan opposes the death penalty for all crimes but terrorism, because the death penalty has never proven to be a deterrent for committing a crime. Instead, Lankan argues that the United States should place a greater emphasis on preventing crime and rehabilitating first-time offenders. Lankan also believes that citizens should not be allowed to own handguns, because those guns are most frequently used to commit crimes. However, Lankan is not opposed to ownership of other types of firearms.

The environment is a serious concern for Lankan, who supports tax credits for both individuals and businesses who voluntarily commit to reducing carbon emissions through the use of solar power, hybrid cars, and other methods. Lankan also supports tax credits for businesses that invest in alternative energy research and feels that the government should offer other incentives to the oil and auto-manufacturing industries to encourage them to turn to alternative fuel production and consumption.

On foreign policy, Lankan worries that the United States is viewed abroad as an aggressive, imperial nation. Lankan would like to see the United States play a lead role in strengthening the United Nations and expects that this would take some of the pressure off the U.S. military to act as the world's police force. Lankan also wants to expand the State Department's role in military planning.

Lankan supports providing publicly subsidized health insurance to needy children and to any elderly or disabled person who applies for it. Lankan also feels that publicly subsidized health insurance for the needy should cover 100 percent of prescription drug costs.

Reducing poverty levels is important to Lankan, who grew up in extreme poverty and now supports universal, full-day preschool and kindergarten for all children living in poverty. Lankan wants to expand subsidized housing and Medicaid, the publicly subsidized health insurance program for the poor, to include new immigrants. Lankan also supports time limits on welfare benefits so that people will move toward financial independence rather than relying on government handouts.

Lankan is in favor of an immigration policy that encourages undocumented immigrants to apply for permanent resident status rather than deporting people who are in the country illegally. Lankan wants to see the process for becoming a citizen become less rigorous and time-consuming and thinks that a more straightforward approach for attaining citizenship will discourage people from coming to the United States illegally. Lankan also wants to put in place a program that will encourage businesses to help undocumented-immigrant employees apply for citizenship.

Cory Mathews

Cory Mathews is a decorated veteran of the U.S. Air Force. Mathews served as a combat physician during Operation Desert Storm and earned a Purple Heart after saving the lives of three fellow soldiers when their helicopter was shot down. Upon returning from Desert Storm, Mathews worked as an emergency room physician before running for office. After serving two terms as a Democrat in the Florida legislature, Mathews was elected to the U.S. House of Representatives and has served five consecutive terms. Mathews has been married for more than 20 years and has two daughters, ages 19 and 14.

Mathews opposes the death penalty except for instances of terrorism. To keep communities safe and to prevent crime, Mathews wants to expand federal funding for community-policing initiatives.

Mathews is a strong environmentalist who has coauthored and consistently voted in favor of clean air and water laws and legislation to enact tougher restrictions on car emissions. To help the United States end its dependence on oil, Mathews wants to encourage the development of alternative fuel sources. As president, Mathews would work to end subsidies for oil and gas companies and reinvest the savings in research to develop alternative fuel sources.

Mathews believes that although the United States needs to be a strong and independent nation, it also needs to rely on diplomacy, rather than military action, to solve global problems. Except for instances in which U.S. security is directly threatened or the United States is directly attacked, Mathews would like to see the United Nations take more responsibility for peacekeeping missions. Mathews believes that the lives of our young people are too precious to squander and that U.S. military action should be used only as a last resort.

At home, Mathews would like to see Medicaid, the publicly subsidized health insurance program for the poor, expanded to include any children who do not have health insurance. Mathews also wants to allow the federal government to bargain with drug companies in the United States and abroad to acquire the safest drugs at the lowest prices for people on Medicaid.

During a lengthy career in public service, Mathews has fought to roll back tax cuts that help the wealthiest individuals in order to fund public education and social programs for the poor. Mathews is a strong believer in the need to eradicate poverty in America. Through a minimum wage hike and additional job-training programs, Mathews believes that the United States can eliminate poverty and strengthen the middle class.

Although illegal immigration is a problem, the only way the United States will solve the problem is by offering a realistic solution that appeals both to Americans and to undocumented immigrants. Mathews proposes that a guest worker program be created. This would allow people to come to the United States for up to three years to obtain work. At the end of that three years, they could continue to work in the United States if they begin the process of becoming a citizen. Otherwise, they would need to return home. Anyone currently in the United States illegally, Mathews believes, should be admitted immediately to the guest-worker program. The government should also provide English-language classes for people enrolled in the program, as not knowing English is often a major impediment to applying for citizenship.

Taylor Andrews

Taylor Andrews attended Oxford University in England as a Rhodes Scholar, eventually earning a PhD in political science. Andrews then spent several decades as a professor at a prestigious university in California before becoming the president of a university in New Jersey. Andrews has been married for 27 years and has a son and daughter, ages 22 and 20. After a distinguished career as a scholar, Andrews retired from education and ran for governor of New Jersey. Andrews is currently serving a second term as New Jersey's governor.

Andrews supports minimum-sentencing laws for criminals but wants to increase funding for local law enforcement in order to make streets safer and to prevent crime. Andrews supports the death penalty as currently used. Andrews does not support any additional limits on an individual's right to own weapons and feels that the United States needs to focus on criminals who possess weapons illegally, not citizens who own them legally.

Andrews is a strong believer in the power of unregulated business to improve the American quality of life. Andrews thinks that minimal environmental restrictions are necessary, but also believes there is no need for additional restrictions. Instead, Andrews feels that government needs to focus on areas of the country, such as toxic waste sites, that need to be cleaned up. Cleaning up these sites and rebuilding on them, Andrews believes, will create jobs and provide future sites for businesses and homes.

Andrews believes that the United States needs to be a moral leader in the world. It should fight for freedom and democracy wherever there is a need. While this will ideally involve diplomacy rather than military action, Andrews says that the country should not hesitate to use its military when U.S. interests are threatened or attacked. However, Andrews feels that American forces should never be deployed to another country without having an exit strategy.

Andrews advocates keeping the current publicly subsidized health insurance programs, Medicare and Medicaid, but wants the federal government to provide no additional funding for health programs and no federal funds for stem cell research or cloning.

Andrews feels strongly that any American can succeed with hard work and perseverance. The answer to society's problems is not to require the federal government to put more money into social programs but to encourage individuals to take responsibility for themselves. Andrews wants to see federal tax cuts across all income levels so that Americans can keep more of the money they earn. Additional tax cuts for U.S. businesses will encourage those businesses to use the additional revenue to create more jobs. Andrews also wants to allow faith-based organizations to compete for federal funds to provide social services for the poor, rather than the federal government providing those services.

Finally, Andrews feels that the government needs to do more to encourage legal immigration and discourage illegal immigration. Andrews feels that the most effective way to do that would be to create a guest worker program that allows people to come to the United States for up to three years to obtain work. At the end of the three years, they could continue to work in the United States if they begin the process of becoming a citizen. Otherwise, they would need to return home. Anyone currently in the United States illegally would need to return to his or her home country to apply for the guest worker program.

Casey McMahon

Casey McMahon is a Hollywood star who became politically active while campaigning for Ronald Reagan when he ran for president. McMahon then decided to run for the Senate and served three terms as a U.S. senator from California. McMahon has been married twice and has no children.

McMahon feels that the best way to prevent crime in America is to keep criminals off the streets. Thus McMahon supports expanding mandatory minimum-sentencing laws and supports the death penalty as currently used. McMahon also feels that it is important for law-abiding Americans to be able to protect themselves and their families and wants to see all bans on an individual's right to own firearms removed. Instead of preventing law-abiding citizens from owning firearms, McMahon wants the government to step up its efforts to seize illegal firearms to prevent them from being used in criminal activities.

McMahon feels that it is not the government's responsibility to protect the environment and wants to see current environmental restrictions on businesses rolled back. Instead of imposing legal restrictions, the government should offer businesses tax incentives for voluntary compliance. Global warming is definitely a problem, but McMahon feels that its threat is exaggerated by alarmists who want the government to prevent manufacturing and energy companies from being successful.

Around the globe, the United States needs to act to promote its national interests, ideally using diplomacy and multinational actions, but should act alone if necessary. Freedom and democracy are basic human rights, and the United States should fight for them wherever there is a need.

The current publicly subsidized health insurance plans, Medicare and Medicaid, must be maintained to prevent a health care crisis in the United States. But McMahon wants the government to allow private companies to administer parts or all of the plans in order to make them more cost efficient. McMahon also opposes allowing Medicaid to cover any part of the cost of an abortion.

McMahon opposes having the federal government provide social services. Instead, federal funds should be distributed to states based on their poverty rates. States should then be responsible for administering any social service programs appropriate for their population. This will allow states to focus on the issues most important to their citizens. McMahon also supports a federal law requiring all states to fund full-day kindergarten in districts with a child poverty rate above 20 percent.

Illegal immigration is a serious problem. McMahon believes that the way to solve the problem is to strengthen security at U.S. borders and enact much stricter punishments for people who enter this country illegally. McMahon proposes adding 20,000 troops to guard the borders. Because deporting undocumented immigrants often does not deter them from reentering the country, and because putting them in jail actually punishes U.S. taxpayers, McMahon thinks that the business owners who hire undocumented immigrants should be punished with fines and jail time. When business owners stop hiring undocumented immigrants, people will stop coming to this country illegally.

J. A. Curley

J. A. Curley served as an economic adviser to presidents Ronald Reagan and George H. W. Bush. Afterward, Curley founded a conservative interest group designed to reduce the size of the federal government and then ran for attorney general of South Carolina. Curley served two terms as attorney general and one term as South Carolina's governor. Curly is married with six children, ages 12 to 22.

Curley feels that the United States should have a zero-tolerance policy for criminal behavior and that increasing the penalties for crimes is the best deterrent for criminal behavior. For this reason, Curley supports the expansion of mandatory minimum-sentencing laws and wants the death penalty to be applied automatically to felonies that involve drug trafficking or terrorism.

Curley wants to see national parks privatized so that companies can efficiently manage them and determine the best use for the land. In some instances, Curley argues, there might be better uses—such as mineral or oil extraction—for the land than preservation. Curley disputes global warming as a theory perpetuated by alarmists and does not support increased federal funding for alternative fuel research or any laws that would require businesses to adopt costly, environmentally friendly policies.

The United States, Curley feels, is the champion of democracy and freedom and should defend those ideals wherever they are threatened. Curley feels that the United States should act alone to promote the country's national interests when necessary and has called for the UN headquarters to be moved from New York City to Switzerland.

Curley has also called for an end to the publicly subsidized health care programs, Medicare and Medicaid. Instead, federal health insurance programs should be opened to private-sector competition to decrease the cost of administering such programs. Curley also opposes the use of federal funds for stem cell research, abortion, and cloning.

Curley has called for an end to federally funded welfare programs, arguing that it is not the government's responsibility to provide social services. A much more fiscally responsible approach to helping people, Curley argues, is to provide full federal funding for faith-based social service agencies that can administer social services to the needy.

The United States has long been overly tolerant of people who enter this country illegally, Curley believes. Since deportation does not seem to deter undocumented immigrants from returning illegally, the United States needs to do more to protect its borders. Curley wants the government to build a fence along the length of the U.S.-Mexico border to prevent undocumented immigrants from crossing into the country. Curley also wants to station 10,000 to 15,000 soldiers along the border with Canada to prevent illegal immigration across that unprotected border. Anyone who wants to come to the United States can go through the legal immigration process.

Interest Group Profiles

Liberal Interest Group on the Environment: Protect Our Planet

You are a member of the board of directors of an environmental group called Protect Our Planet. Your interest group needs to build relationships with candidates and politicians in order to change environmental policies in the United States and abroad. You are particularly concerned with global warming and feel that the U.S. government needs to immediately pass laws to restrict greenhouse gas emissions. You also want the United States to stop the destruction of ancient forests that clean our air and act as cooling agents for our planet. Every year, millions of acres of land are cleared for development, which contributes to global warming and threatens our Earth's future. You also want to protect the oceans from coastal development, which is wreaking havoc on marine life, and from offshore oil drilling and irresponsible fishing practices, both of which slaughter marine life.

Liberal Interest Group on Energy: Association for Eco-Friendly Fuel

You are a member of the board of directors of a think tank called Association for Eco-Friendly Fuel. Your interest group does research on the need for, and possibility of, eco-friendly fuel sources. You want the U.S. government to adopt more eco-friendly fuels for automobiles, such as E85 (an ethanol-based fuel produced from plants like sugar cane and corn), hydrogen (which can be produced in practically unlimited quantities from renewable energy sources), and electricity (which costs less than gasoline and causes no harmful emissions). You want the government to offer tax incentives for companies producing automobiles and fuel that decrease or eliminate the emission of harmful greenhouse gases.

Liberal Interest Group on Crime: Socially Responsible Crime Prevention

You are a member of the board of directors of Socially Responsible Crime Prevention. Your interest group is staunchly opposed to the death penalty. DNA testing has recently led to the release of a number of prisoners after long stints in prison for crimes they did not commit. You do not want to see anyone unjustly put to death. Instead, you advocate that more funds should be spent on crime prevention, including crime-prevention education for young children. You also want to outlaw firearm distribution and ownership. Firearms are used in one out of three instances of violent crime, and your organization feels that the best way to prevent violent crime is to eliminate the ownership of firearms. Once all firearms are outlawed, the government can more easily crack down on the illegal distribution of weapons.

Liberal Interest Group on Health Care: Health Care for Everyone

You are a member of the board of directors of Health Care for Everyone, an interest group that believes that health care is a fundamental right for all citizens, not just those who can afford it. Your group is seeking to convince the government to provide universal health care for all Americans. Every year, people suffer, and sometimes die, because they do not have health insurance and cannot get the health care they require to treat their illnesses. Because so many employed Americans do not have health insurance, you want the government to ensure that there is a federally funded program to provide everyone with health care. Your plan is for the government to tax all businesses a set amount per employee to cover the cost of the program. All health care providers and pharmacies would legally be required to accept the government's health care plan. This would eliminate the need for private health insurance companies and would ensure that all Americans get the care they need and deserve.

Liberal Interest Group on Social Services: Citizens for One America

You are a member of the board of directors of Citizens for One America. This interest group focuses on ensuring that all Americans receive the social services they need to help them become more productive members of society. Many Americans are locked in a cycle of poverty that is determined by the situation they are born into, and your group wants to help them break that cycle. Your group is advocating that the tax cuts on the wealthiest 1% of Americans be scaled back. Those tax dollars could then be used to fund essential social programs aimed at eliminating poverty, including job-training programs, day-care tuition assistance for low-income families, and early childhood education.

Liberal Interest Group on Immigration: Citizens United for Fair Immigration

You are a member of the board of directors of Citizens United for Fair Immigration, an interest group whose mission is to make the immigration process easier to navigate and more nondiscriminatory. Currently, it takes a long time and involves many steps to complete the process of becoming a U.S. citizen. Your group wants to make the process shorter and more expedient so that people will be more likely to immigrate legally. You also want to eliminate quotas that limit the number of people who can immigrate. Instead, you want the United States to take as many (or as few) immigrants as are likely to make good, productive U.S. citizens. Your group also wants to grant amnesty to all undocumented immigrants currently living in the United States.

Conservative Interest Group on the Environment: Good Cents for Earth

You are a member of the board of directors for Good Cents for Earth. As the name of your organization implies, your group believes that business and the environment do not need to be at odds. You are opposed to most environmental regulations on businesses. You agree that minimal laws to protect the air, land, and water might be necessary. But you also believe that other environmental laws, such as the ban on oil drilling in protected areas like the Arctic National Wildlife Refuge or restrictions on automobile emissions, hurt the American people by limiting their options and making products more expensive. Eliminating such bans would allow businesses to fully develop American industry to its potential, creating new jobs and additional wealth in the process. Your group will be satisfied if you can get some of the current environmental regulations rolled back and prevent further regulations.

Conservative Interest Group on Energy: Association of Petroleum Distributors

You are a member of the board of directors of an interest group representing major petroleum distributors. The companies you represent want less government interference in their businesses. The demand for oil, not only in the United States but worldwide, is rising dramatically. To meet that need, the companies you represent want more freedom to drill for oil in the United States. These companies also recognize that automobile emissions from gasoline-fueled cars are harming the environment. Thus they are willing to work to make gas cleaner (resulting in lower levels of greenhouse gas emissions) or to develop alternative fuels, such as ethanol- or hydrogen-based fuels (both of which limit emissions). However, if these companies move into developing alternative fuels, they expect significant government subsidies (funding) to help fund research and the cost of changing their production models.

Conservative Interest Group on Crime: Safety on Our Streets

You are a member of the board of directors of Safety on Our Streets, an interest group primarily concerned with making the United States safer. You believe that the key to a safe America is to keep dangerous criminals locked up for life. Your group strongly supports the death penalty as the best way to prevent criminals from repeating their crimes and to save U.S. taxpayers money. However, you are opposed to limitations on the legal ownership of firearms. Your group claims that the Second Amendment protects Americans' rights to own firearms for their own protection. Your organization has done studies showing that the greatest deterrent for violent crime is criminals' fear that the victims they target may possess firearms. Rather than disarming responsible citizens who own legally registered firearms, the government should instead spend more time and money recovering illegal firearms from criminals.

Conservative Interest Group on Health Care: Association of American Health Care Providers

You are a member of the board of directors of the Association of American Health Care Providers, an interest group representing the entire spectrum of health care providers, from hospital staff to in-home health care providers. Your group wants to provide the best possible care, at the lowest cost, with the shortest wait time, to all patients. Your group strongly believes that the current U.S. health care system, in which individuals obtain private health insurance to cover most of their health care needs, is the best way to meet these goals. The fact that U.S. health care is among the best in the world is proof that the system works. Your group wants the government to invest in the current system by providing grants and subsidies to doctors and hospitals to help keep the costs of treatment down. You also want the government to provide additional funding for Medicare (health care for the elderly) and Medicaid (health care for the poor) so that everyone receives the treatment they deserve.

Conservative Interest Group on Social Services: Americans United for Responsible Choices

You are a member of the board of directors of Americans United for Responsible Choices, an interest group dedicated to improving the government's role in providing social services. Your organization argues that the government wastes too much money, especially on expensive and unsuccessful social service programs. Your group agrees that welfare programs aimed at ending poverty, such as job-training programs and early childhood education, are necessary. However, you feel that the government is inefficient in administering these programs, resulting in a large and wasteful bureaucracy. Instead, you would like to see private corporations or faith-based organizations compete for federal funds that are currently dedicated to social services. The group that wins each contract would then provide that service at a lower cost and in a more efficient manner than the government currently does, resulting in programs that would accomplish their mission without wasting taxpayer money.

Conservative Interest Group on Immigration: Citizens United for Better Immigration

You are a member of the board of directors of Citizens United for Better Immigration, a group representing citizens who are concerned about the problems of immigration. Your group argues that higher immigration rates lead to increased violence and a greater strain on our social welfare system, costing Americans billions of tax dollars every year. You would like to see immigration restricted to college-educated individuals and their spouses and children. On the issue of illegal immigration, your group wants the government to step up its efforts to prevent undocumented immigrants from entering the country by building fences along common entrance points or by using U.S. soldiers to secure the border. Your group also wants the government to do more to root out undocumented immigrants currently in the country and deport them.

Creating a Candidate or Interest Group Web Site

You will work with your group to create a Web site to help others understand the views of your candidate or interest group.

Step 1 Use the examples below as a guide for designing a poster version of your Web site.

- Underlined headings on the examples must appear on your Web site.

- You must write a slogan appropriate for your candidate or interest group and display it prominently.

Step 2 Create position statements or talking points for your Web site.

Candidate groups: Create brief position statements explaining your candidate's views for each issue on the Web site template below.

Interest group representatives: Create at least three talking points that explain why the issues you represent are important and how you want them handled by elected officials.

Step 3 Add color and other creative touches to make your Web site visually appealing.

Candidate Web Site Example

George Washington

★ Integrity ★ Leadership ★ Experience ★

| Home | About | Get Involved | Multimedia | Blog | Contribute |

Why you should vote for George Washington

Important Issues Facing Our Nation
Click on an issue to learn more about our candidate's position.

Crime

Energy

Environment

Foreign Policy

Health Care

Social Services

Immigration

Interest Group Web Site Example

Americans for Education

| Home | About | Get Involved | For the Press | Legislation | Contribute |

About us:

On the Issues:
Learn more about our group's views on the issues below.

1.

2.

3.

Recording Details About the Meet-and-Greet

Use this sheet to record exchanges of Power Tokens and endorsements during the meet-and-greet.

Power Tokens: Power Tokens represent the additional assistance that an interest group can give to a candidate during an election. Sometimes this assistance comes as a financial donation to the campaign or as a promise to encourage its membership to vote for the candidate. In exchange, the candidate promises to support the interest group's issue.

Endorsements: Candidates often seek endorsements from interest groups. When an interest group endorses a candidate, the group is telling its membership and others who believe in the cause that the group supports a particular candidate and that the candidate supports the group's cause.

Rules Governing the Use of Power Tokens and Endorsements

- Each interest group has a set number of Power Tokens. Interest groups may give all of their tokens to one candidate or divide them among multiple candidates.

- Each interest group can officially endorse only one candidate (or no candidates).

- Interest groups cannot give, and candidates cannot receive, endorsements or Power Tokens unrealistically. If a candidate accepts Power Tokens or an endorsement from an interest group whose cause the candidate could not realistically support, the candidate will be penalized by having Power Tokens confiscated.

Record information in the table as you participate in the meet-and-greet.

Your group name: _____

Interest Group or Candidate	What the Candidate Promised to the Interest Group	What the Interest Group Gave to the Candidate

Power Tokens

Power Token	Power Token	Power Token	Power Token	Power Token
Power Token	Power Token	Power Token	Power Token	Power Token
Power Token	Power Token	Power Token	Power Token	Power Token
Power Token	Power Token	Power Token	Power Token	Power Token
Power Token	Power Token	Power Token	Power Token	Power Token
Power Token	Power Token	Power Token	Power Token	Power Token

Candidate and Interest Group Meet-and-Greet

You will now prepare for and participate in a meet-and-greet between political candidates and interest group representatives.

Step 1 Prepare for the meet-and-greet.

- Create a name tag that includes the name of your candidate or interest group, your role (such as Campaign Manager or Board of Directors Member), and a slogan for the candidate's campaign or the interest group.

- Review Student Handout 8E. Write your group's name in the appropriate place. Then identify each interest group or candidate you want to meet with during the meet-and-greet. Write that candidate's or interest group's name in the first column of the table. If you run out of space, use the back of the handout to record additional information.

Step 2 Participate in the meet-and-greet.

Candidate groups: Your goal is to meet with board members representing the interest groups whose causes align with your candidate's beliefs. If you are willing to make an interest group's issue one of your campaign's main issues, try to negotiate for Power Tokens from the interest group in exchange for their support. You also want endorsements from as many interest groups as possible. Use Student Handout 8E to record Power Tokens and endorsements you give or receive during the meet-and-greet.

Interest group representatives: Your goal is to determine which candidate, if any, your group will endorse. The best way to ensure that your goals are met is to align yourself with a candidate who has a good chance of winning the election. You can give Power Tokens to as many candidates as you wish. However, you may endorse only one candidate. Use Student Handout 8E to record Power Tokens and endorsements you give or receive during the meet-and-greet.

Mastering the Content

1. What is the primary goal of political parties?
    A. to create a national platform
    B. to get their candidates elected
    C. to collect campaign contributions
    D. to attract members who agree on issues

2. Which of these is the most common form of individual involvement with a political party?
    A. attending a party rally or meeting
    B. making a financial contribution to the party
    C. registering to vote as a member of the party
    D. working on the campaign of a party candidate

3. How do lobbyists help government officials to function more effectively?
    A. by setting the public agenda
    B. by funding public election campaigns
    C. by selecting candidates for public office
    D. by providing information on public issues

4. The National Women's Party (1913–1930) and the Right to Life Party (1970–present) are examples of which type of third party?
    A. splinter party
    B. ideological party
    C. single-issue party
    D. economic protest party

5. The idea that political power should be distributed and shared among various groups in society is known as
    A. centrism.
    B. pluralism.
    C. socialism.
    D. libertarianism.

6. Which political party in the United States had the longest continuous existence?
    A. Democrats
    B. Federalists
    C. Progressives
    D. Republicans

7. Who are the main sponsors of political action committees (PACs)?
    A. think tanks
    B. third parties
    C. interest groups
    D. grassroots organizations

8. Which of these is the best example of grassroots mobilization?
    A. a public demonstration
    B. a political party convention
    C. a meeting with policymakers
    D. a paid television advertisement

9. Which of these is found in a party platform?
    A. a description of the party's structure
    B. a statement of the party's principles
    C. a list of the party's campaign contributors
    D. a plan for getting the party's candidates elected

10. Which of these is the first step in the policymaking process?
    A. agenda setting
    B. policy adoption
    C. policy evaluation
    D. issue identification

Exploring the Essential Question

*Political parties and interest groups: How do they influence our
political decisions?*

Interest groups work in many ways to affect public opinion, political parties,
and, ultimately, government policy decisions. The table below shows four of the
thousands of interest groups active in the United States today.

Four Representative Interest Groups

Group	Membership	Mission	Activities
Business Roundtable	Heads of major U.S. corporations	To ensure economic growth and a productive U.S. work-force	Research and position papers Policy formulation Lobbying
United Farm Workers of America	27,000 farmworkers	To provide farmworkers with the inspiration and tools to improve their lives	Labor organizing Contract negotiations Lobbying
Sierra Club	1,300,000 citizen supporters	To explore and protect wild places and promote the responsible use of Earth's ecosystems	Grassroots mobilization Litigation News releases
National Education Association	3,200,000 public schoolteachers	To create great public schools for every student	Workshops and training Lobbying Legal actions

1. Based on what you have learned about political parties, which of these four
   interest groups most likely has the largest proportion of Republican members?
   Why do you think so?

2. Choose one of these chosen interest groups to discuss. Identify the group and
   explain how it might claim to serve the public interest while protecting the
   interests of its members.

3. Choose one of the activities of your chosen interest group to discuss. Explain
   how that activity might be used to support the group's mission.

4. Suppose you were a member of the interest group you chose. What might you
   do to help it carry out its mission?

Public Opinion and the Media

To what extent do the media influence your political views?

PREVIEW

Analyze Adlai Stevenson's 1952 campaign poster, shown at the beginning of Chapter 9, and record responses to these questions:

- What details do you see?
- According to the poster, why should people vote for Stevenson?
- To whom is this poster designed to appeal?
- Do you think such a poster could actually influence people's views in an election?
- What other kinds of political media messages have you been exposed to? Did they have any influence on your political views?

READING NOTES

After you read each section, answer the corresponding questions in your notebook.

Section 9.2

1. List six forces that shape political socialization. Rank them in order from 1 (most influence on my political socialization) to 6 (least influence). For the top two items on your list, briefly explain why they have influenced your political socialization.

2. Create a simple diagram or illustration to represent each of the three ways that public opinion is shaped. Label each illustration.

3. Why is public opinion important in a democracy?

Section 9.3

1. Explain the difference between straw polls and the scientific sampling process.

2. Create a simple flowchart to show the steps of the polling process. Begin with the sentence shown below.

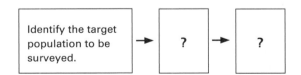

3. Create a symbol to represent each of these types of polls: *benchmark polls, tracking polls, exit polls,* and *push polls.* Then write one or two sentences explaining whether you think each type of poll should be used in political campaigns.

Section 9.4

1. Create a simple T-chart. In the first column, list at least three traditional media sources. In the second column, list at least five forms of "new" media. Check off all the forms of media that you have seen or used. Below your chart, identify at least two pros and one con of the new media.

2. What is the role of a free press in a democracy?

3. Describe two ways in which public officials can attract and shape media coverage.

4. Are the media biased? Explain your answer.

Section 9.5

How important do you think a candidate's image is during a political campaign? Use at least two of these terms in your answer: *media consultant, issue ad, image ad, photo op, soap opera story, mudslinging.*

PROCESSING

Write a paragraph in response to each question.

1. Are campaign commercials a good source of information about candidates? Why or why not?

2. How much influence do you think political advertising has on voters during elections? Why?

Creating a Campaign Commercial

Follow these steps to create a campaign commercial for your candidate.

Step 1 Carefully read the information you receive about your assigned candidate, and review the profile of your opponent. Identify these things:

- experience that qualifies your candidate to be president
- why your candidate will appeal to the public
- what differentiates your candidate from the opponent

Step 2 Identify the focus of your commercial, including

- the candidate's message.
- the type of advertisement: positive, negative, or issue based.
- the persuasive technique or techniques you will use.

Step 3 Create a storyboard for your commercial. Use the template you are given to prepare a commercial that will convince people to vote for your candidate or against your opponent. Your commercial must

- include every member of your group in some way, such as acting as the candidate, being interviewed, holding a sign, or providing narration.
- use at least one persuasive advertising technique.
- set the scene with appropriate props or costumes.
- include music or background visuals.
- be 30 seconds in length.

Step 4 Practice your commercial in preparation for recording it or presenting it to the class.

Candidate Profiles

Cory Mathews (Democrat)

Cory Mathews is a decorated veteran of the U.S. Air Force. Mathews served as a combat physician during Operation Desert Storm and earned a Purple Heart after saving the lives of three fellow soldiers when their helicopter was shot down. Upon returning from Desert Storm, Mathews worked as an emergency room physician before running for office. After serving two terms as a Democrat in the Florida legislature, Mathews was elected to the U.S. House of Representatives and has served five consecutive terms. Mathews has been married for more than 20 years and has two daughters, ages 19 and 14.

Mathews opposes the death penalty except for instances of terrorism. To keep communities safe and to prevent crime, Mathews wants to expand federal funding for community policing initiatives.

Mathews is a strong environmentalist who has coauthored and consistently voted in favor of clean air and water laws and legislation to enact tougher restrictions on car emissions. To help the United States end its dependence on oil, Mathews wants to encourage the development of alternative fuel sources. As president, Mathews would work to end subsidies for oil and gas companies and reinvest the savings in research to develop alternative fuel sources.

Mathews believes that although the United States needs to be a strong and independent nation, it also needs to rely on diplomacy, rather than military action, to solve global problems. Except for instances in which U.S. security is directly threatened or the United States is directly attacked, Mathews would like to see the United Nations take more responsibility for peacekeeping missions. Mathews believes that the lives of our young people are too precious to squander and that U.S. military action should be used only as a last resort.

At home, Mathews would like to see Medicaid, the publicly subsidized health insurance program for the poor, expanded to include any children who do not have health insurance. Mathews also wants to allow the federal government to bargain with drug companies in the United States and abroad to acquire the safest drugs at the lowest prices for people on Medicaid.

During a lengthy career in public service, Mathews has fought to roll back tax cuts that help the wealthiest individuals in order to fund public education and social programs for the poor. Mathews is a strong believer in the need to eradicate poverty in America. Through a minimum-wage hike and additional job-training programs, Mathews believes that the United States can eliminate poverty and strengthen the middle class.

Although illegal immigration is a problem, the only way the United States will solve the problem is by offering a realistic solution that appeals both to Americans and to undocumented immigrants. Mathews proposes that a guest worker program be created. This would allow people to come to the United States for up to three years to obtain work. At the end of that three years, they could continue to work in the United States if they begin the process of becoming a citizen. Otherwise, they would need to return home. Anyone currently in the United States illegally, Mathews believes, should be admitted immediately to the guest-worker program. The government should also provide English-language classes for people enrolled in the program, as not knowing English is often a major impediment to applying for citizenship.

Taylor Andrews (Republican)

Taylor Andrews attended Oxford University in England as a Rhodes Scholar, eventually earning a PhD in political science. Andrews then spent several decades as a professor at a prestigious university in California before becoming the president of a university in New Jersey. Andrews has been married for 27 years and has a son and daughter, ages 22 and 20. After a distinguished career as a scholar, Andrews retired from education and ran for governor of New Jersey. Andrews is currently serving a second term as New Jersey's governor.

Andrews supports minimum-sentencing laws for criminals but wants to increase funding for local law enforcement in order to make streets safer and to prevent crime. Andrews supports the death penalty as currently used. Andrews does not support any additional limits on an individual's right to own weapons and feels that the United States needs to focus on criminals who possess weapons illegally, not citizens who own them legally.

Andrews is a strong believer in the power of unregulated business to improve the American quality of life. Andrews thinks that minimal environmental restrictions are necessary, but also believes there is no need for additional restrictions. Instead, Andrews feels that government needs to focus on areas of the country, such as toxic waste sites, that need to be cleaned up. Cleaning up these sites and rebuilding on them, Andrews believes, will create jobs and provide future sites for businesses and homes.

Andrews believes that the United States needs to be a moral leader in the world. It should fight for freedom and democracy wherever there is a need. While this will ideally involve diplomacy rather than military action, Andrews says that the country should not hesitate to use its military when U.S. interests are threatened or attacked. However, Andrews feels that American forces should never be deployed to another country without having an exit strategy.

Andrews advocates keeping the current publicly subsidized health insurance programs, Medicare and Medicaid, but wants the federal government to provide no additional funding for health programs and no federal funds for stem cell research or cloning.

Andrews feels strongly that any American can succeed with hard work and perseverance. The answer to society's problems is not to require the federal government to put more money into social programs but to encourage individuals to take responsibility for themselves. Andrews wants to see federal tax cuts across all income levels so that Americans can keep more of the money they earn. Additional tax cuts for U.S. businesses will encourage those businesses to use the additional revenue to create more jobs. Andrews also wants to allow faith-based organizations to compete for federal funds to provide social services for the poor, rather than the federal government providing those services.

Finally, Andrews feels that the government needs to do more to encourage legal immigration and discourage illegal immigration. Andrews feels that the most effective way to do that would be to create a guest worker program that allows people to come to the United States for up to three years to obtain work. At the end of the three years, they could continue to work in the United States if they begin the process of becoming a citizen. Otherwise, they would need to return home. Anyone currently in the United States illegally would need to return to his or her home country to apply for the guest worker program.

Storyboard for Campaign Commercial

Use the storyboard template below to design your campaign commercial. In the sections labeled "On screen," quickly explain what viewers will see during this part of the commercial. In the "Narration" sections, briefly explain what the actors and narrators will say.

1	2
On screen: **Narration:**	**On screen:** **Narration:**
3	4
On screen: **Narration:**	**On screen:** **Narration:**
5	6
On screen: **Narration:**	**On screen:** **Narration:**

Mastering the Content

1. The process by which people form their political attitudes and values is called
   A. political correctness.
   B. political engagement.
   C. political participation.
   D. political socialization.

2. Which of the following is the best definition of public opinion?
   A. the sum of many individual views
   B. what journalists think about issues
   C. the beliefs of one or more interest groups
   D. how politicians express common attitudes

3. Which of the following is the most important reason why a scientific poll is more accurate than a straw poll?
   A. the type of questions asked
   B. the number of people surveyed
   C. the method of sampling employed
   D. the means of contacting people used

4. The founders of our country saw a free press as a safeguard against
   A. negative campaigning.
   B. the abuse of power.
   C. the rise of parties.
   D. political gridlock.

5. To test the appeal of campaign messages, media consultants often use
   A. focus groups.
   B. push polls.
   C. spin doctors.
   D. think tanks.

6. The release of confidential information to the news media by an unnamed source is known as which of the following?
   A. a staged event
   B. a trial balloon
   C. a sound bite
   D. a leak

7. How can the company conducting an opinion poll reduce the margin of error?
   A. ask fewer questions
   B. survey a larger sample
   C. use mail instead of phone
   D. limit the survey to college graduates

8. Which of these persuasive techniques takes advantage of people's desire to conform?
   A. bandwagon
   B. card-stacking
   C. name-calling
   D. transfer

9. The primary purpose of staged events and photo opportunities is to
   A. attract press coverage.
   B. discuss issues in depth.
   C. collect small donations.
   D. hear the views of voters.

10. How do political analysts determine the voting patterns of women and men?
    A. conduct exit polls
    B. examine the ballots
    C. review election results
    D. interview election judges

Exploring the Essential Question

To what extent do the media influence your political views?

The extent to which we are influenced by the media depends, in part, on how much we trust what we hear, read, and see in the news media. The question of trust in the media was posed in a 2006 opinion poll. Study the results below, and answer the questions that follow.

CBS News/*New York Times* Poll

In general, how much trust and confidence do you have in the news media—such as newspapers, TV, and radio—when it comes to reporting the news fully, accurately, and fairly: a great deal, a fair amount, not very much, or none at all?

	A Great Deal	A Fair Amount	Not Very Much	None at All	Unsure
All	15%	48%	28%	8%	1%
Republicans	9%	43%	35%	13%	0%
Democrats	22%	53%	21%	4%	0%
Independents	13%	49%	29%	8%	1%

Source: CBS News/*New York Times*, Jan. 20–25, 2006.

1. Based on this poll, about what percentage of Americans trust the news media much or all of the time?

2. Which group—Republicans, Democrats, or Independents—is most trusting of the news media? The least trusting?

3. Based on these results, which group is most likely to believe the news media are biased? What kind of bias is that group likely to see in news reporting?

4. What answer would you give if you were asked this survey question? Explain why you chose the answer you did.

Political Campaigns and Elections

Elections and voting: Why should they matter to you?

Speaking of Politics

As you complete the Reading Notes, use these terms in your answers:

plurality	caucus
winner-take-all system	party base
primary election	stump speech
general election	coattail effect

PREVIEW

Each event listed below is a step in the process of running for president. Based on what you know about elections, record the steps in the most logical order in your notebook. Then answer this question: *Do you think this process helps or hinders us in electing the best individual as president?*

- form a campaign organization
- run in primaries and caucuses
- participate in televised debates
- announce candidacy
- conduct electoral vote
- attend national convention
- raise funds
- hold popular vote
- build a coalition of supporters
- develop a campaign strategy

READING NOTES

Section 10.2

Create the table below in your notebook. Record any applicable dates when each group gained voting rights, and briefly explain what rights were gained at that time. Then answer the questions that follow.

Group	Voting Rights Gained
White males	
African Americans	
Women	
American Indians	
18-year-olds	

1. Do you think Americans take voting for granted today? Why or why not?

2. What steps have been taken to increase voter turnout?

Section 10.3

Create a campaign to-do list for a presidential candidate trying to secure the party's nomination. Your list should have nine steps: *form an exploratory committee, join the race, set up a campaign organization, raise funds, develop a campaign strategy, campaign, run in primaries and caucuses,* and *attend the national convention.* Record the steps in your notebook, and note what needs to be done to accomplish each one. See the example below.

Step	To Do
Form an exploratory committee.	• Gather a group of advisers to evaluate chances for election. • Test the waters to determine the level of public support.
Join the race.	

Section 10.4

Create a list of important campaign terms. The list must include a brief description of each of these terms: *presidential election, midterm election, off-year election, term limits, stump speech, polling place, battleground states,* and *electoral vote.*

Section 10.5

Answer these questions:

1. How is money raised in political campaigns?

2. Do you see this as a problem? Why or why not?

3. What is one suggestion you would make for changing the role of money in political campaigns?

Section 10.6

Make a very simple sketch of an American voter. Around the body, draw spokes with explanations of how each of these factors influences whether a person is likely to vote: *age, education,* and *income.* Then add spokes with explanations of how each of these factors influences whom Americans vote for: *party affiliation, issues,* and *candidate characteristics.*

PROCESSING

Imagine that you have been hired by the Federal Election Commission to suggest one way to improve the U.S. electoral system. What would you suggest? Include the following information in your response:

- What changes would be involved?

- How would your suggestion change the electoral system?

- Why would your suggested change improve the electoral system?

Candidate Positions on Issues

Pat Donnellson (Democrat)

Below are your positions on four issues of interest to voters.

Foreign Policy

The United States is damaging its reputation around the world by not using diplomacy in its actions toward other countries. The United States should

- work with the United Nations to solve global conflicts.

- not take military action without UN approval, unless the United States is directly attacked by another country.

- create a U.S. Department of Peace with a cabinet-level position for the secretary of peace.

Crime and Punishment

Only education and weapons restrictions—not additional severe punishment—will help lower crime rates. The United States should

- adopt a constitutional amendment to ban the death penalty, which does not prevent crime and has been shown to have been inappropriately applied in the past.

- invest heavily in education and community policing, which will help curb violence.

- outlaw the private ownership of any type of firearm, no matter what its intended use.

Environment

The most serious crisis facing our country and the world is global warming. The United States should

- require trucks and SUVs to meet the same emission standards as cars.

- set a goal of having all cars run on alternative fuels by 2025.

- raise the gas tax. This would pay for research into alternative fuels. It would also provide government subsidies for oil companies that transition into producing alternative fuels or for auto manufacturers that transition into producing vehicles that run on alternative fuels.

- provide federal funding for mandated environmental education in schools.

Social Services for the Poor

Our social services do not effectively help eliminate poverty. The United States should

- create government-subsidized health insurance that would be available to all Americans.

- allow individuals to subscribe to private health insurance plans, but tax those plans to help pay for government-sponsored health care.

- raise the annual income figure that the federal government uses to define poverty so that more people will qualify for welfare (transitional aid), which will help them work their way out of poverty.

- make housing a right for all Americans.

Terry Lankan (Democrat)

Below are your positions on four issues of interest to voters.

Foreign Policy

The United States is developing a reputation as an aggressive empire. The United States should

- play a lead role in strengthening the United Nations to take some of the pressure off the U.S. military to act as the world's police force.
- expand the State Department's role in military planning to focus more on diplomacy.

Crime and Punishment

The government should focus on crime prevention. The United States should

- eliminate the death penalty for all crimes but terrorism, because the death penalty has never proven to be a deterrent for criminals.
- place a greater emphasis on preventing crime and on rehabilitation programs for first-time offenders.
- eliminate an individual's right to own handguns because such weapons are most frequently used to commit crimes. Ownership of other types of firearms, such as rifles, should remain legal.

Environment

The government needs to be active in protecting the environment and preventing global warming. The United States should

- offer tax credits for individuals and businesses that voluntarily reduce carbon emissions through the use of solar power, hybrid cars, and other methods.
- provide tax credits for businesses that invest in alternative energy research. Offer other government incentives to the oil and auto-manufacturing industries to encourage them to turn to alternative fuel production and consumption.

Social Services for the Poor

The United States should do more to reduce poverty levels and enable more people to live middle-class lifestyles. The United States should

- expand government-subsidized health insurance programs to include any elderly or disabled person or any child who applies for it.
- cover 100 percent of prescription drug costs for anyone on publicly subsidized health insurance.
- provide universal, full-day preschool and kindergarten for all children living in poverty.
- expand subsidized housing and Medicaid to include new immigrants.
- limit the amount of time someone can receive welfare (transitional aid) benefits. This will ensure that people are moving toward financial independence rather than relying on government handouts.

Cory Mathews (Democrat)

Below are your positions on four issues of interest to voters.

Foreign Policy

Although the United States needs to remain a strong and independent nation, it also needs to rely on diplomacy with other nations—rather than military action—to solve global problems. The United States should

- encourage the United Nations to take a more active role in peacekeeping missions.
- take military action against other nations only if U.S. security is directly threatened or the United States is directly attacked.
- use military action only as a last resort to avoid squandering the lives of our young people.

Crime and Punishment

Increased crime-prevention measures are a far more effective method of keeping us safe than are additional punishments for crime. The United States should

- eliminate the death penalty except for cases involving terrorism.
- keep communities safe and prevent crime by expanding federal funding for community-policing initiatives.

Environment

This country needs to be a global leader in the fight against global warming. The United States should

- enact tougher regulations on automobile emissions.
- enact stricter clean air and water laws.
- develop alternative fuel sources in order to help the country reduce its dependence on oil.
- end subsidies to oil and gas companies and reinvest that money in research to develop alternative fuel sources.

Social Services for the Poor

We need to continue to help the poor rise above poverty. The United States should

- expand government-subsidized health insurance for the poor (Medicaid) to include any children who do not have health insurance for any reason.
- allow the federal government to bargain with drug companies in the United States and abroad to acquire the safest drugs at the lowest prices for people who have publicly subsidized health insurance.
- roll back tax cuts that help the wealthiest individuals in order to fund social and educational programs for the poor.
- work to eliminate poverty through a minimum wage hike and additional job-training programs.

Taylor Andrews (Republican)

Below are your positions on four issues of interest to voters.

Foreign Policy

This country needs to be a moral leader in the world. The United States should

- fight for freedom and democracy wherever there is a need.
- use diplomacy rather than military action when possible, but not hesitate to use military force when U.S. interests are threatened or attacked.
- never get involved in other countries' affairs without an exit strategy.

Crime and Punishment

Increasing the punishment for crimes will help deter criminal activity. The United States should

- support mandatory minimum-sentencing laws for criminals in all states.
- increase funding for local law enforcement to make streets safer and to prevent crime.
- retain the death penalty as currently used.
- not enact any additional limits on an individual's right to own weapons. The country must focus on criminals who possess weapons illegally, not on citizens who own them legally.

Environment

Americans can thank unregulated business for improving their quality of life. The United States should

- keep minimal environmental restrictions, but should not enact any additional regulations that might affect a company's ability to do business.
- focus on areas of the country, like toxic waste sites, that need to be cleaned up.
- rebuild on these cleaned-up areas to create jobs as well as new sites for businesses and homes.

Social Services for the Poor

Instead of expanding social services, the government needs to get Americans to focus on hard work and perseverance. The United States should

- keep the current government-subsidized health insurance programs (Medicare and Medicaid), but provide no additional funding for health programs.
- allow faith-based organizations to compete for federal funds to provide social services for the poor, rather than the federal government providing those services.
- enact federal tax cuts across all income levels so that Americans can keep more of the money they earn.
- enact additional tax cuts for U.S. businesses and encourage them to use the additional revenue to create more jobs and help people work their way out of poverty.

Casey McMahon (Republican)

Below are your positions on four issues of interest to voters.

Foreign Policy

We need to promote our national interests abroad. The United States should

- ideally emphasize diplomacy and multinational actions, but act alone if necessary.

- promote and protect our interests in other countries, even if doing so requires military action.

- fight for freedom and democracy—which are basic human rights—wherever there is a need.

Crime and Punishment

The best way to prevent crime is to keep criminals off the streets. The United States should

- expand mandatory minimum-sentencing laws.

- retain the death penalty as currently used.

- allow law-abiding Americans to be able to protect themselves and their families by legally owning any type of firearm.

- step up its efforts to seize illegal firearms to prevent them from being used in criminal activities.

Environment

It is not the government's responsibility to protect the environment. The United States should

- roll back current environmental regulations that affect businesses.

- offer tax incentives to businesses for voluntary compliance with minimum environmental regulations.

- recognize that the problem of global warming is exaggerated by alarmists who want the government to prevent manufacturing and energy companies from being successful.

Social Services for the Poor

We need to remove the federal government from the business of providing social services. The United States should

- keep the current government-subsidized health insurance programs (Medicare and Medicaid) to prevent a health care crisis.

- allow private companies to administer parts or all of the plans in order to make those plans more cost efficient.

- distribute federal funds to states based on their poverty rates. States should then be responsible for administering any social services appropriate for their populations. This will allow states to focus on the issues most relevant to their citizens.

- enact a federal law requiring all states to fund a full day of kindergarten in districts with a child poverty rate greater than 20 percent.

J. A. Curley (Republican)

Below are your positions on four issues of interest to voters.

Foreign Policy

This country should be the champion of democracy and freedom around the world. The United States should

- defend the ideals of democracy and freedom wherever they are threatened.
- act alone to promote the country's national interests.
- move the UN headquarters from New York City to Switzerland.

Crime and Punishment

The government should have a zero-tolerance policy for criminal behavior. The United States should

- increase penalties for crimes, because punishment is the best deterrent.
- expand mandatory minimum-sentencing laws.
- apply the death penalty automatically to felonies involving drug trafficking and terrorism.
- remove any possibility of parole for criminals who commit violent felonies.

Environment

Our natural resources should be used in ways that are most beneficial to all. The United States should

- privatize national parks so that companies can efficiently manage them and determine the best use for the land. In some instances, there might be better uses—such as mineral or oil extraction—for the land than preservation.
- recognize that global warming is a theory perpetuated by alarmists. The government should not provide federal funding for research into alternative fuels.
- not enact any laws that would require businesses to adopt costly environmentally friendly policies.

Social Services for the Poor

The government should rely on private businesses and faith-based charities to provide social services. The United States should

- end government-subsidized health care programs (Medicare and Medicaid).
- turn Medicare and Medicaid programs over to private health insurance providers to decrease the cost of administering such programs.
- end all federally funded welfare programs. It is not the government's responsibility to provide social services.
- provide full federal funding for faith-based social service agencies, which can then administer social services to the needy.

National Town Hall Meeting Prep for Candidates

You are about to participate in one of the most important events in the election process. In a national town hall meeting, average Americans get to ask questions of the candidates. Prepare for the national town hall meeting by doing the following:

Step 1 Create a nameplate for the meeting. Then prepare a 10-second introduction, including your name, the office or position you currently hold, and a brief statement about why you are running for president. Finally, prepare a 30-second closing statement encouraging people to vote for you.

Step 2 Develop talking points on the major issues of the campaign. Your talking points should consist of the two or three points you definitely want to make about each issue. They must include at least one relevant statistic per issue.

Issue	Talking Points
Foreign policy	
Crime and punishment	
Environment	
Social services for the poor	

Statistics on the Issues

The statistics below relate to the four issues that the candidates will be debating. Some of the statistics are estimates, based on the most recent data available.

Foreign Policy

- Amount spent on U.S. foreign aid, 2008: **$20,300,000,000**
- Percentage of U.S. federal budget spent on defense, 2008: **20%**
- Defense budget, 2008: **$600,000,000,000**
- Amount spent on defense per person, 2007: **$1,992**
- U.S. military spending as percentage of GDP: **4%**
- World military spending as percentage of GDP: **2%**
- U.S. soldiers killed in action, 1993–1999: **6,742**
- U.S. soldiers killed in action, 2000–2006: **9,550**

Crime and Punishment

- U.S. crime rate, 1960: **2%**
- U.S. crime rate, 2003: **4%**
- Percentage of former prisoners rearrested for new crimes within 3 years of being released: **67%**
- Percentage of U.S. population incarcerated, 2006: **0.75%**
- Percentage of world population incarcerated, 2006: **0.17%**
- Jails in the U.S.: **1,558**
- Percentage of U.S. population who have been victims of assault: **1.2%**
- Percentage of U.S. population who have been victims of property crime: **10%**
- U.S. rank among countries with the most crimes committed: **1**
- Percentage of homicides that involve a firearm: **40%**
- Prisoners executed in the U.S., 2006: **53**
- U.S. death row inmates released after evidence of their innocence emerged, 1973–2007: **124**
- Prisoners on death row in the U.S. as of January 1, 2007: **3,350**

Environment

- Five hottest years on record, as of 2007: **1880, 2002, 2003, 2005, 2006**
- U.S. rank as a producer of greenhouse gases: **1**
- Number of national science academies issuing statements that "climate change is real" and asking that governments take "prompt action" on the problem: **11**
- Percentage of Americans who believe global warming is a serious threat now: **38%**
- Percentage of Americans who believe global warming will be a serious problem in the future: **85%**
- U.S. oil consumption, as a percentage of total world oil consumption: **25%**
- Percentage of the largest U.S. industrial plants and water treatment facilities that are in serious violation of pollution standards: **25%**
- U.S. areas that are protected: **3,481 (13.4% of U.S. land)**
- Percentage of U.S. territory still considered wild: **36%**
- Percentage decrease in carbon monoxide in the air under the Clean Air Act, 1990–2006: **62%**

Social Services for the Poor

- Percentage of Americans living below the poverty line, 2004: **12%**
- Percentage of federal budget spent on aid to the needy, 2007: **16%**
- Percentage of federal budget spent on Medicare and Medicaid, 2007: **15% and 7%, respectively**
- Percentage of Americans under 18 without health care, 2006: **12%**
- Percentage of Americans age 19–29 without health care, 2006: **31%**
- Percentage of Medicare funds spent on administration: **3%–10%**
- Percentage of private health insurance plans spent on administration: **12%**
- Percentage of federal budget spent on Title I (education program for children in poverty), 2008: **0.004%**

National Town Hall Meeting Prep for the Audience

You are about to participate in one of the most important events in the election process. Your job at the national town hall meeting will be to learn as much as possible about the candidates in order to decide who should be elected president.

To prepare for the meeting, read about the positions of all six candidates and review the statistics on the four issues that they will debate. For each issue, identify the candidate or candidates whose positions you are particularly interested in. Record that information below. Also write a question for that candidate or candidates. Incorporate statistics related to the issues into your questions, where appropriate.

Issue	Candidates and Positions	Questions for Candidates
Foreign policy		
Crime and punishment		
Environment		
Social services for the poor		

Overview of the Candidates

Pat Donnellson (Democrat)

Donnellson wants to focus on diplomacy, rather than military action, to solve global problems. Working with the United Nations and creating a U.S. Department of Peace should be the basis of U.S. foreign policy. Donnellson wants the federal government to provide government-sponsored health care and to help more people qualify for government aid to work their way out of poverty. Donnellson wants to have all cars run on alternative fuels by 2025 and wants to tax gas to pay for research into alternative fuels. Donnellson also wants the United States to adopt a constitutional amendment banning the death penalty, invest in community policing, and outlaw the private ownership of any type of firearm.

Terry Lankan (Democrat)

Lankan wants the United States to help strengthen the United Nations so that the U.S. military will not have to act as the world's police force. Lankan wants to expand government-subsidized health insurance to cover more people and wants universal, full-day preschool and kindergarten for all children living in poverty. Lankan thinks there should be limits on how long people can receive welfare (transitional aid). The government should also offer tax credits to individuals and businesses that reduce carbon emissions or invest in alternative energy research. Lankan also wants to eliminate the death penalty except for crimes of terrorism and does not think individuals should be allowed to own handguns.

Cory Mathews (Democrat)

Mathews believes that the United States should take military action against other nations only if U.S. security is directly threatened or if the country is directly attacked. Mathews wants Medicaid to include any children who do not have health insurance, wants to roll back tax cuts on the wealthiest individuals to fund social programs and education for the poor, and wants a minimum wage hike and more job-training programs. Mathews wants the country to enact tougher environmental regulations and to develop alternative fuel sources. Mathews also wants to increase crime-prevention measures by expanding federal funding for community-policing initiatives.

Taylor Andrews (Republican)

Andrews believes that the United States must fight for freedom and democracy wherever there is a need and should not hesitate to use military action when U.S. interests are threatened. Andrews wants to allow faith-based organizations to use federal funds to provide social services for the poor and plans to enact tax cuts across all income levels and for businesses. Andrews believes that only the current environmental regulations are necessary. Rather than enacting new restrictions, the United States should focus on cleaning up areas like toxic waste sites. Andrews believes that increasing the punishment for crimes through mandatory minimum-sentencing laws will help deter criminal activity.

Casey McMahon (Republican)

McMahon believes that the United States should promote its national interests abroad, even if doing so requires military action. Instead of the federal government providing social services, McMahon wants private companies to administer government-subsidized health care programs and wants to distribute federal funds to the states. States would then be responsible for administering social services. McMahon would like to roll back current environmental regulations and instead offer businesses tax incentives for voluntary compliance with minimum environmental restrictions. McMahon wants to expand mandatory minimum-sentencing laws and retain the death penalty.

J. A. Curley (Republican)

Curley believes that the United States needs to defend the ideals of democracy and freedom wherever they are threatened and should act alone to promote the country's national interests. Curley wants to end government-subsidized health care programs, as well as all federally funded welfare programs. The United States needs to use the country's natural resources, including lands currently protected, in ways that benefit the most people. Curley thinks that the United States should not buy into the theory of global warming. Curley feels that there should be a zero-tolerance policy for criminal behavior and advocates increased penalties, expanded mandatory minimum-sentencing laws, and greater use of the death penalty.

The National Town Hall Meeting and State Primaries

Follow these steps to participate in the national town hall meeting and to vote in the state primaries.

Step 1 Arrange the classroom for the national town hall meeting. Consult the diagram to set up the classroom and to determine where you will sit.

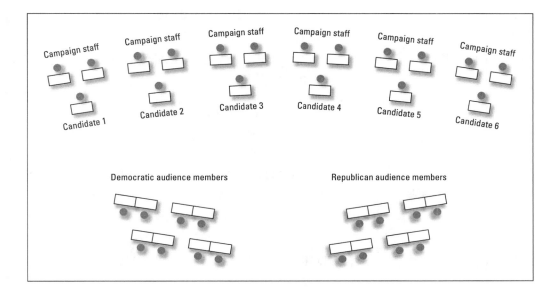

Step 2 Participate in the national town hall meeting.
- Every candidate will give a 10-second introduction.
- The moderator (teacher) will move around the audience with a microphone and allow one audience member from each small group to ask the candidates a question.
- The questioner will begin, *This question is for (candidate's name)* . . .
- After a candidate answers a question, the moderator will ask whether any other candidates want to respond. One or two other candidates may then offer opposing viewpoints or ask a question of the candidate about his or her answer.
- Each new question from the audience must be addressed to a new candidate.
- At the end of the national town hall meeting, each candidate will have 30 seconds to summarize why he or she should be the next president.

Step 3 Vote in the state primaries.
- Each voter represents a different state that holds a closed primary.
- Use your ballot to cast your vote for a candidate from the party that you have been supporting.

Ballots for the State Primaries

OFFICIAL BALLOT
DEMOCRAT
State Primary Election

INSTRUCTIONS TO VOTERS
To vote, fill in the oval opposite your choice, like this: ⬤

For President
Vote for not more than ONE.

PAT DONNELLSON ◯   TERRY LANKAN ◯
CORY MATHEWS ◯

OFFICIAL BALLOT
REPUBLICAN
State Primary Election

INSTRUCTIONS TO VOTERS
To vote, fill in the oval opposite your choice, like this: ⬤

For President
Vote for not more than ONE.

TAYLOR ANDREWS ◯   CASEY McMAHON ◯
J. A. CURLEY ◯

OFFICIAL BALLOT
DEMOCRAT
State Primary Election

INSTRUCTIONS TO VOTERS
To vote, fill in the oval opposite your choice, like this: ⬤

For President
Vote for not more than ONE.

PAT DONNELLSON ◯   TERRY LANKAN ◯
CORY MATHEWS ◯

OFFICIAL BALLOT
REPUBLICAN
State Primary Election

INSTRUCTIONS TO VOTERS
To vote, fill in the oval opposite your choice, like this: ⬤

For President
Vote for not more than ONE.

TAYLOR ANDREWS ◯   CASEY McMAHON ◯
J. A. CURLEY ◯

OFFICIAL BALLOT
DEMOCRAT
State Primary Election

INSTRUCTIONS TO VOTERS
To vote, fill in the oval opposite your choice, like this: ⬤

For President
Vote for not more than ONE.

PAT DONNELLSON ◯   TERRY LANKAN ◯
CORY MATHEWS ◯

OFFICIAL BALLOT
REPUBLICAN
State Primary Election

INSTRUCTIONS TO VOTERS
To vote, fill in the oval opposite your choice, like this: ⬤

For President
Vote for not more than ONE.

TAYLOR ANDREWS ◯   CASEY McMAHON ◯
J. A. CURLEY ◯

OFFICIAL BALLOT
DEMOCRAT
State Primary Election

INSTRUCTIONS TO VOTERS
To vote, fill in the oval opposite your choice, like this: ⬤

For President
Vote for not more than ONE.

PAT DONNELLSON ◯   TERRY LANKAN ◯
CORY MATHEWS ◯

OFFICIAL BALLOT
REPUBLICAN
State Primary Election

INSTRUCTIONS TO VOTERS
To vote, fill in the oval opposite your choice, like this: ⬤

For President
Vote for not more than ONE.

TAYLOR ANDREWS ◯   CASEY McMAHON ◯
J. A. CURLEY ◯

Preparing for the National Nominating Convention

As your party's nominee, you will facilitate making the decisions of who will do what in your campaign. Next to each task below, write the names of the people in your political party who will complete that task either before or during the national nominating convention for your party.

Create a Banner Make a large banner for the convention. The banner should include the year of the convention, the name of the political party, a slogan, and any other appropriate creative touches. Hang the banner in an appropriate location or hold it up on stage during the convention.

Create Signs Make signs in support of the presidential candidate, the vice presidential candidate, and your political party. Typical signs seen at conventions include such slogans as "New York Loves Hillary Clinton" or "America Is Reagan Country." Slogans used on signs should not repeat the slogan created for chanting during the convention. Signs should have appropriate creative touches and use a lot of red, white, and blue. Make enough signs so that everyone in your party, except the candidates, has one to carry during the convention.

Choose Music Choose one song or create a short compilation of songs that will serve as your candidates' background music. The music should include a catchy theme song that can be used again and again at campaign appearances. Music cannot have any inappropriate lyrics.

Write a Slogan Create a slogan that can be used as a chant for your party during the convention. The slogan should be something that will get people excited about your party and your candidate. Teach the rest of your party how to chant the slogan prior to the convention. At the convention, enthusiastically lead the chanting of the slogan during the appropriate times.

Choose a Master of Ceremonies Choose an MC to write brief introductions for the keynote speaker and the presidential candidate. Introductions should be about 15 seconds long and should heavily praise the speakers (they are great people, the best thing to happen to your party, and so on). The MC is also responsible for keeping the crowd excited and for cuing standing ovations (at least five of them) during introductions and speeches at the convention.

Choose a Keynote Speaker Choose someone to write and deliver a keynote address during the convention. The keynote speaker's address should glorify your political party, criticize the opposing party or candidates, and predict victory for your candidates in November. Coordinate the speech with the presidential nominee so that the two speeches are not repetitive. The keynote needs to be delivered eloquently and should last for one minute or less.

Choose the Vice President This is ultimately the presidential nominee's choice, but he or she may wish to consult other party members about the choice. The vice presidential candidate can be a former presidential candidate or anyone in the party who will increase the likelihood of the presidential nominee being elected. You may wish to keep this decision a secret (make sure you ask your vice presidential nominee ahead of time) until you make the announcement at the convention. Or you might want to tell other members of your party so that they can use this information in creating signs, banners, and slogans.

Write a Presidential Acceptance Speech Write and deliver a speech accepting the nomination for the office of president of the United States. The speech should briefly highlight the reasons you are the right person for the office, thank other candidates who ran against you for their current support, praise the merits of party harmony, and outline no fewer than three issues that you feel most strongly about. Your speech should predict victory in November. The speech should end by announcing your vice presidential running mate and should briefly highlight one or two important qualities of that person. The candidate needs to participate in writing this speech and needs to eloquently deliver the speech during the convention. The speech should last for one minute or less.

The National Nominating Conventions

You will now participate in the national nominating convention for your party. The two national nominating conventions will be held one at a time.

Agenda for the National Nominating Conventions

You will see only brief segments of each party's national nominating convention. Each convention will be organized as follows:

Step 1 Music plays, delegates march in with signs and banner, music fades as delegates chant their slogan.

Step 2 Delegates hold signs and cheer during appropriate times throughout the convention. The MC cues delegates on when to cheer, including standing ovations during speeches.

Step 3 The MC welcomes the delegates and introduces the keynote speaker.

Step 4 The keynote speaker addresses the convention.

Step 5 The MC introduces the party's presidential nominee.

Step 6 The presidential nominee delivers an acceptance speech.

Step 7 The vice presidential nominee joins the presidential nominee on stage. They wave to the audience and shake hands with delegates.

Step 8 Music plays again, everyone cheers for the candidates as they exit the stage, delegates march out carrying signs and chanting their slogan.

The Role of the Press

During each convention, the students who are members of the opposing party will act as *independent* members of the press. Press members will need to record information to report on the following:

- How inspiring was this convention? Provide specific details.
- Should people vote for this presidential and vice presidential candidate? Why or why not?

The Presidential Election

You will now participate in the campaigning portion of the presidential election.

Step 1 Except for the presidential and vice presidential nominees from each party, all students now represent individual states (they are no longer members of particular political parties). Consult the projected list to determine which state you have been assigned to represent. Create a large nametag that displays the name of your state and its number of electoral votes.

Step 2 Examine the projected electoral map. Using the four corners of the U.S. on the floor, find the approximate geographic location of your state and stand there.

Nominees: While students are positioning themselves, discuss this question with your running mate: *Which states should we focus on in our campaign, and why?*

Step 3 Conduct the campaigning session. Follow these rules:

- You have 10 minutes for this mock campaign session. Presidential and vice presidential nominees can visit as many states as they want—together or separately—to encourage those states to vote for them.

- When a nominee makes a campaign stop, he or she can talk to multiple states in the area.

- No state can stop a nominee as he or she is traveling. A nominee is free to visit the states he or she chooses and may visit some states more than once or not at all.

State	Electoral Votes	Student
California	55	
Texas	34	
New York	31	
Florida	27	
Pennsylvania	21	
Illinois	21	
Ohio	20	
Michigan	17	
New Jersey	15	
North Carolina	15	
Georgia	15	
Virginia	13	
Massachusetts	12	
Indiana	11	
Tennessee	11	
Washington	11	
Missouri	11	
Arizona	10	
Maryland	10	
Minnesota	10	
Wisconsin	10	
Alabama	9	
Colorado	9	
Louisiana	9	
South Carolina	8	
Kentucky	8	

State	Electoral Votes	Student
Connecticut	7	
Oklahoma	7	
Oregon	7	
Iowa	7	
Arkansas	6	
Kansas	6	
Mississippi	6	
Nebraska	5	
Nevada	5	
New Mexico	5	
Utah	5	
West Virginia	5	
New Hampshire	4	
Hawaii	4	
Idaho	4	
Rhode Island	4	
Maine	4	
Montana	3	
Alaska	3	
Delaware	3	
District Of Columbia	3	
North Dakota	3	
South Dakota	3	
Vermont	3	
Wyoming	3	

Mastering the Content

1. The emphasis on elections in the United States most reflects which constitutional principle?
   A. individual rights
   B. popular sovereignty
   C. checks and balances
   D. separation of powers

2. In which kind of primary election would a registered independent be unable to vote?
   A. open
   B. closed
   C. blanket
   D. nonpartisan

3. The most common way people become candidates for public office is through
   A. popular drafts.
   B. party caucuses.
   C. petition drives.
   D. self-announcement.

4. In which type of election is voter turnout likely to be the greatest?
   A. primary election
   B. midterm election
   C. off-year election
   D. presidential election

5. Which of the following groups benefited most from the Voting Rights Act of 1965?
   A. women
   B. 18- to 20-year-olds
   C. Native Americans
   D. African Americans

6. Televised debates and radio ads are examples of which of the following campaign approaches?
   A. retail politics
   B. microtargeting
   C. winner-take-all
   D. wholesale politics

7. What is the main criticism leveled against the Electoral College system for electing presidents?
   A. It takes too long.
   B. It is undemocratic.
   C. It discourages voting.
   D. It costs too much money.

8. What is the main source of funding for election campaigns?
   A. public financing
   B. contributions from PACs
   C. personal wealth of candidates
   D. donations from individual citizens

9. What was one purpose of the Bipartisan Campaign Reform Act of 2002, also known as the McCain-Feingold Act?
   A. to limit the use of soft money in campaigns
   B. to make voter registration more convenient
   C. to ban the participation of PACs in campaigns
   D. to promote the use of more accurate voting machines

10. Which of these is the most likely reason for a donor to contribute to two opposing campaigns?
    A. to encourage others to donate as well
    B. to reduce the risk of a third-party victory
    C. to show support for the two-party system
    D. to gain access to whichever candidate wins

Exploring the Essential Question

Elections and voting: Why should they matter to you?

In 1992, President George H. W. Bush was approaching the end of his first term and hoping to win election to a second term. The diagram below summarizes the stages of that year's election process. The candidates who actively campaigned in the Democratic and Republican primaries are shown, along with the votes cast at each party's nominating convention. The results of the general election are shown as well.

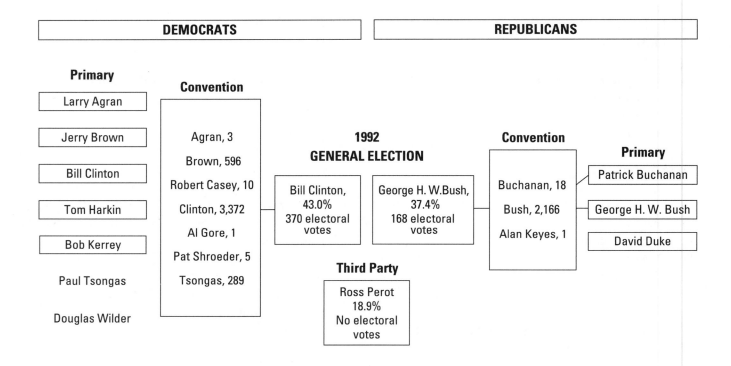

1. Which candidate had the second largest number of votes at the Democratic National Convention? At the Republican National Convention?

2. During the primary elections, why did one major party have so many more serious contenders than the other?

3. How was it possible for a candidate who won nearly 20 percent of the popular vote to receive no votes in the Electoral College?

4. Using the 1992 election as an example, explain how a third-party candidate who does not win the election may significantly influence the election results.

Lawmakers and Legislatures

What makes an effective legislator?

As you complete the Reading Notes, use these terms in your answers:

constituent

pork

standing committee

joint committee

conference committee

appropriations

joint resolution

casework

PREVIEW

Analyze the photograph of Congressman Joe Schwarz and read about his background.

Biographical Information

Congressman Joe Schwarz
Republican, Michigan Seventh District
Born: November 15, 1937, in Battle Creek, Michigan
Education: B.A. University of Michigan, 1959; M.D. Wayne State University, 1964
Occupation: Doctor, U.S. Navy 1965–1967, served in Vietnam; served in the Central Intelligence Agency, 1968–1970; private medical practice, 1970–present
Previous political experience: Battle Creek city commissioner, 1979–1985; mayor of Battle Creek, 1985–1987; Michigan State Senate, 1987–2002; elected to U.S. House of Representatives, 2004

Now answer these questions:

1. From the photograph and biography, what facts do you know about Congressman Schwarz?

2. What things about Joe Schwarz do you think are typical for a member of Congress? What things might be atypical?

3. What aspects of his background do you think would help make Joe Schwarz an effective legislator? Explain.

4. What things do you think Congressman Schwarz and his staff will need to do, or learn to do, to help him be an effective legislator?

READING NOTES

Section 11.2

1. List two formal and two informal qualifications for a member of Congress today (not 40 or 50 years ago). Do you think the informal qualifications for education and occupation help make an effective legislator? Why or why not?

2. Study the apportionment map in Section 11.2, and record information about any change to apportionment in your state. Then describe the process that determined why your state gained or lost representatives or why it stayed the same.

3. Explain the difference between a delegate and a trustee. Which do you think makes a more effective legislator, and why?

4. Create a bar graph or circle graphs to show the percentage of incumbents who have been reelected in the House and Senate since 1945. List three factors that help explain your graph or graphs.

Section 11.3

1. Fill in the blanks to complete this analogy: *The Senate "cools" legislation from the House like a _____ cools _____.* Create a simple illustration for your analogy. Finally, list at least two important differences between the House and the Senate that might allow the Senate to "cool" legislation from the House.

2. Which leadership position in Congress has the most power? List some specific powers of that position.

3. Create a simple table listing the five types of committees in Congress. Include these things in your table for each type of committee:
   - an appropriate symbol
   - one or two of the committee's important functions
   - a concrete example of that type of committee (if possible)

4. Sketch a simple graph showing what has happened to the size of House and Senate staff since 1930. Then list two or three important jobs congressional staffers do.

5. Suppose you are a member of Congress and want to create a new caucus. Come up with a creative name for your caucus, and explain what issues or topics your caucus would focus on.

Section 11.4

1. According to Article I of the Constitution, what are the specific, or enumerated, powers of Congress? What part of the Constitution allows Congress to broaden its power beyond those enumerated powers?

2. Create a simple diagram that shows the six ways in which Congress checks the other two branches of government. Label each check, and indicate which other branch each check applies to.

3. Draw the spoke diagram below in your notebook. Fill in each rectangle with a key power of Congress.

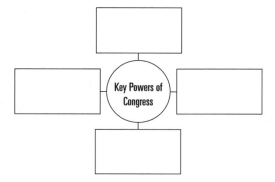

From each of those key powers, add at least two more spokes with important pieces of information about that power of Congress.

4. Create a political cartoon that shows why casework is such an important aspect of being an effective legislator.

Section 11.5

1. Create a Venn diagram comparing state legislatures with Congress. Identify at least three significant similarities and at least four important differences between the two. Be specific.

2. Overall, do you think term limits are a good idea? Why or why not?

PROCESSING

Create a report card that evaluates how effective a legislator is.

- Select one of your own members of Congress—representative or senator—or another national or state legislator.

- Identify three to five criteria that you will use to evaluate that legislator's effectiveness. Use topics from the chapter—such as committee assignments, casework, and getting reelected—or other criteria that you think are important.

- Find information about what your selected legislator has done in each area. Consider starting your search on the legislator's own Web site, or visit Congresspedia, which has useful information and links for every member of Congress.

- Based on your research, design a report card and assign a letter grade for each item, along with supporting evidence—such as facts, statistics, or quotations—to justify the grade. Then give an overall grade for the legislator's effectiveness, along with a summary explaining the grade.

New Congressional Staff Orientation

You and your partner are the staff members for a newly elected member of Congress. You will now analyze information from eight orientation packets to learn about different aspects of being an effective legislator. When you receive a packet, place the placard(s) and the handout with the placard questions and reading questions face up on the desk. Place the handout with the excerpt from *Freshman Orientation* by Edward Sidlow face down. Then follow these steps:

Step 1 Carefully analyze the information on the placard(s).

Step 2 Discuss each of the placard questions.

Step 3 Turn the other handout face up, and carefully read the excerpt from *Freshman Orientation*.

Step 4 Discuss each of the reading questions.

Step 5 Find the corresponding section of your new congressional staff orientation notes. Record at least three things you learned that will help your new member of Congress be an effective legislator.

Step 6 Organize all of the packet materials, exchange them for a new orientation packet, and repeat these steps.

Selecting Congressional Office Space

Placard Questions

Carefully analyze the information on the placards, and then discuss these questions with your partner:

1. What interesting details do you see on the two maps?

2. Who has offices inside the U.S. Capitol building? Why do you think these people have their offices there?

3. In which buildings do most members of the House of Representatives have their offices?

4. Of the three possible office spaces listed below, which would you recommend that your member of Congress select and why?

   • Second-floor office suite in the Rayburn Building

   • Third-floor office suite in the Longworth Building

   • First-floor (ground level) office suite in the Cannon Building (One of the three offices in this suite is not connected to the other two offices, but is instead a few yards down the hall.)

Reading Questions

Read Excerpt A from *Freshman Orientation,* and then discuss these questions with your partner:

1. Do you think Congressman Schwarz and his chief of staff selected office space that will help him be an effective legislator? Explain.

2. What have you learned that will help your new member of Congress be an effective legislator?

Excerpt A from *Freshman Orientation* by Edward I. Sidlow

After his November [2004] victory . . . Joe Schwarz found himself one of thirty-nine—twenty-four Republicans, fifteen Democrats—newly elected members of the House of Representatives in the 109th Congress. The arrival of these newcomers on Capitol Hill, coupled with the departure of the members whose seats they had filled, set off the ritual, complicated game of "Room Draw"—or, more candidly, "grab that space." Offices now vacated would first be made available to members who had served in the preceding Congress, some of whom would choose to move to a more spacious office, or to one with a better view, leaving their old offices for the freshman class to divvy up. Then, according to custom, a lottery would be held for new members, assigning numbers to indicate the order in which they could select an office from the spaces available. Among those taking office in 2005, the member drawing number 1 had the widest choice; the member with number 39 had the most limited selection. Since Joe Schwarz had drawn number 38, he and Matt Marsden [his chief of staff] were not hopeful about the office space they would get. "When you are that far down the list," Matt noted, "it's silly to have great expectations."

To Matt's surprise, however a first-floor office in the Cannon Building was still available when it was Joe's turn to select his space. A first-floor location means no long waits for elevators on the way from the office to the floor of the House for votes and debate . . .

The Cannon Building, which was opened in 1908 and named for Joe Cannon, the powerful Speaker of the House from 1903 to 1911, is the oldest of three House office buildings. It is situated [southeast] of the Capitol Rotunda, on the other side of Independence Avenue. Across the street is the Library of Congress, and a block or so away is the U.S. Supreme Court.

Schwarz's new office space, measuring about 1,000 square feet, was due to receive fresh paint and new carpeting before the congressman and his staff moved in. While the first-floor location could be seen as a plus, the space itself is a bit awkward, since the rooms are not entirely contiguous . . . While somewhat inconvenient, the divided configuration does allow the staff a sense of independence, and it affords the boss a fair amount of peace and quiet. Besides, freshmen members don't have a lot of choice in these matters.

Hiring Congressional Staff

Placard Questions

Carefully analyze the information on the placards, and then discuss these questions with your partner:

1. What interesting things do you see in the organizational chart for Congressman Schwarz's Capitol Hill office?

2. What might you hypothesize about the age, background, and experience of these D.C. staffers?

3. How is Congressman Schwarz's Washington, D.C., staff similar to and different from that of an average House member?

4. How are Congressman Schwarz's district staff and offices similar to and different from that of an average House member? What might explain the differences?

Reading Questions

Read Excerpt B from *Freshman Orientation,* and then discuss these questions with your partner:

1. How effective do you think Congressman Schwarz and his chief of staff were in selecting staff to help him be an effective legislator? Explain.

2. What have you learned that will help your new member of Congress be an effective legislator?

Excerpt B from *Freshman Orientation* by Edward I. Sidlow

Having taken on the title of chief of staff, Matt [Marsden's] . . . most immediate task was to hire someone to supervise the Washington-based staff—someone with Capitol Hill experience and a thorough understanding of the congressional systems and the policymaking process. Matt interviewed four people for the job, and then had Joe meet with each of them. Eventually, they chose Chuck Yessaian, who, in his mid-twenties, was the youngest of the job candidates . . .

Chuck had moved to D.C. in January 2001 without any solid job prospects. He . . . interviewed for an entry-level position on the staff of the House Transportation and Infrastructure Committee . . .

Chuck described his early position on the committee staff as "the lowest staff assistant imaginable . . . I was really a glorified furniture mover" . . . In late winter of 2003, he interviewed for a position as legislative assistant (LA) in the office of Fred Upton (R-Mich.) . . . After being on the Hill for just a little over three years, then, Chuck was ready in late 2004 to make the jump to legislative director in the Schwarz office—an impressive accomplishment . . .

In his new position, Yessaian inherited three newly appointed legislative assistants . . . Mark Ratner . . . had worked for Joe during his days in the Michigan state senate and then had served briefly as a substitute teacher before rejoining Schwarz on the campaign trail. Louis Meizlish was a recent graduate of the University of Michigan and a veteran of the campaign as well . . . Meghan Kolassa, a thirty-one-year-old attorney and a life-long friend of Joe's daughter Brennan, had worked for Schwarz when he was in the state senate . . .

A fourth hire was Rob Blackwell, who . . . had first met Dr. Joe Schwarz as a frightened youngster whose tonsils needed to be removed. Afterward, the two stayed in touch, and after working on the congressional campaign, Rob was invited to join the staff in Washington. His job description included . . . "everything from helping out with the schedule, to being Joe's bodyman"* . . .

Chuck Yessaian hired two additional legislative assistants to round out the Hill staff . . . For the more general LA position, [he hired] Jared Page . . . Then twenty-five years old, Jared had . . . earned a bachelors degree in political science and a masters in public policy, both from the University of Michigan. His first taste of politics had come during the summer of 2000, when . . . he worked for Joe Schwarz, who was then a state senator . . .

The second LA position . . . required someone [with] a detailed understanding of military matters and at least the potential for receiving the security clearance necessary for working with the classified information . . . Having received approximately fifty applications for this position, Chuck interviewed about six candidates. Finally, as Chuck put it, he "stepped outside the box a bit on Aaron's hire—a senior LA with no Hill experience is rather unconventional." In his mid-thirties, Aaron Taliaferro had completed nearly ten years of active service in the air force . . . Aaron had worked directly with Secretary of Defense Donald Rumsfeld, and he had the highest security clearance one could get. Chuck also thought that Aaron would fit in well with the rest of the Schwarz office staff . . .

A little more than twelve weeks since the Swearing-In, Congressman Schwarz's office was up and running.

---

*A *bodyman* is the person who shuttles the elected official from place to place; holds the coat, briefcase, or suitcase; and knows when to have a container of coffee, as opposed to bottled water or soda on hand.

Requesting Committee Assignments

Placard Questions

Carefully analyze the information on the placards, and then discuss these questions with your partner:

1. What interesting information do you find in Congressman Schwarz's biography?

2. What interesting information do you see about Michigan's Seventh District?

3. Suppose you were a member of Congressman Schwarz's staff. Based on information from his background and his district, which *three* committee assignments would you recommend that he request from his party leaders? Why?

Reading Questions

Read Excerpt C from *Freshman Orientation,* and then discuss these questions with your partner:

1. Do you think Congressman Schwarz's final committee assignments put him in the best position to be an effective legislator? Why or why not?

2. What have you learned that will help your new member of Congress be an effective legislator?

Excerpt C from *Freshman Orientation* by Edward I. Sidlow

The committee system is absolutely central to the policy-making process. Congress handles roughly 10,000 bills in any given two-year cycle; this enormous workload must be divided in some manageable way. Standing committees . . . provide the structure for handling the volume of bills introduced, and they are essential to a House member's life on the Hill . . .

After the victory in the 2004 primary, Joe Schwarz and [his chief of staff] Matt Marsden began discussing the committee assignments that would be commensurate with Joe's interests and ability to benefit the Seventh District . . . They quickly agreed that an assignment to the Committee on Education and the Workforce would be great. Joe believed deeply in the importance of education and . . . because of his medical training, he had a particular appreciation for science education . . . Consequently, Joe and Matt determined that a seat on the Science Committee was also attractive . . .

Because farming is a major industry in Michigan's Seventh District, . . . a seat on Agriculture would be welcomed. The Transportation and Infrastructure Committee also seemed an attractive possibility, in part because Interstate 94, which runs east-to-west through the district, is badly in need of repair and widening in some places . . .

For a number of reasons, an assignment to the Armed Services Committee would be desirable. First, the Hart-Dole-Inouye Federal Center in Battle Creek is a huge Department of Defense operation that employs numerous constituents, and it had to be protected in a time of budget shortages and military reorganization. There is also a National Guard base in the Seventh District, and base relocations were looming in the near future. Joe's intelligence experience in the CIA and his service in Vietnam might appear . . . to have made him a natural for an appointment to Armed Services. His freshmen status, however, worked against him, since, typically, freshmen are not assigned to that powerful committee . . .

New Republican House members request their committee assignments by submitting a letter indicating their preferences to the party's Steering Committee . . . There is no guarantee that the new members' preferences will be honored . . . The reality is that freshmen are going to do what the leadership tells them to do when it comes to committee assignments . . .

On his visits to Washington between the election and the Swearing-In, [Joe] met with as many members of the Steering Committee as possible. More than simply courtesy calls, . . . these meetings actually gave Joe a chance to introduce himself and talk about his interests and abilities, and, ultimately, to reinforce in person the committee requests he had made in writing.

Meanwhile, experienced members of the new congressman's staff also spoke to their counterparts on the staffs of the Steering Committee members . . . Chuck Yessaian, Joe's legislative director, bluntly described the process: "Staff members lobby like crazy on behalf of their congressmen, and are sometimes relentless in doing so" . . .

Congressman Schwarz and his staff were pleased when Joe's committee assignments—Agriculture, Science, and Armed Services—were delivered by letter from the Office of the Speaker of the House.

Choosing and Working in Caucuses

Placard Questions

Carefully analyze the information on the placards, and then discuss these questions with your partner:

1. How many members does the Mainstream Tuesday Group have? The Republican Study Committee?

2. About which issues is the RSC most concerned? On which issues does the Mainstream Tuesday Group want to focus?

3. What are some key similarities between the RSC and the Mainstream Tuesday group? What are some important differences?

4. If you were a member of Congressman Schwarz's staff, which caucus would you recommend that he join and why?

Reading Questions

Read Excerpt D from *Freshman Orientation,* and then discuss these questions with your partner:

1. Do you think that Congressman Schwarz's choice of caucuses and the work he did with them helped to make him an effective legislator? Why or why not?

2. What have you learned that will help your new member of Congress be an effective legislator?

Excerpt D from *Freshman Orientation* by Edward I. Sidlow

Caucuses, which are usually bipartisan and centered around specific public policy areas, are informal groupings of House members . . . There are numerous caucuses to choose from, allowing those who join to keep tabs on particular issues they care about and enabling interested parties outside of Congress to know which legislators are engaged in which policies . . .

Congressman Schwarz joined nearly three dozen caucuses covering a wide range of subjects. He became a member of the Northern Border Caucus, the Automotive Caucus, and the Passenger Rail Caucus—all directly related to the politics of Michigan. He also sat in six different health caucuses and nine caucuses focused in some way on foreign policy and international relations . . . For some congressmen and -women, membership in a caucus is little more than a statement of interest in a subject area, while others are more active in the meetings and discussions that a caucus may sponsor. For freshmen legislators, caucus memberships allow a quick and easy introduction to members of both parties who have similar policy interests and concerns.

Beyond these issue-specific caucuses, another of Joe's memberships played a significant role in his Hill life and in his ability to work with like-minded colleagues. The Tuesday Group, once referred to as a "casual caucus of pragmatic Republicans," . . . became more active in the 109th Congress than it had been in the past, meeting almost every week that Congress was in session—though, ironically, on Wednesday. The group originally intended to meet on the second day of the week, but the weekly congressional calendar now typically runs from Tuesday through Thursday, reserving Monday and Friday for travel. As a result, Wednesday became the second "work day" of most weeks, and, as Washington logic would have it, the Tuesday Group meets on Wednesday . . .

[One Tuesday Group discussion] centered on a bill before the House to allow oil drilling on the Arctic Continental Shelf . . . Like many of the moderates who make up the Tuesday Group, Representative Schwarz was a friend of the environment, and he described the group's resistance to the original proposal in positive terms:

> The Tuesday Group thought the bill was so imperfect that we decided we would withhold our support unless changes were made. We really had an effect there . . . the thirty or so members of the group made it clear that we would withhold votes and the bill's sponsors and party leadership would not have enough support to pass the bill. Many of the changes we wanted were made overnight— enough so that twenty or so of us could support it.

Working on Legislation

Placard Questions

Carefully analyze the information on the placard, and then discuss these questions with your partner:

1. What interesting information do you see on the diagram?

2. Approximately what percentage of bills and joint resolutions introduced in 2005 were actually signed into law?

3. According to the diagram, between which steps in the process do most bills "die"?

4. Who are some of the groups or individuals that might kill a bill and keep it from becoming law? Why might they oppose a particular bill?

Reading Questions

Read Excerpt E from *Freshman Orientation,* and then discuss these questions with your partner:

1. In this example, do you think Congressman Schwarz's actions contributed to making him an effective legislator? Why or why not?

2. What have you learned that will help your new member of Congress be an effective legislator?

Excerpt E from *Freshman Orientation* by Edward I. Sidlow

The issue of stem-cell research had inspired vigorous debate in recent years, fueled in part by the active support of prominent advocates such as Nancy Reagan, who spoke out on the promise of research efforts in the treatment of Alzheimer's, the devastating disease that afflicted former president Ronald Reagan . . . Although it was passionately opposed in the fundamentalist religious community . . . embryonic stem-cell research had broad support in the scientific community . . .

On February 15, 2005, [Republican] Congressman Michael Castle of Delaware . . . introduced H.R. 810 . . . The Stem Cell Research Enhancement Act of 2005 sought to provide funding for the use of cells derived from embryos that were going to be discarded by fertility clinics . . . The bill quickly garnered 200 cosponsors, representing an impressive display of bipartisan support.

Still, the proponents of H.R. 810 knew that they were fighting an uphill battle. President Bush had vowed publicly to veto any effort by Congress to increase the federal government's role in stem-cell research. Moreover, the right wing of the Republican Party in Congress . . . was vehemently opposed to any such legislation and hoped to prevent this bill . . . from coming to the House floor for a vote . . .

Supporters of the legislation firmly believed that if they failed to demonstrate how seriously invested in the bill they were, it would never get a floor vote. They therefore adopted a proactive strategy that essentially called for threatening the Speaker of the House. Representative Castle drafted a letter, signed by several members of the Tuesday Group [a moderate Republican caucus], to make it clear that if H.R. 810 were not given an up-or-down vote, they would not vote with the Republican leadership in support of President Bush's budget. When the Speaker learned of the existence of this letter, which had not yet been sent, he allowed a group of about ten moderates, including Congressman Schwarz, to meet with him to discuss bringing the bill to the floor . . .

In the meeting, Schwarz spoke last—and he spoke longer than anyone else.

If people are opposed to stem-cell research on some religious or moral basis, fine. I would not try to sway a person from the rock of their beliefs . . . [But] every expert in the finest universities . . . will tell you . . . that embryonic stem-cell research can provide powerful findings that will lead to treatments of some very tragic diseases . . . It's not my place or anyone else's to pass judgment on the religious beliefs of others. But don't argue the science with me. If you argue the science with me, you are dead wrong.

. . . The day after the meeting with [Speaker] Hastert, word got out that the Speaker would agree to bring H.R. 810 to the floor. Joe was approached by the House Republican Conference Chair, . . . who told him "The Speaker is giving you this vote because of your presentation, Joe" . . . H.R. 810 passed the House on May 24, 2005, by a vote of 238–194 . . . In July of 2006, the bill passed the Senate and was sent to the president.

Note: President Bush vetoed the bill on July 19, 2006. The House was unable to override the veto with the necessary two-thirds majority, and the Stem Cell Research Enhancement Act died on the House floor the same day.

Doing Constituent Casework

Placard Questions

Carefully analyze the information on the placard, and then discuss these questions with your partner:

1. About how many constituent letters and e-mails are received by Congressman Cooper's staff each month?

2. About how many casework folders does Congressman Frank's staff work on each month?

3. What are the three most common types of casework issues that Congressman Frank's staff works on?

4. Why do you think casework is such an important part of what members of Congress and their staff do?

Reading Questions

Read Excerpt F from *Freshman Orientation,* and then discuss these questions with your partner:

1. Do you think doing constituent casework is a good use of Congressman Schwarz and his staff's time? Do these examples show that Congressman Schwarz is an effective legislator? Why or why not?

2. What have you learned that will help your new member of Congress be an effective legislator?

Excerpt F from *Freshman Orientation* by Edward I. Sidlow

Casework is the provision of favors and services that members of Congress can offer to their constituents . . . As the scope of the federal government has grown and bureaucratic red tape has increased, so too has the amount of time spent on casework. In fact, casework activity probably takes up as much time as lawmaking and pork-barreling combined . . .

The congressman regarded constituent casework as a major part of his job . . . "You spend a huge amount of time on it," Schwarz explained. "The people in the district offices and in Washington are working on constituent things all the time—*all* the time—and they are remarkably good at it" . . .

The congressman himself got personally involved in some constituent matters.

Some of the ones I love involve World War II veterans . . . My high school biology teacher is a good example. He served with distinction in the China-Burma-India theater, in the army air force, and just had his 90th birthday. His medals had been misplaced somewhere along the line. I became personally involved in that. We did everything we could and we were able to get his medals replaced. You just love to help people in that way . . .

Congressman Schwarz saw constituent service for what it is—a fact of congressional life and a significant part of the job description. The ability to help constituents with their individual needs, moreover, is one of the essential advantages of incumbents when it comes time to stand for reelection. Challengers are simply not in a position to cut through the bureaucratic maze of Washington on behalf of people in the district, while members of Congress are uniformly willing to commit considerable staff time to servicing the district through casework. By word of mouth, news of favors provided by members of Congress gets around.

Some other constituent requests came on the heels of truly tragic circumstances . . . One situation that particularly touched Dawn [Saylor, one of Schwarz's constituent relations representatives] involved a woman with an inoperable brain tumor who suffered numerous seizures on a daily basis. "One day," Dawn recounted,

this woman's husband took off and left her and three children. The next day she received a letter from the Social Security Administration, informing her that her claim for Social Security disability was denied . . . There were times when I was on the phone with her that I just couldn't hold back the tears.

Dawn was able to help this woman by expediting the appeals process on the denial of disability. Ultimately, the appeal was resolved in the constituent's favor, and the woman did get some financial relief. Being able to help a constituent in need brought Dawn a great deal of satisfaction.

Protecting the Interests of the District

Placard Questions

Carefully analyze the cartoon on the placard, and then discuss these questions
with your partner:

1. What interesting details do you see in the cartoon?

2. Based on this cartoon, what are some ways that legislators protect or work for
   the interests of their districts?

3. Why might legislators act in these ways?

4. What might be the consequences if all legislators acted this way, all the time?

Reading Questions

Read Excerpt G from *Freshman Orientation,* and then discuss these questions
with your partner:

1. How did Congressman Schwarz and his staff protect the interests of his
   district? Should he act this way all the time? Why or why not?

2. What have you learned that will help your new member of Congress be an
   effective legislator?

Excerpt G from *Freshman Orientation* by Edward I. Sidlow

In late April [2005], the *Kalamazoo Gazette* published a short piece about the efforts of [Joe] Schwarz and his colleague Fred Upton to protect the military facilities located in Battle Creek. The Pentagon was awaiting a report from the Base Realignment and Closure Commission (BRAC), . . . which was to recommend a list of bases for closing . . .

Aaron Taliaferro joined the Schwarz staff about three weeks before the BRAC list was to be released. Brought in as a senior legislative assistant because of his military background, he was acutely aware that if any recommended closures or relocations included facilities in Michigan's Seventh Congressional District, his job was to launch an all-out effort to get the recommendation reversed . . .

When the BRAC recommendations were released, . . . [the Battle Creek] Air National Guard Base . . . was recommended for closure. Aaron noted that Congressman Schwarz . . . "rolled up his sleeves and simply said, 'We've got to save that base'" . . .

Aaron approached the task of reversing the recommendation methodically.

I thought like a military analyst. First, identify the problem. OK, the problem is, we're on the list. The way to get off the list is quite straightforward. Invalidate the findings that resulted on our being on the closure list . . .

According to Aaron, Lt. Col. Dave San Clemente, the operations officer on the base . . . "did a Herculean amount of data gathering and analysis for us . . . and was absolutely essential to our work." San Clemente's efforts made up a large portion of the presentation to be made before the BRAC commission at a June meeting in St. Louis.

That meeting was an opportunity for Congressman Schwarz to make a public appeal for the Battle Creek base . . . The chance to make their case to the commission, face-to-face, "was critical," Aaron said . . .

The presentation was a success. Aaron took particular satisfaction from the comments made by one commissioner . . . who singled out Michigan at a press conference at the conclusion of the day's hearings "for a very information-based, factual, logical, and coherent presentation" . . .

The final BRAC recommendation was expected in late August. In the time between the June meeting in St. Louis and the final decision, Aaron met personally with eight of the nine commissioners . . .

Aaron also used every contact he could to persuade [another] Commissioner . . . to make a site visit to the Battle Creek Air National Guard Base . . .

On Friday, August 26, 2005, the BRAC final report was released. To the delight of Congressman Schwarz and all who had worked with him on this issue, the initial recommendation to close the Air National Guard Base in Battle Creek was overturned . . .

Newspaper editorials applauded Schwarz and his efforts to keep the base open . . . Schwarz's colleague Fred Upton was also effusive in his praise—the reversal of the decision to close the Battle Creek base, Upton claimed, was "a testament to the vigorous effort led by Joe Schwarz."

Running for Reelection

Placard Questions

Carefully analyze the information on the placard, and then discuss these
questions with your partner:

1. In general, what percentage of incumbents in the House and Senate are
    reelected?

2. Why do you think such a high percentage of legislators are reelected?

3. In general, who spends more money in campaigns: incumbents or challengers?
    Is that trend increasing or decreasing?

4. What connections might you make between the information on these two
    sets of graphs?

Reading Questions

Read Excerpt H from *Freshman Orientation,* and then discuss these questions
with your partner:

1. How effective was the reelection campaign that Congressman Schwarz and
    his staff ran?

2. What have you learned that will help your new member of Congress be an
    effective legislator?

Excerpt H from *Freshman Orientation* by Edward I. Sidlow

It is conventional wisdom that incumbent members of Congress have considerable advantages over challengers in an election campaign. Incumbents typically enjoy greater name recognition and easier access to the media. They also tend to have a wider network of contacts and donors . . . Moreover, incumbent[s] . . . have the opportunity to sponsor and support legislation that is beneficial to their districts . . .

In politics, however, there are no absolutes . . .

The Schwarz team learned in November 2005 that they would have a political struggle on their hands in the bid to win reelection to the House of Representatives. Tim Walberg—evangelical pastor, former state legislator, and recent unsuccessful congressional candidate—announced that he was going to challenge Congressman Schwarz in the Republican primary . . .

In April, an article in the *Lansing State Journal* carried the headline "Race for Schwarz's Seat Begins in Earnest" . . .

Less than two weeks later, the race for the Republican nomination in the Seventh District was again a top story in the *Lansing State Journal*. This time the headline proclaimed, "Walberg Camp's Cash Race Outpacing Schwarz," and the accompanying article stated that in the first quarter of 2006, Walberg had raised $179,361, while Schwarz reportedly had raised $153,873 . . .

By May, the campaign strategies of both candidates had become very clear. Schwarz was running on his record, as the campaign slogan displayed on billboards along I-94 proclaimed: *Congressman Joe Schwarz—Real Representation, Real Results.* The Walberg strategy was to paint Joe Schwarz as a liberal whose values were not in step with those of voters in the district . . .

During the spring and summer, the congressman returned to the district as often as possible . . . The Schwarz staff scheduled Joe's weekends around . . . the annual summer events in towns throughout the district, . . . [including] the Cereal Festival in Joe's hometown, Battle Creek. At the Cereal Festival, which ran for three days in June, one of the major events was the annual staging of the world's longest breakfast table, at which the local companies, Kellogg and Post, feed breakfast to as many people as show up. This is the kind of event that a hometown congressman certainly would not miss . . .

In July, a *Detroit News* story called the Schwarz-Walberg race the most contentious congressional primary election in Michigan. The article made mention of Schwarz's impressive array of endorsements [including President Bush] but suggested that the race was the "ripest" in the state for an upset. The story noted that Walberg . . . "has flooded the airwaves with messages calling Schwarz 'outrageously liberal.'" Schwarz's reaction to the liberal label—"It's pretty amusing because if one looks at my voting record, it's pretty much pure vanilla Republican" . . . —was quoted . . .

As the election drew near, it was a rare day that residents in Michigan's Seventh District did not receive several pieces of mail supporting one or another of the candidates . . . The barrage of mail from both campaigns was designed to keep the candidates' names before the voters, and it made the race in Michigan's Seventh District very expensive.

New Congressional Staff Orientation Notes

For each orientation topic, write at least three important things you learned that will help your new member of Congress be an effective legislator.

Topic A: Selecting Congressional Office Space	Topic B: Hiring Congressional Staff
Topic C: Requesting Committee Assignments	**Topic D: Choosing and Working in Caucuses**
Topic E: Working on Legislation	**Topic F: Doing Constituent Casework**
Topic G: Protecting the Interests of the District	**Topic H: Running for Reelection**

Joe Schwarz and the 2006 Election

On primary election night, the Schwarz campaign was back at Schuler's Restaurant in Marshall, Michigan . . . Key staffers once more gathered in an upstairs conference room . . . The mood was anxious. Everyone who had worked on the campaign expected a tight race, much like the primary two years earlier that had ended in celebration . . .

Rebecca Schneider, the congressman's district director, . . . recounted,

It was kind of eerie. There was a weird energy in the room . . . It was pretty clear that if you were not directly involved with gathering election returns, you were not welcome in there. It was tense. As the numbers came in, it grew more tense, and it became clear that the folks inside the war room did not want noise or distraction . . . But I could see in . . . the boss's face, that things were not going well.

As the evening wore on, the congressman spent more and more time in the office off the lobby of the war room . . .

Eventually, Joe did go downstairs and indicated to the crowd his sense that things were not going well for the campaign . . . A short time later, Joe went downstairs again, and, flanked by his daughter and his chief of staff, conceded the race . . .

The final vote tally of the Republican primary in Michigan's Seventh District was 53 percent (33,244 votes) for Walberg and 47 percent (29,349 votes) for Schwarz. Joe was disappointed by the turnout, which was less than 15 percent in his home county, and less than 20 percent district-wide . . . "Anybody who studies elections, and understands them, knows that well-organized, aggressive minorities do well in low-turnout elections." Matt Marsden was a bit less circumspect . . . : "I'm guessing a lot of people woke up after the election and said . . . 'Maybe I should have gotten out and voted.'"

On September 7, 2006, Congressman Schwarz reflected on his defeat in the Sunday edition of the *Washington Post,* beginning, "I am the political equivalent of a woolly mammoth, a rarity headed for extinction . . . Yes, I'm a moderate." . . . He voiced his concern for the political center, noting that "fewer and fewer sensible . . . candidates will have any chance of being elected," although "politics needs a middle" for effective public policymaking. "Somehow, some way," Joe concluded, "moderates must . . . learn to fight as hard for the policies of the sane and rational center as the far right and far left fight for the extremes."

—from *Freshman Orientation* by Edward I. Sidlow
(Washington, D.C.: CQ Press, 2007)

Mastering the Content

1. Which of these is the best definition of *constituents*?
   A. donors who contribute cash or services to an electoral campaign
   B. residents of an electoral district represented by an elected official
   C. citizens nationwide who benefit from an elected official's programs
   D. voters in an elected official's home state who belong to the same party

2. A conference committee is made up of members from both the
   A. House and Senate.
   B. majority and minority parties.
   C. legislative and executive branches.
   D. Republican and Democratic caucuses.

3. Where do most members of Congress begin their political careers?
   A. as lobbyists
   B. in the military
   C. in local politics
   D. as staff assistants

4. In saying "The power of the speaker of the House is the power of scheduling," Tip O'Neill was referring chiefly to the speaker's power to do which of the following?
   A. choose the hours of breaks and meals
   B. control the meeting dates of committees
   C. determine the timing of national elections
   D. decide which bills will be debated and when

5. What determines the number of seats in the Senate?
   A. The Constitution specifies the exact number of seats.
   B. The number of seats depends on the number of states.
   C. Congress fixed the maximum number of seats in 1911.
   D. The number of seats depends on each state's population.

6. Which of the following might apply to state lawmakers but not to members of Congress?
   A. advantage of incumbency
   B. minimum age qualifications
   C. residency requirements
   D. term limits

7. Which of these powers belongs only to the Senate?
   A. the power to conduct hearings
   B. the power to impeach officials
   C. the power to initiate tax bills
   D. the power to ratify treaties

8. Which of these groups handles most of the detailed work of lawmaking in Congress?
   A. joint committees
   B. select committees
   C. standing committees
   D. conference committees

9. Which of these events triggers reapportionment of seats in the House of Representatives?
   A. a change in House leadership
   B. a census conducted every 10 years
   C. the election of representatives every 2 years
   D. the decision of the House to authorize redistricting

10. What do the powers of oversight, confirmation, impeachment, ratification, override, and amendment have in common?
    A. They keep Congress from becoming too powerful.
    B. They enable Congress to dominate the other two branches.
    C. They help Congress check the power of the other two branches.
    D. They force the two chambers of Congress to cooperate with each other.

Exploring the Essential Question

What makes an effective legislator?

Part of a legislator's job is to help his or her constituents. The diagram below shows ways in which members of the U.S. House of Representatives serve their congressional districts. Refer to the diagram as you answer the questions that follow.

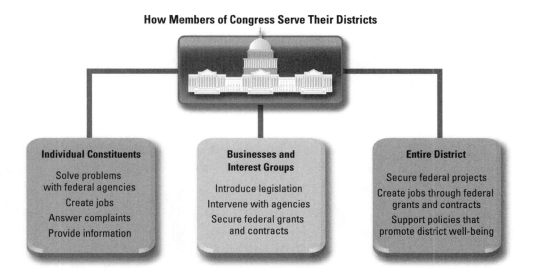

How Members of Congress Serve Their Districts

Individual Constituents
Solve problems with federal agencies
Create jobs
Answer complaints
Provide information

Businesses and Interest Groups
Introduce legislation
Intervene with agencies
Secure federal grants and contracts

Entire District
Secure federal projects
Create jobs through federal grants and contracts
Support policies that promote district well-being

1. Define *pork*. Use information from the diagram to support your definition.
2. Explain how what you see in the diagram might affect a challenger seeking to unseat an incumbent in an election.
3. Describe a problem that you, or someone you know, might take to your representative or senator. Explain why a legislator might be more effective at addressing that problem than you could be.
4. Based on the diagram, identify three qualities that a legislator might need to serve his or her constituents effectively. Explain how each quality would be helpful.

Congressional Lawmaking

How do laws really *get made?*

Speaking of Politics

As you complete the Reading Notes, use these terms in your answers:

congressional page   hold

seniority rule   rider

filibuster   Christmas tree bill

cloture   logrolling

PREVIEW

Think of a bill that you would like to see passed into law to improve the lives of high school seniors across the country. Give your bill a catchy title, and write a two- or three-sentence description of its main features.

Now draw a mental flowchart of the steps you think it would take to get your bill passed into law, from beginning to end. Include as many steps as you think are necessary, with a minimum of three. (A mental flowchart is a representation of what you think is true. There are no wrong answers as long as you rely only on what is in your head.)

After you complete your mental flowchart, star the step that you think is particularly important. Then briefly explain why you think that step is so important.

READING NOTES

Complete the following tasks for each section.

Section 12.2

Create a spoke diagram like the one below. On each spoke, note one important task or ceremony that is completed at the start of each new Congress. Then select one of these tasks, and explain how it might be used to influence or affect how laws really get made.

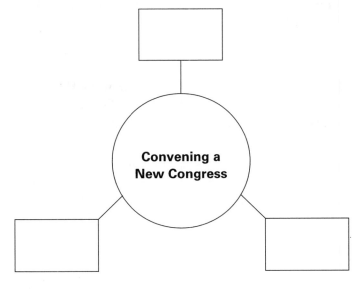

Section 12.3

1. Given the current makeup of Congress, choose which of the following members would *most likely* be selected as chair of the House Armed Services Committee, and explain why.

   Congressperson W: Democrat, 28 years in Congress, 12 years on committee

   Congressperson X: Republican, 24 years in Congress, 18 years on committee

   Congressperson Y: Republican, 20 years in Congress, served as a military officer

   Congressperson Z: Democrat, 16 years in Congress, former Democratic candidate for president

2. Create a flowchart showing three phases that typically occur when subcommittees consider a bill. For each phase, list two or three important things that happen during that step in the legislative process.

3. Imagine that you are a member of the majority on the House Rules Committee. You are reviewing a bill that the speaker of the House strongly supports. What kind of rule—closed or open—would you likely ask for this bill and why?

Section 12.4

1. Create a Venn diagram comparing how the House and Senate conduct debates, amend bills, and vote on bills. List at least three similarities and three differences in your diagram.

2. List at least four groups or individuals who typically influence or pressure legislators. Which of these groups or individuals do you think should have the most impact on how laws really get made? Why?

Section 12.5

Create a flowchart of all the possible things that can happen to a bill after it passes the House and Senate. Be sure your diagram includes these terms: *conference committee, presidential veto,* and *congressional override.*

PROCESSING

Based on what you have learned in this chapter, create a new mental flowchart that shows the steps that take place when a law really gets made. Your flowchart should include

- all of the important steps in the formal process for how a law gets made. Color all these steps one color.

- all the other factors that influence how a law really gets made. Place these factors at the appropriate places in the formal process. Color these factors a second color.

- at least three of these terms: *congressional page, seniority rule, filibuster, cloture, hold, rider, Christmas tree bill,* and *logrolling.*

Then answer this question: *Do you think our system makes it too hard to get a bill passed into law? Why or why not?*

Organizing the House

Follow this procedure to organize the new House of Representatives.

Step 1: Set up the House.

☐ Arrange the classroom like the House of Representatives chamber by moving desks so they resemble the map at right.

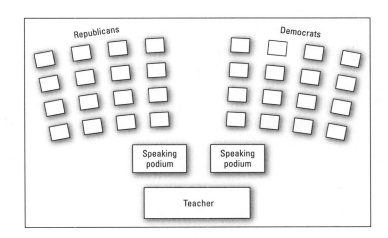

Step 2: Select party leaders.

☐ Organize yourselves by political party as indicated on the map.

☐ Party members who want to hold one of the party leadership positions should raise their hands (a minimum of three people per party). Party leaders should have strong leadership skills, be able to speak in front of others, and be good at persuading others.

☐ Each party votes for its leaders. For the majority party, the person with the most votes will be speaker of the House. The one with the second most votes will be majority leader. The one with the third most votes will be majority whip. For the minority party, the person with the most votes will be minority leader and the one with the second most votes will be minority whip.

☐ Record the names of party leaders on the board.

Step 3: Assign members of Congress to committees.

☐ *Majority and minority leaders:* Obtain the party caucus notes from your teacher.

☐ *Party members:* Check your role card to confirm your committee assignment.

☐ *Party leaders:* Consult the party caucus notes to review the upcoming bills in each committee, and explain to your party members how you want them to vote.

☐ *Party members:* Write on the back of your role card whether your party leader supports or opposes the bill.

Step 4: Swear in the new speaker of the House.

☐ *Everyone:* Take your seat in the House chamber, according to the map.

☐ *Dean of the House (longest-serving member):* Swear in the speaker of the House by administering the following oath:

Dean: Do you solemnly swear that you will support and defend the Constitution of the United States against all enemies, foreign and domestic; that you will bear true faith and allegiance to the same; that you take this obligation freely, without any mental reservation or purpose of evasion; and that you will well and faithfully discharge the duties of the office on which you are about to enter, so help you God?

Speaker: I do.

Dean (handing gavel to new speaker): Congratulations, (Madam/Mister) Speaker.

House members: *Enthusiastic or polite applause, depending on whether the speaker is from your party.*

Step 5: Swear in the new Congress.

☐ *Speaker of the House:* Swear in all members of the House by administering the following oath:

Speaker: Do you solemnly swear or affirm that you will support and defend the Constitution of the United States against all enemies, foreign and domestic; that you will bear true faith and allegiance to the same; that you take this obligation freely, without any mental reservation or purpose of evasion; and that you will well and faithfully discharge the duties of the office on which you are about to enter, so help you God?

House members: I do. *Enthusiastic applause from all.*

House of Representatives Role Cards

Role Card 1

Name:

State: Alabama   **Political party:** Republican
Years in House: 32 (You are dean of the House.)
Committee assignment: Judiciary
About your constituents: In general, your constituents are moderately conservative. A small majority supports giving the government all tools necessary to fight terrorism and opening up protected areas for oil and natural gas drilling. A small majority opposes increasing the minimum wage for workers.

Role Card 2

Name:

State: Alaska   **Political party:** Republican
Years in House: 28
Committee assignment: Energy and Commerce
About your constituents: In general, your constituents are moderately conservative. A small majority supports giving the government all tools necessary to fight terrorism and opening up protected areas for oil and natural gas drilling. A small majority opposes increasing the minimum wage for workers.

Role Card 3

Name:

State: Arizona   **Political party:** Republican
Years in House: 26
Committee assignment: Education and Labor
About your constituents: In general, your constituents are moderately conservative. A small majority supports giving the government all tools necessary to fight terrorism and opening up protected areas for oil and natural gas drilling. A small majority opposes increasing the minimum wage for workers.

Role Card 4

Name:

State: Connecticut   **Political party:** Republican
Years in House: 24
Committee assignment: Judiciary
About your constituents: In general, your constituents are very conservative. A large majority supports giving the government all tools necessary to fight terrorism and opening up protected areas for oil and natural gas drilling. A large majority opposes increasing the minimum wage for workers.

Role Card 5

Name:

State: Florida   **Political party:** Republican
Years in House: 22
Committee assignment: Energy and Commerce
About your constituents: In general, your constituents are very conservative. A large majority supports giving the government all tools necessary to fight terrorism and opening up protected areas for oil and natural gas drilling. A large majority opposes increasing the minimum wage for workers.

Role Card 6

Name:

State: Georgia   **Political party:** Republican
Years in House: 20
Committee assignment: Education and Labor
About your constituents: In general, your constituents are very conservative. A large majority supports giving the government all tools necessary to fight terrorism and opening up protected areas for oil and natural gas drilling. A large majority opposes increasing the minimum wage for workers.

Role Card 7

Name:

State: Idaho   **Political party:** Republican

Years in House: 18

Committee assignment: Judiciary

About your constituents: In general, your constituents are moderately conservative. A small majority supports giving the government all tools necessary to fight terrorism and opening up protected areas for oil and natural gas drilling. A small majority opposes increasing the minimum wage for workers.

Role Card 8

Name:

State: Kentucky   **Political party:** Republican

Years in House: 16

Committee assignment: Energy and Commerce

About your constituents: In general, your constituents are moderately conservative. A small majority supports giving the government all tools necessary to fight terrorism and opening up protected areas for oil and natural gas drilling. A small majority opposes increasing the minimum wage for workers.

Role Card 9

Name:

State: Montana   **Political party:** Republican

Years in House: 14

Committee assignment: Education and Labor

About your constituents: In general, your constituents are moderately conservative. A small majority supports giving the government all tools necessary to fight terrorism and opening up protected areas for oil and natural gas drilling. A small majority opposes increasing the minimum wage for workers.

Role Card 10

Name:

State: Nebraska   **Political party:** Republican

Years in House: 12

Committee assignment: Judiciary

About your constituents: In general, your constituents are moderately liberal. A small majority opposes laws that threaten people's civil liberties or that would open up protected areas for oil and natural gas drilling. A small majority supports increasing the minimum wage for workers.

Role Card 11

Name:

State: Nevada   **Political party:** Republican

Years in House: 10

Committee assignment: Energy and Commerce

About your constituents: In general, your constituents are moderately liberal. A small majority opposes laws that threaten people's civil liberties or that would open up protected areas for oil and natural gas drilling. A small majority supports increasing the minimum wage for workers.

Role Card 12

Name:

State: New Hampshire   **Political party:** Republican

Years in House: 8

Committee assignment: Education and Labor

About your constituents: In general, your constituents are moderately liberal. A small majority opposes laws that threaten people's civil liberties or that would open up protected areas for oil and natural gas drilling. A small majority supports increasing the minimum wage for workers.

Role Card 13

Name:

State: North Carolina   **Political party:** Republican
Years in House: 6
Committee assignment: Judiciary
About your constituents: In general, your constituents are very conservative. A large majority supports giving the government all tools necessary to fight terrorism and opening up protected areas for oil and natural gas drilling. A large majority opposes increasing the minimum wage for workers.

Role Card 14

Name:

State: Ohio   **Political party:** Republican
Years in House: 4
Committee assignment: Energy and Commerce
About your constituents: In general, your constituents are very conservative. A large majority supports giving the government all tools necessary to fight terrorism and opening up protected areas for oil and natural gas drilling. A large majority opposes increasing the minimum wage for workers.

Role Card 15

Name:

State: Oklahoma   **Political party:** Republican
Years in House: 2
Committee assignment: Education and Labor
About your constituents: In general, your constituents are very conservative. A large majority supports giving the government all tools necessary to fight terrorism and opening up protected areas for oil and natural gas drilling. A large majority opposes increasing the minimum wage for workers.

Role Card 16

Name:

State: Pennsylvania   **Political party:** Republican
Years in House: 0 (This is your first year.)
Committee assignment: Judiciary
About your constituents: In general, your constituents are moderately conservative. A small majority supports giving the government all tools necessary to fight terrorism and opening up protected areas for oil and natural gas drilling. A small majority opposes increasing the minimum wage for workers.

Role Card 17

Name:

State: South Dakota   **Political party:** Republican
Years in House: 0 (This is your first year.)
Committee assignment: Energy and Commerce
About your constituents: In general, your constituents are moderately conservative. A small majority supports giving the government all tools necessary to fight terrorism and opening up protected areas for oil and natural gas drilling. A small majority opposes increasing the minimum wage for workers.

Role Card 18

Name:

State: Texas   **Political party:** Republican
Years in House: 0 (This is your first year.)
Committee assignment: Education and Labor
About your constituents: In general, your constituents are moderately conservative. A small majority supports giving the government all tools necessary to fight terrorism and opening up protected areas for oil and natural gas drilling. A small majority opposes increasing the minimum wage for workers.

Role Card 19

Name:

State: California   **Political party:** Democratic

Years in House: 30

Committee assignment: Judiciary

About your constituents: In general, your constituents are moderately liberal. A small majority opposes laws that threaten people's civil liberties or that would open up protected areas for oil and natural gas drilling. A small majority supports increasing the minimum wage for workers.

Role Card 20

Name:

State: Colorado   **Political party:** Democratic

Years in House: 28

Committee assignment: Energy and Commerce

About your constituents: In general, your constituents are moderately liberal. A small majority opposes laws that threaten people's civil liberties or that would open up protected areas for oil and natural gas drilling. A small majority supports increasing the minimum wage for workers.

Role Card 21

Name:

State: Illinois   **Political party:** Democratic

Years in House: 26

Committee assignment: Education and Labor

About your constituents: In general, your constituents are moderately liberal. A small majority opposes laws that threaten people's civil liberties or that would open up protected areas for oil and natural gas drilling. A small majority supports increasing the minimum wage for workers.

Role Card 22

Name:

State: Iowa   **Political party:** Democratic

Years in House: 24

Committee assignment: Judiciary

About your constituents: In general, your constituents are very liberal. A large majority opposes laws that threaten people's civil liberties or that would open up protected areas for oil and natural gas drilling. A large majority supports increasing the minimum wage for workers.

Role Card 23

Name:

State: Kansas   **Political party:** Democratic

Years in House: 22

Committee assignment: Energy and Commerce

About your constituents: In general, your constituents are very liberal. A large majority opposes laws that threaten people's civil liberties or that would open up protected areas for oil and natural gas drilling. A large majority supports increasing the minimum wage for workers.

Role Card 24

Name:

State: Louisiana   **Political party:** Democratic

Years in House: 20

Committee assignment: Education and Labor

About your constituents: In general, your constituents are very liberal. A large majority opposes laws that threaten people's civil liberties or that would open up protected areas for oil and natural gas drilling. A large majority supports increasing the minimum wage for workers.

Role Card 25

Name:

State: Maryland   **Political party:** Democratic
Years in House: 18
Committee assignment: Judiciary
About your constituents: In general, your constituents are moderately liberal. A small majority opposes laws that threaten people's civil liberties or that would open up protected areas for oil and natural gas drilling. A small majority supports increasing the minimum wage for workers.

Role Card 26

Name:

State: Massachusetts   **Political party:** Democratic
Years in House: 16
Committee assignment: Energy and Commerce
About your constituents: In general, your constituents are moderately liberal. A small majority opposes laws that threaten people's civil liberties or that would open up protected areas for oil and natural gas drilling. A small majority supports increasing the minimum wage for workers.

Role Card 27

Name:

State: Michigan   **Political party:** Democratic
Years in House: 14
Committee assignment: Education and Labor
About your constituents: In general, your constituents are moderately liberal. A small majority opposes laws that threaten people's civil liberties or that would open up protected areas for oil and natural gas drilling. A small majority supports increasing the minimum wage for workers.

Role Card 28

Name:

State: Minnesota   **Political party:** Democratic
Years in House: 12
Committee assignment: Judiciary
About your constituents: In general, your constituents are moderately conservative. A small majority supports giving the government all tools necessary to fight terrorism and opening up protected areas for oil and natural gas drilling. A small majority opposes increasing the minimum wage for workers.

Role Card 29

Name:

State: Missouri   **Political party:** Democratic
Years in House: 10
Committee assignment: Energy and Commerce
About your constituents: In general, your constituents are moderately conservative. A small majority supports giving the government all tools necessary to fight terrorism and opening up protected areas for oil and natural gas drilling. A small majority opposes increasing the minimum wage for workers.

Role Card 30

Name:

State: New Jersey   **Political party:** Democratic
Years in House: 8
Committee assignment: Education and Labor
About your constituents: In general, your constituents are moderately conservative. A small majority supports giving the government all tools necessary to fight terrorism and opening up protected areas for oil and natural gas drilling. A small majority opposes increasing the minimum wage for workers.

Role Card 31

Name:

State: New Mexico   **Political party:** Democratic

Years in House: 6

Committee assignment: Judiciary

About your constituents: In general, your constituents are very liberal. A large majority opposes laws that threaten people's civil liberties or that would open up protected areas for oil and natural gas drilling. A large majority supports increasing the minimum wage for workers.

Role Card 32

Name:

State: New York   **Political party:** Democratic

Years in House: 4

Committee assignment: Energy and Commerce

About your constituents: In general, your constituents are very liberal. A large majority opposes laws that threaten people's civil liberties or that would open up protected areas for oil and natural gas drilling. A large majority supports increasing the minimum wage for workers.

Role Card 33

Name:

State: Oregon   **Political party:** Democratic

Years in House: 2

Committee assignment: Education and Labor

About your constituents: In general, your constituents are very liberal. A large majority opposes laws that threaten people's civil liberties or that would open up protected areas for oil and natural gas drilling. A large majority supports increasing the minimum wage for workers.

Role Card 34

Name:

State: Vermont   **Political party:** Democratic

Years in House: 0 (This is your first year.)

Committee assignment: Judiciary

About your constituents: In general, your constituents are moderately liberal. A small majority opposes laws that threaten people's civil liberties or that would open up protected areas for oil and natural gas drilling. A small majority supports increasing the minimum wage for workers.

Role Card 35

Name:

State: Virginia   **Political party:** Democratic

Years in House: 0 (This is your first year.)

Committee assignment: Energy and Commerce

About your constituents: In general, your constituents are moderately liberal. A small majority opposes laws that threaten people's civil liberties or that would open up protected areas for oil and natural gas drilling. A small majority supports increasing the minimum wage for workers.

Role Card 36

Name:

State: Wisconsin   **Political party:** Democratic

Years in House: 0 (This is your first year.)

Committee assignment: Education and Labor

About your constituents: In general, your constituents are moderately liberal. A small majority opposes laws that threaten people's civil liberties or that would open up protected areas for oil and natural gas drilling. A small majority supports increasing the minimum wage for workers.

Party Caucus Notes

Party Caucus Notes for Republican Party Leaders

Read this information to the members of your party:

- *Raise your hand if you are assigned to the Judiciary Committee.* This committee will debate the Keep Americans Safe Act. This bill would give the president the power to have e-mails and phone calls intercepted without having to obtain a warrant from a U.S. court. The party leadership strongly supports this bill and urges party members to vote in favor of it.

- *Raise your hand if you are assigned to the Energy and Commerce Committee.* This committee will debate the Energy Independence Act. This bill would open up federal lands and offshore coastal waters to oil and gas drilling. The party leadership strongly supports this bill and urges party members to vote in favor of it.

- *Raise your hand if you are assigned to the Education and Labor Committee.* This committee will debate the Fair Minimum Wage Act. This bill would raise the federal minimum wage. The party leadership strongly opposes this bill in its current form and urges party members to amend it in committee or defeat it.

Party Caucus Notes for Democratic Party Leaders

Read this information to the members of your party:

- *Raise your hand if you are assigned to the Judiciary Committee.* This committee will debate the Keep Americans Safe Act. This bill would give the president the power to have e-mails and phone calls intercepted without having to obtain a warrant from a U.S. court. The party leadership strongly opposes this bill in its current form and urges party members to amend it in committee or defeat it.

- *Raise your hand if you are assigned to the Energy and Commerce Committee.* This committee will debate the Energy Independence Act. This bill would open up federal lands and offshore coastal waters to oil and gas drilling. The party leadership strongly opposes this bill in its current form and urges party members to amend it in committee.

- *Raise your hand if you are assigned to the Education and Labor Committee.* This committee will debate the Fair Minimum Wage Act. This bill would raise the federal minimum wage. The party leadership strongly supports this bill and urges party members to vote in favor of it.

Working in Committee

Follow this procedure to work in your House committee.

Step 1: Set up the House committee meeting areas.

☐ Set up three meeting areas, like the one shown at right, around the classroom.

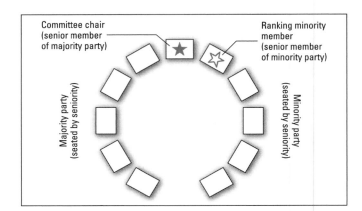

Committee chair (senior member of majority party)

Ranking minority member (senior member of minority party)

Majority party (seated by seniority)

Minority party (seated by seniority)

Step 2: Organize your committee.

☐ Go to your assigned committee area and select your committee chair. The chair must be from the majority party and is often the member with the most seniority.

☐ The committee chair takes the center seat. The ranking minority member (the minority member with the most seniority) sits next to the committee chair.

☐ Committee members of the majority party sit next to the committee chair, in order of seniority. Committee members of the minority party sit next to the ranking minority member, in order of seniority.

Step 3: Hold hearings on proposed bills.

The committee chair does the following:

☐ Call the committee meeting to order by saying, *The (name of committee) is now in session. We will be discussing H.R. Bill (number of bill).*

☐ Distribute copies of the proposed bill to committee members, and read the bill aloud.

☐ Select committee members to read the expert testimony aloud.

Step 4: Write amendments to the bill.

☐ Within each committee, break into two groups by party.

☐ Review the instructions from your party leaders and the information about your constituents.

☐ Within your group, draft two or more amendments that will make the bill more appealing to your constituents. You can delete language, change language, or add new language to the bill. Each amendment must be clear and easy to understand, be no more than 30 words, and include the name of the amendment's main author or authors.

☐ Have the teacher review each proposed amendment to make sure that it meets the criteria listed above. Make any necessary changes.

☐ Pass all proposed amendments to the committee chair. The chair will select the order in which the amendments will be discussed.

Step 5: Mark up the bill.

Move back to your assigned seats for the committee meeting. The committee chair will do the following:

☐ Read the first amendment aloud. Then ask the amendment's main author to briefly explain how the amendment improves the bill.

☐ Give each committee member an opportunity to comment on the proposed amendment.

☐ After all members have commented, call for a vote. If the amendment is approved, the chair amends his or her copy of the bill to reflect the new amendment.

☐ Continue this process for the remaining amendments or until time runs out.

Step 6: Report the proposed bill.

☐ The committee chair reads the new, amended bill aloud. The chair then calls for a final vote on whether to report the bill favorably to the House floor. If the bill is approved, the chair prepares a copy of the approved bill, including amendments, and gives it to the teacher.

H.R. Bills and Expert Testimony

H.R. Bill 1: Keep Americans Safe Act

To amend the regulations by which the President can authorize the interception of electronic communication in order to protect the safety of American citizens.

1   *Be it enacted by the Senate and House of Representatives of the United States*

2   *of America in Congress assembled.*

3   Allow the President to authorize government officials to intercept any electronic

4   (e-mail), wireless (cell), or telephone communication they suspect relates

5   to possible terrorist activity, *without* having to first prove probable cause and

6   obtain a warrant from a U.S. court. This warrantless surveillance authorization

7   would relate *only* to electronic or telephone communication between someone in the

8   United States and someone in a foreign country. Surveillance of e-mail or phone

9   communication within the United States could only be done if a warrant is obtained

10   from a U.S. court. However, the President has the right to suspend this restriction

11   for 90 days in the event of a terrorist attack or if the President determines that the

12   country is under imminent threat.

13

Expert Testimony in Favor of the Keep Americans Safe Act

I thank the members of the Judiciary Committee for the opportunity to present testimony in support of the Keep Americans Safe Act. In today's world, enemies of the United States use all tools at their disposal to plan terrorist attacks against us. Congress must ensure that our law enforcement and intelligence communities have the proper tools to fight a 21st-century war against these enemies.

Another terrorist attack inside the United States would likely be masterminded by terrorist leaders who are outside our country. Suppose U.S. intelligence learns the phone number of a suspected terrorist in a foreign country. Under current law, if they wanted to listen to calls between this suspected terrorist and someone in the United States, they would have to obtain a warrant from a U.S. court. To obtain such a warrant, they would have to show probable cause that the person in the United States involved in this communication is a foreign spy or terrorist. However, by law, they are not permitted to get a warrant to find out whether the person is a spy or terrorist. This kind of constraint needlessly—and perhaps dangerously—ties the hands of U.S. intelligence officials. The Keep Americans Safe Act would allow U.S. intelligence to monitor these phone calls, or any other electronic or wireless communication, immediately, without having to go through the process of obtaining a warrant.

Some U.S. intelligence officials have complained that the process of getting a warrant takes too long. Clearly our enemies will not put their plans to harm American citizens on hold while U.S. intelligence officers work to obtain a warrant. This bill would address this concern by allowing the president to suspend the requirement of warrants for electronic, wireless, or phone communication within the United States in the event of a terrorist attack or if the president determines that the country is under imminent threat of attack.

As I stated, it is Congress's job to ensure that U.S. law enforcement and intelligence are equipped with the proper tools to fight a 21st-century war against our enemies. The Keep Americans Safe Act provides them with those tools.

The following organizations support this bill:

- **Central Intelligence Agency** The CIA's primary function is to obtain and analyze information about foreign governments, corporations, and persons and to report such information to the appropriate branches of the government.
- **Federal Bureau of Investigation** The FBI's mission is "to protect and defend the United States against terrorist and foreign intelligence, to uphold and enforce the criminal laws of the United States, and to provide leadership and criminal justice services to federal, state, municipal, and international agencies and partners."
- **National Association of Chiefs of Police** Part of the mission of this association is to encourage educational activities and services, to promote enforcement and security, and to encourage communication between law officers. It has 60,000 eligible members.

Expert Testimony in Opposition to the Keep Americans Safe Act

Committee members, thank you for the opportunity to speak with you today. I find the title of this bill—the Keep Americans Safe Act—very ironic, since I consider it to be quite dangerous. Benjamin Franklin once said, "Those who would give up essential Liberty, to purchase a little temporary Safety, deserve neither Liberty nor Safety." Supporters of this bill claim that it will provide safety. But it actually threatens all Americans and their civil liberties.

The Fourth Amendment of the Constitution makes it clear that if the federal government wants to listen in on the communication of an American, it must obtain a warrant from a U.S. court. Such a warrant is issued if government officials show that there is probable cause of wrongdoing. This is a simple case of government checks and balances. We agree with supporters of the bill who argue that surveillance is necessary to counter terrorist threats. However, they make no good argument why such surveillance should be conducted without a judicial warrant.

For example, proponents of this bill claim that the process for obtaining warrants takes too long. But we have reviewed records that show that this process is efficient in actual emergencies. We have also heard that emergency warrants have been obtained quickly, often the same day and sometimes within minutes. Finally, we have heard that warrants can be approved orally when necessary. Certainly, this bill could be amended so that in emergency situations, judges are available 24/7 to hear and approve requests for warrants.

We also find very troublesome the provisions in this bill that would allow the president to suspend the requirement to obtain warrants for intercepted communications in the case of a terrorist attack or an imminent threat. This language is so vague that it basically hands any present or future president the power to claim that there is an imminent threat to avoid ever having to obtain warrants. At the very least, this bill should be amended to eliminate this provision.

The essence of the constitutional protection for individual liberties is the division of powers and the checks and balances among the three branches of government. The requirement that the president must obtain a judicial warrant before intercepting communications of Americans is an example of the checks and balances that protect our rights and liberties.

Let's fight terrorism. But let us fight it the right way—consistent with our Constitution and in a manner that serves as a model for the rest of the world. Let us show Benjamin Franklin that we deserve *both* liberty and safety.

The following organizations oppose this bill:

- **American Civil Liberties Union** The ACLU's mission is to preserve the First Amendment rights of freedom of speech, assembly, the press, and religion; the right to equal protection under the law, regardless of race, sex, religion, or national origin; the right to due process; and the right to privacy. The ACLU has approximately 500,000 members.

- **Electronic Frontier Foundation** The EEF's primary goal is to educate the press, policymakers, and the general public about civil liberties issues related to technology and to act as a defender of those liberties. It has a membership of about 50,000 concerned citizens.

- **American Library Association** The ALA promotes the right of every individual to seek and receive information from all points of view without restriction. It provides free access to all sides of a question, cause, or movement. It is the oldest and largest library association in the world, with approximately 65,000 members.

H.R. Bill 2: Energy Independence Act

To establish a program for leasing federal lands for the exploration, development, and production of oil and natural gas.

1   *Be it enacted by the Senate and House of Representatives of the United States*

2   *of America in Congress assembled.*

3   Direct the Secretary of the Interior to establish a program for leasing areas under

4   control of the federal government for exploration, development, and production

5   of oil and natural gas. The areas open for these projects would include wildlife

6   refuges—such as the Arctic National Wildlife Refuge (ANWR)—and coastal

7   ocean areas at least 3 miles from the land along the Pacific, Atlantic, and Gulf

8   coasts. Revenue from the lease agreements would be divided equally between the

9   federal government and the states where these areas are located. All oil or natural

10 gas produced from these projects would be for domestic, U.S. use only.

11

12

Expert Testimony in Favor of the Energy Independence Act

I appreciate the opportunity to testify before this committee and explain why the proposed Energy Independence Act should be passed. As you know, the United States currently imports well over 50 percent of its oil. This dependence on foreign oil makes our country vulnerable to the actions of oil-producing countries. By exploring and developing additional crude oil supplies in the United States, we could take pressure off rising gasoline prices and ease the burden of rising energy costs on all Americans.

The following statistics explain how this bill will help the United States achieve these goals:

- It is projected that oil reserves in the Arctic National Wildlife Refuge (ANWR) alone will eventually result in 1 million barrels of oil per day. This represents an increase of 20 percent over our current domestic production.

- The Interior Department estimates that this bill would open access to about 19 billion barrels of recoverable oil and 86 trillion cubic feet of natural gas that lie beneath the coastal waters from New England to southern Alaska.

- In addition to adding to the nation's energy supply, oil and natural gas development projects would create hundreds of thousands of jobs for Americans. The ANWR project alone could create 50,000 to 65,000 jobs across the country.

- Federal and state treasuries would be enhanced by billions of dollars from the lease agreements made available by this bill. Estimates for the ANWR project are $4.2 billion for the first five years. Coastal states like Louisiana could see their annual revenues increase from about $32 million to $860 million.

Critics of this bill will try to scare you with grave predictions of environmental disasters and damage to wildlife. However, studies of existing oil and gas development projects in Alaska show that local animal populations are as healthy and as large as in areas that do not have oil development.

The bottom line is that this country needs to become more energy independent. There may be other ideas that will help the country become energy independent in the future, but this bill leads us in that direction now. It will also create jobs and add sorely needed revenue to state and federal governments. I strongly urge you to support the Energy Independence Act.

The following organizations support this bill:

- **American Petroleum Institute** API's mission is "to influence public policy in support of a strong, viable U.S. oil and natural gas industry essential to meet the energy needs of consumers in an efficient, environmentally responsible manner." The institute has 400 corporate members.

- **Texas Oil and Gas Association** TXOGA concentrates on legislation, regulation, and public/industry affairs so that "it may be responsive to the ever-growing demands made on the [oil and gas] industry by federal, state, and local governments and by the general public." The association has approximately 2,000 members, about 500 of whom are executives of the state's largest energy companies.

- **Alaska State Chamber of Commerce** The mission of this organization is to drive positive change for Alaska's business environment. The board of directors includes elected members and representatives from Alaska's 30 local chambers of commerce.

Expert Testimony in Opposition to the Energy Independence Act

Thank you for the opportunity to speak before the committee and explain why the Energy Independence Act should be opposed. As you know, the United States consumes about 25 percent of the world's oil each year, but it holds only 2 percent of the world's oil reserves. The sponsors of the Energy Independence Act would have you believe that passing this bill will dramatically alter this imbalance. But the facts do not support their claims.

- The projected oil increase from the proposed Arctic National Wildlife Refuge (ANWR) project would reduce gas prices by a whopping 1¢ per gallon. That decrease would not be seen until about 20 years from now. Even a former oil company engineer admitted, "The enthusiasm of government officials about ANWR exceeds that of [the oil] industry . . . and the evidence so far about ANWR is not promising."

- Supporters of the bill try to assure the public that there is no danger of accidents that will harm the environment. But as recently as March 2006, an Alaskan pipeline leaked more than 200,000 gallons of crude oil.

- There is absolutely no need for the bill's provision to open up coastal ocean waters to new oil and gas drilling. The oil and gas industry already has access to the majority of oil and gas off the U.S. coast. Some 80 percent of the known oil and gas reserves are located in areas where drilling is already allowed, mainly off the Gulf Coast of Texas and Louisiana.

- Supporters of this bill point out the potential economic benefits for coastal states. But they conveniently ignore the risk of billions of dollars in lost revenue to the tourist and recreation industries if there were an oil spill.

The most important argument of all is that the Energy Independence Act does the exact opposite of what its title says. This bill facilitates America's continued dependence on nonrenewable energy sources such as oil. At the very least, this bill should include provisions requiring vehicles in this country to be more fuel efficient. It should also include provisions that require businesses and families to conserve more energy. Finally, it should include incentives for companies to develop clean and renewable energy sources. A bill that included those kinds of provisions would truly make the United States energy independent.

The following organizations oppose this bill:

- **Sierra Club** The Sierra Club's mission is to explore, enjoy, and protect Earth's wild places; to protect Earth's ecosystems and resources; to protect and restore the natural and human environment; and to use all lawful means to carry out these objectives. It has more than 1.3 million members.

- **League of Conservation Voters** The league's mission is "to advocate for sound environmental policies and to elect pro-environmental candidates who will adopt and implement such policies." The league has more than 250,000 voters.

- **Sustainable Energy Coalition** The SEC "promotes increased federal support for energy efficiency and renewable energy technologies and reduced federal support for unsafe or polluting energy resources." It represents more than 60 national and state organizations.

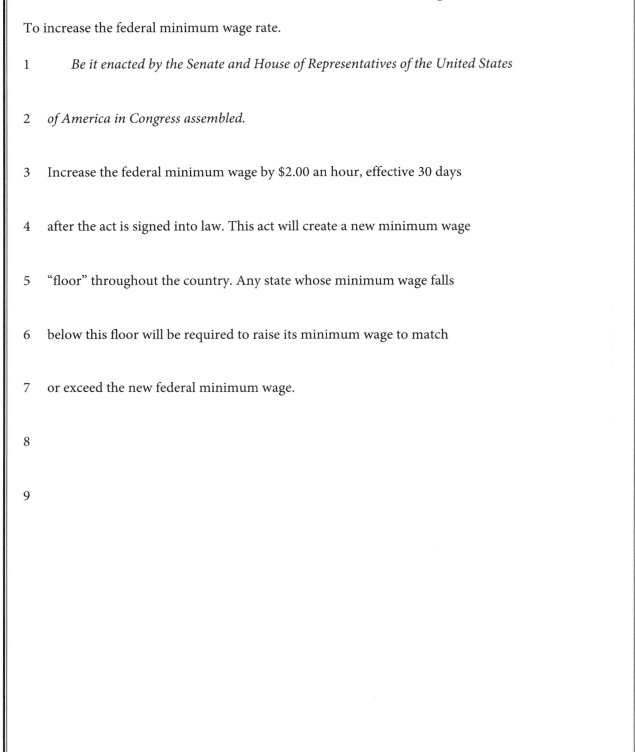

H.R. Bill 3: Fair Minimum Wage Act

To increase the federal minimum wage rate.

1   *Be it enacted by the Senate and House of Representatives of the United States*

2   *of America in Congress assembled.*

3   Increase the federal minimum wage by $2.00 an hour, effective 30 days

4   after the act is signed into law. This act will create a new minimum wage

5   "floor" throughout the country. Any state whose minimum wage falls

6   below this floor will be required to raise its minimum wage to match

7   or exceed the new federal minimum wage.

8

9

Expert Testimony in Favor of the Fair Minimum Wage Act

I am here today to explain why the Fair Minimum Wage Act is an important piece of legislation that deserves your support. These are some of the important reasons why the federal minimum wage should be increased:

- The purchasing power of the current federal minimum wage has fallen for the past seven years. This means that workers earning minimum wage have essentially been getting a pay cut each of those years.

- Leading economists, including Nobel Prize winners and past presidents of the American Economics Association, have stated that "increases in . . . minimum wages in the range of $1.00 to $2.50 . . . can significantly improve the lives of low-income workers and their families, without the adverse effects that critics have claimed."

- Some opponents of this bill argue that raising the minimum wage does not really help low-income families. However, according to statistics, each of the following groups would receive a disproportionate benefit from a raise in the federal minimum wage: single parents with children under 18, women, African Americans, and Hispanics.

- Some critics of this bill argue that an increase in the minimum wage actually hurts low-income workers. They say that because of the increased cost of wages, businesses, particularly small ones, will not hire as many workers or will have to fire some workers. However, there is little evidence of job loss associated with minimum wage increases. Recent studies indicate that employers may be able to absorb some of the costs of an increase in the minimum wage through decreased absenteeism and increased worker morale and productivity.

Certainly there is room for compromise on this bill around such details as how quickly the wage increase will be implemented or whether the increase comes all at once or in stages. But the minimum wage increase proposed in this bill will not hurt small businesses. It will also significantly improve the lives of low-income workers. It is long overdue. I urge you to support this bill.

The following organizations support this bill:

- **Let Justice Roll Living Wage Campaign** This nonpartisan coalition of more than 90 faith-based, community, labor, and business organizations is committed to raising the minimum wage.

- **Service Employees International Union** SEIU is an organization of more than 1.9 million members united by the belief in the dignity and worth of workers and the services they provide and is dedicated to improving the lives of workers and their families.

- **Association of Community Organizations for Reform Now** ACORN is "the nation's largest community organization of low- and moderate-income families, working together for social justice and stronger communities," including specific campaigns for better job conditions. ACORN has more than 350,000 member families.

Expert Testimony in Opposition to the Fair Minimum Wage Act

I am here today to explain why the Fair Minimum Wage Act, despite the good intentions of its sponsors, is not a sound piece of legislation. Undoubtedly, the supporters of this bill believe that it will help low-income workers without adversely affecting businesses or the overall economy. Unfortunately, the facts do not support these claims.

- A recent study by an employment policy research center suggests that as a result of the previous minimum wage increase of only 50¢ an hour, 645,000 entry-level jobs were destroyed, despite the robust economy at the time of that increase.

- The proposed increase of $2.00 an hour will force small business employers to eliminate entry-level jobs, reduce hours and benefits for current employees, and possibly dismiss current employees.

- By implementing the entire $2.00-an-hour increase just 30 days after the bill is signed into law, rather than phasing it in incrementally over several years, business owners will have very little time to prepare for the significant increase in wage costs that they will have to bear.

- If small businesses try to pass along the extra cost associated with a minimum wage increase by raising prices, their customers are likely to go to other, larger competitors who are more able to absorb this increased wage burden. If these small businesses go out of business, their workers will suffer.

- Statistics show that an increase in the minimum wage does little to help the intended beneficiaries: low-income families. According to the Employment Policy Foundation, less than 1 percent (0.9%) of current minimum wage earners belong to families with a total family income of $20,000 or less.

An increase in the minimum wage that is this large and this fast will damage businesses, particularly small ones, and will reduce the number of entry-level jobs for low-skilled workers. I urge you to vote against this bill. At the least, members of this committee should consider reducing the size of this wage increase and implementing a more gradual phase-in of the wage increase.

The following organizations oppose this bill:

- **National Federation of Independent Businesses** The NFIB's mission is to promote and protect the right of its members to own, operate, and grow their businesses. The federation's efforts are focused on the impact of current and proposed legislation on small and independent businesses. It has approximately 350,000 members.

- **Small Business Legislative Council** The SBLC's mission is to maximize the influence of business on legislative and federal policy issues of importance to the entire small business community. The council has more than 60 trade and professional organizations as members.

- **National Restaurant Association** The NRA promotes a pro-restaurant agenda on important restaurant issues, such as minimum wage and food safety, before Congress and federal regulatory agencies. The association includes 935,000 restaurants.

Floor Debates and Final Voting

Follow this procedure for debating and voting on the proposed bills.

Step 1: Set up the House.

☐ Follow the map at right to arrange the classroom like the House of Representatives chamber.

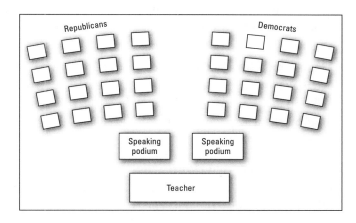

Step 2: Prepare for the floor debate.

☐ *All House members:* Take your seats.

☐ *Speaker of the House:* Select the order in which the bills will be debated. Announce the first bill to be debated, and distribute copies of that bill to all House members.

☐ *Committee chair:* Read the bill and amendments aloud. Allow members to ask any clarifying questions.

☐ House members have five minutes to review the bill and the expert testimony and to consult with members of that committee. They then have 10 minutes to write a one- or two-paragraph statement that explains why they support or oppose the bill. This statement begins, *Mister (or Madam) Speaker, I rise to speak in support of (or in opposition to) H.R. Bill (bill number).*

☐ The committee chair and ranking minority member each have six one-minute speaking slots for their party for the floor debate. Each puts together a list of which six party members will speak and in which order. They submit this to the speaker.

Step 3: Hold the floor debate.

The speaker will officiate the debate as follows:

☐ Call the House to order by banging the gavel and announcing, *The House will now come to order.*

☐ Take turns recognizing Republican and Democrat speakers from the list submitted by the committee chair and the ranking minority member. Each speaker has one minute. Republicans speak from the podium on their side of the room and Democrats from their podium.

☐ When all speakers have finished, bang the gavel and announce, *Debate on H.R. Bill (bill number) is ended.*

Step 4: Prepare for final House vote on the first bill.

☐ Before the final vote, House members will have 10 minutes to carefully review their role cards to see how their constituents feel about the bill. They should also consult with party leaders to see how they want party members to vote.

☐ House members can also meet informally with members from the other party to make logrolling deals. To do so, agree that you will vote with the other person on an upcoming bill if he or she votes with you on this bill. If you make a logrolling deal, you must stick to it.

Step 5: Hold the final House vote.

☐ After the 10-minute review period, the speaker officiates the voting by banging the gavel and announcing, *The House will now come to order.*

☐ The speaker calls for a voice vote as follows:

Speaker: All those in favor of the bill say "aye."

House members in favor (in unison): Aye!

Speaker: All those opposed to the bill say "no."

House members opposed (in unison): No!

Speaker: The ayes (or nos) have the majority. H.R. Bill (bill number) is approved (or defeated).

☐ If members think the speaker has incorrectly judged the voice vote, they may request a standing vote. The speaker then calls for a standing vote as follows:

Speaker: All those in favor of the bill, please stand. (Speaker counts those standing.)

Speaker: All those opposed to the bill, please stand. (Speaker counts those standing).

Speaker: The ayes (or nos) have the majority. H.R. Bill (bill number) is approved (or defeated).

House members: *If you support the bill, clap for the bill if it passes.*

Step 6: Debate the remaining bills.

☐ Repeat Steps 2 to 5 for the remaining bills or until time runs out.

Floor Vote Strategy Notes

Strategy Notes for the Speaker of the House

Meet individually with members of your own party, particularly any who might vote against the party on this bill. Tell them, *I am expecting you to (support/ oppose) this bill. If you vote with the party on this bill, you can expect my full support in your next reelection campaign.*

Strategy Notes for the Majority Leader

Meet individually with members of your own party, particularly any who might vote against the party on this bill. Tell them, *The party leaders are expecting you to (support/oppose) this bill. If you vote with the party on this bill, I will try to move you to a more prestigious committee, where you can do more to help your constituents.*

Strategy Notes for the Majority Whip

Meet individually with members of your own party, particularly any who might vote against the party on this bill. Tell them, *The party leaders are expecting you to (support/oppose) this bill. If you vote with the party on this bill, you can count on our full support for your upcoming piece of legislation.*

Strategy Notes for the Minority Leader

Meet individually with members of your own party, particularly any who might vote against the party on this bill. Tell them, *The party leaders are expecting you to (support/oppose) this bill. If you vote with the party on this bill, I will try to move you to a more prestigious committee, where you can do more to help your constituents.*

Strategy Notes for the Minority Whip

Meet individually with members of your own party, particularly any who might vote against the party on this bill. Tell them, *The party leaders are expecting you to (support/oppose) this bill. If you vote with the party on this bill, you can count on our full support for your upcoming piece of legislation.*

Floor Vote Memos

Memo from the President

Dear Congressperson,

I was happy to come to your district last year and give a speech at the fundraising dinner for your campaign. In return, I am expecting that you will vote with the party on this particular bill, which is very important to me.

Memo from the President

Dear Congressperson,

I was happy to come to your district last year and give a speech at the fundraising dinner for your campaign. In return, I am expecting that you will vote with the party on this particular bill, which is very important to me.

Memo from an Interest Group Lobbyist

Dear Congressperson,

I represent one of the powerful interest groups who support this bill. I want to remind you of the generous contribution our organization made to your recent campaign. Please know that you can expect our continued support if you help pass this bill.

Memo from an Interest Group Lobbyist

Dear Congressperson,

I represent one of the powerful interest groups who support this bill. I want to remind you of the generous contribution our organization made to your recent campaign. Please know that you can expect our continued support if you help pass this bill.

Memo from a Key Constituent

Dear Congressperson,

I am sure you remember all my family and friends who volunteered to work on your campaign last year. You were very thankful and told me to contact you if there was ever anything you could do in return. Now I would like to ask you to vote against this bill.

Memo from a Key Constituent

Dear Congressperson,

I am sure you remember all my family and friends who volunteered to work on your campaign last year. You were very thankful and told me to contact you if there was ever anything you could do in return. Now I would like to ask you to vote against this bill.

Memo from an Interest Group Lobbyist

Dear Congressperson,

I represent one of the powerful interest groups who oppose this bill. I want to remind you of the generous contribution our organization made to your recent campaign. Please know that if you help defeat this bill, you can expect our continued support.

Memo from an Interest Group Lobbyist

Dear Congressperson,

I represent one of the powerful interest groups who oppose this bill. I want to remind you of the generous contribution our organization made to your recent campaign. Please know that if you help defeat this bill, you can expect our continued support.

Memo from a Key Constituent

Dear Congressperson,

I am sure you remember the important fundraising dinner I hosted for you at my home during your last campaign. You were grateful and told me to contact you if there was ever anything you could do in return. Now I would like to ask you to vote in favor of this bill.

Memo from a Key Constituent

Dear Congressperson,

I am sure you remember the important fundraising dinner I hosted for you at my home during your last campaign. You were grateful and told me to contact you if there was ever anything you could do in return. Now I would like to ask you to vote in favor of this bill.

Mastering the Content

1. What is meant by logrolling?
   A. trading votes
   B. delaying legislation
   C. meeting with lobbyists
   D. doing favors for constituents

2. A high school junior who works as a messenger in the House or Senate is called a congressional
   A. cadet.
   B. intern.
   C. page.
   D. plebe.

3. What is the process used in the Senate to end a filibuster called?
   A. cloture
   B. devolution
   C. prior restraint
   D. vote of no confidence

4. In their oath of office, lawmakers swear to support and defend
   A. their party.
   B. the Congress.
   C. the Constitution.
   D. their constituents.

5. Which of these is a key factor in choosing committee chairs?
   A. age
   B. seniority
   C. education
   D. experience

6. What is a Christmas tree bill?
   A. a bill approved late in the session
   B. a bill that raises the pay of lawmakers
   C. a bill passed as a favor to the president
   D. a bill that has attracted many unrelated riders

7. Before a bill can be sent to the president, both chambers of Congress must vote to
   A. approve the same version.
   B. restore the original language.
   C. have a supermajority in favor.
   D. authorize the president to change it.

8. How can Congress override a presidential veto?
   A. Congress must wait until after the next election to reconsider the bill.
   B. Congress must agree to amend the bill to meet the president's objections.
   C. Congress must approve the bill again by a majority vote in both chambers.
   D. Congress must approve the bill again by a two-thirds vote in both chambers.

9. What does a committee or subcommittee do during markup?
   A. call outside experts to testify
   B. determine the final language of a bill
   C. place a bill on the calendar for discussion
   D. take an initial informal vote before debate

10. Which kind of vote in Congress tells constituents how their lawmakers voted?
    A. voice vote
    B. roll-call vote
    C. standing vote
    D. up-or-down vote

Exploring the Essential Question

How do laws really *get made?*

Public Law 107-110, No Child Left Behind, tied federal funding of public education to the performance of schools. Read highlights of its history as H.R.1 below, and then answer the questions.

Events in Legislative History of H.R.1, March 2001 to January 2002

Mar. 22 H.R.1, "To close the achievement gap with accountability, flexibility, and choice, so that no child is left behind," introduced by Representative John Boehner from Ohio

Mar. 23 Referred to House Committee on Education and the Workforce

   Mar. 29   Committee hearings

   May 8   Committee markup session

   May 9   Committee vote to report amended bill: 41 aye, 7 nay

May 14 Reported by committee to the House as amended

   May 16   Rules Committee provided for consideration of the bill with two hours of general debate and limits on amendments

   May 17   House adopted Rules Committee recommendation

May 23 Passed in House: 384 aye to 45 nay

May 25 Received in Senate and placed on calendar

June 14 H.R.1 amended and passed in Senate, 91–8, replacing a related Senate bill

   July 10   Senate wanted its amendment, asked for a conference

   July 18   House rejected amendment, agreed to conference

   July 19, Aug. 1, Sep. 25, Oct. 30, Nov. 30   Conference committee meetings

   Dec. 13   Conference report filed. House passed final version of H.R.1: 381–41

   Dec. 18   Senate passed final version of H.R.I: 87–10

Jan. 4 Presented to president

Jan. 8 Signed by president to become Public Law 107-110

---

1. What activity related to H.R.1 took place on March 29, 2001?

2. Was the House debate on H.R.1 conducted under a closed or open rule? What does this tell you about the speaker of the House's view on the bill?

3. Some people say that most of the work of Congress happens in committee. Does the history of H.R.1 support this view? Why or why not?

4. If you had had a strong opinion on this bill, when and how might you have voiced your views most effectively?

Chief Executives and Bureaucracies

What qualities do modern presidents need to fulfill their many roles?

Speaking of Politics

As you complete the Reading Notes, use these terms in your answers:

reprieve	bureaucracy
pardon	pocket veto
cabinet	administration
executive order	whistle-blower

PREVIEW

Carefully examine the appointments in the daily diary of a modern president. Then answer these questions:

1. What observations can you make about the president's schedule on this day?

2. Why do you think the president has so many different types of appointments?

3. Based on this daily diary, what are some of the president's roles and responsibilities?

4. What qualities do you think the president needs to fulfill these many roles?

READING NOTES

Complete the given tasks as you read each section.

Section 13.2

Compare the job descriptions of national, state, and local chief executives by completing a table like the one below.

Chief Executives				
Level of Government	Title	Qualifications (formal and informal)	How are they elected?	How can they be removed from office?
National				
State				
Local				

Section 13.3

1. Briefly explain how one of the presidents described in this section defined or exercised the powers of the presidency.

2. In what ways do you think presidents today are more powerful today than they were in the past?

Section 13.4

1. Describe the roles of the modern president by completing a spoke diagram like the one below. For each role, identify at least three powers or responsibilities and create a simple symbol.

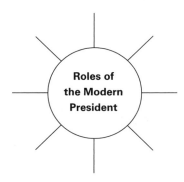

Roles of the Modern President

2. What checks does the president have on the legislative and judicial branches?

Section 13.5

Fill in a table like the one below by summarizing the main function of each group in the executive branch. Include at least two examples of individuals, departments, or agencies within each group.

The President			
White House Staff	Executive Office of the President	Executive Departments	Independent Agencies

Section 13.6

Create an analogy that evaluates the role and impact of government bureaucracies on the lives of Americans by completing this statement: *Government bureaucracies are like . . .*

Use one of these options to complete your analogy, or create your own:

- an overbearing parent who controls your life
- an overloaded computer hard drive that keeps crashing
- a well-oiled engine that keeps a car running
- an emergency room doctor who saves lives

Illustrate your analogy with a simple drawing. Then write at least two statements beginning with the word *because* to explain your analogy.

PROCESSING

Create and conduct an opinion survey to evaluate the current president's job performance.

- Your survey will have nine questions. The first eight questions will focus on the eight presidential roles. For each of these questions, provide a brief description of that role and then ask, *Do you approve or disapprove of the way the president is performing in this role?* Add a final question that assesses the president's overall job performance.
- Conduct the survey by polling at least 10 individuals outside your class.
- Compile your survey results for each of the nine questions. Then write a paragraph summarizing your results.

Appointments in a Modern President's Daily Diary

Location
THE WHITE HOUSE
WASHINGTON, D.C

Date APRIL 24
Day THURSDAY

TIME	ACTIVITY
5:30 a.m.	The President received a wake-up call.
8:32 a.m.	The President participated in a meeting to discuss Federal Trade Commission legislation with selected Members of Congress.
9:30 a.m.	The President met with Shimon Perez, Chairman of the Labor Party of the State of Israel.
11:02 a.m.	The President met to discuss the economy and inflation with representatives of the metals and metal product industries.
11:55 a.m.	The President met with Hamilton Jordan, Chief of Staff.
1:20 p.m.	The President participated in a meeting to discuss the Administration's anti-inflation program and fair housing initiatives with Hispanic leaders.
2:03 p.m.	The President participated in a ceremony to receive diplomatic credentials from the ambassadors of St. Lucia, the Bahamas, Haiti, Lesotho, El Salvador, and Japan.
3:37 p.m.	The President talked with the Chairman of the Joint Chiefs of Staff, General David C. Jones.
4:19 p.m.	The President met to discuss the upcoming Presidential campaign.
5:27 p.m.	The President talked with the First Lady in Detroit, Michigan.
8:06 p.m.	The President met with the Vice President, Secretary of State, Secretary of Defense, and other White House advisers.
12:15 a.m.	The President retired.

President Franklin Roosevelt

A Day in the Life of President Franklin Roosevelt

President Franklin D. Roosevelt took office in 1933 during the nation's worst economic crisis, the Great Depression. In 1933, some 13 million Americans—nearly one-fourth of the workforce—were unemployed. This unemployment had a cascading effect. The unemployed had little to spend, so many business lost customers and had to close—increasing unemployment. In addition to losing their jobs, many people lost their savings and homes. Soup kitchens and breadlines became a common sight in most cities. Promising a New Deal that would help the needy and promote recovery, Roosevelt entered the White House in a landslide victory.

On March 5, 1933, President Roosevelt got to work solving the nation's economic crisis. He focused his first day in office on dealing with problems in the financial sector. Loss of public confidence in the ability of the banking industry to safeguard people's money had caused periodic bank runs. Panicked depositors lined up in front of banks to try to withdraw their money. Those first in line got their money out. But once a bank ran out of cash, it closed its doors. By 1933, one-fifth of the banks that had been in business in the United States in 1930 had failed, and 9 million people had seen their savings vanish.

Roosevelt spent most of his first day in meetings with his cabinet and selected members of Congress. He "concluded that forty-eight different methods of handling the banking situation [were] impossible." After checking with his attorney general about his power to act in this situation, the president decided to proclaim a national banking holiday. This holiday would close all banks temporarily, stopping the steady withdrawal of funds. He also called Congress into a special session to pass the Emergency Banking Act. This law, passed on March 9, reformed the banking system and gave the federal government more power to supervise banks.

Roosevelt would explain all of his actions to the American people in his first fireside chat on the night of March 12. He hoped to restore their confidence in the banking system, and he urged Americans to do their part as well.

Appointments in President Roosevelt's Daily Diary

Location   Date MARCH 5, 1933
THE WHITE HOUSE   Day SUNDAY
WASHINGTON, D.C

TIME	ACTIVITY
9:00 a.m.	The President and his family attended services at St. Thomas' Church.
11:00 a.m.	The President attended a luncheon at the White House with his family and friends.
2:30 p.m.	The President met in the Oval Office with members of the Cabinet, the Vice President, and the Speaker of the House to discuss the banking situation.
3:30 p.m.	The President met with Congressional leaders to discuss calling Congress into special session so he could introduce legislation to address the banking situation.
4:45 p.m.	The President issued a proclamation calling Congress into special session.
6:00 p.m.	The President, Attorney General, Secretary of the Treasury, and other advisers worked on a proclamation to declare a national banking holiday.
7:30 p.m.	The President had supper with his sons.
9:45 p.m.	The President spoke with representatives of the four Press Associations to explain the banking holiday.
11:30 p.m.	The President gave a five minute radio address to the American Legion [an organization for American veterans].
11:36 p.m.	The President met with the Secretary of State about foreign policy issues, including the success of the Nazi Party in the German elections.

Source: Franklin D. Roosevelt Presidential Library and Museum.

President Roosevelt Document 1

Proclamation No. 2038
Calling Congress into Extraordinary Session
March 5, 1933

Whereas public interests require that the Congress of the United States should be convened in extra session at twelve o'clock, noon, on the Ninth day of March, 1933, to receive such communication as may be made by the Executive;

Now, Therefore, I, Franklin D. Roosevelt, President of the United States of America, do hereby proclaim and declare that an extraordinary occasion requires the Congress of the United States to convene in extra session at the Capitol in the City of Washington on the Ninth day of March, 1933, at twelve o'clock, noon, of which all persons who shall at that time be entitled to act as members thereof are hereby required to take notice.

IN WITNESS WHEREOF, I have hereunto set my hand and caused to be affixed the great seal of the United States.

Franklin D. Roosevelt

Source: The American Presidency Project.

President Roosevelt Document 2

First Fireside Chat, March 12, 1933

I want to talk for a few minutes with the people of the United States about banking . . . I want to tell you what has been done in the last few days, why it was done, and what the next steps are going to be . . .

What, then, happened during the last few days of February and the first few days of March? Because of undermined confidence on the part of the public, there was a general rush by a large portion of our population to turn bank deposits into currency or gold—a rush so great that the soundest banks could not get enough currency to meet the demand . . . By the afternoon of March 3d scarcely a bank in the country was open to do business . . .

It was then that I issued the proclamation providing for the nationwide bank holiday, and this was the first step in the Government's reconstruction of our financial and economic fabric.

The second step was the legislation promptly and patriotically passed by the Congress confirming my proclamation and broadening my powers so that it became possible . . . to extend the holiday and lift the ban of that holiday gradually . . .

This bank holiday, while resulting in many cases in great inconveniences, is affording us the opportunity to supply the currency necessary to meet the situation . . .

We had a bad banking situation. Some of our bankers had shown themselves either incompetent or dishonest in their handling of the people's funds. They had used the money entrusted to them in speculations and unwise loans. This was, of course, not true in the vast majority of our banks, but it was true in enough of them to shock the people for a time into a sense of insecurity . . . It was the Government's job to straighten out this situation and do it as quickly as possible. And the job is being performed.

I do not promise you that every bank will be reopened or that individual losses will not be suffered . . . We [the government] shall be engaged not merely in reopening sound banks but in the creation of sound banks through reorganization.

It has been wonderful to me to catch the note of confidence from all over the country. I can never be sufficiently grateful to the people for the loyal support they have given me . . .

After all, there is an element in the readjustment of our financial system more important than currency, more important than gold, and that is the confidence of the people. Confidence and courage are the essentials of success in carrying out our plan. You people must have faith; you must not be stampeded by rumors or guesses. Let us unite in banishing fear. We have provided the machinery to restore our financial system; it is up to you to support and make it work.

It is your problem no less than it is mine. Together we cannot fail.

Source: The American Presidency Project.

Transcript of President Roosevelt Audio Clip

Inaugural Address, March 4, 1933

President Hoover, Mr. Chief Justice, my friends: This is a day of national consecration, and I am certain that on this day my fellow Americans expect that on my induction into the Presidency I will address them with a candor and a decision which the present situation of our people impels. This is preeminently the time to speak the truth, the whole truth, frankly and boldly. Nor need we shrink from honestly facing conditions in our country today. This great Nation will endure as it has endured, will revive, and will prosper. So, first of all, let me assert my firm belief that the only thing we have to fear is . . . fear itself . . .

Our greatest primary task is to put people to work. [applause] This is no unsolvable problem if we face it wisely and courageously. It can be accomplished in part by direct recruiting by the Government itself, treating the task as we would treat the emergency of a war, but at the same time, through this employment, accomplishing great greatly needed projects to stimulate and reorganize the use of our great natural resources.

Hand in hand with that, we must frankly recognize the overbalance of population in our industrial centers and, by engaging on a national scale in a redistribution, endeavor to provide a better use of the land for those best fitted for the land.

I am prepared, under my constitutional duty, to recommend the measures that a stricken nation in the midst of a stricken world may require. These measures, or such other measures as the Congress may build out of its experience and wisdom, I shall seek, within my constitutional authority, to bring to speedy adoption.

But, in the event that the Congress shall fail to take one of these two courses, in the event that the national emergency is still critical, I shall not evade the clear course of duty that will then confront me. I shall ask the Congress for the one remaining instrument to meet the crisis— broad Executive power to wage a war against the emergency, as great as the power that would be given to me if we were in fact invaded by a foreign foe. [applause]

For the trust reposed in me, I will return the courage and the devotion that befit the time. I can do no less.

Source: The American Presidency Project.

President Lyndon Johnson

A Day in the Life of President Lyndon Johnson

President Lyndon B. Johnson took office in 1963 after the assassination of President John F. Kennedy. The former vice president promised to carry on Kennedy's idealistic vision for the American people. He spoke of moving toward a Great Society, where there was abundance and liberty for all and an end to poverty and racial injustice. Johnson promoted this Great Society by declaring the War on Poverty. He introduced a number of legislative initiatives aimed at improving the economic welfare of Americans. He also voiced strong support for the civil rights movement and signed the Civil Rights Act of 1964.

On August 4, 1964, President Johnson continued his commitment to the Great Society by meeting with various members of Congress to discuss his legislative proposals. At 11:06 A.M., he received a telephone call that prompted a dramatic shift in his priorities. In the middle of a meeting with Congressman George Mahon, Johnson was interrupted by an urgent call from Secretary of Defense Robert McNamara. According to McNamara, U.S. ships in the Gulf of Tonkin off the coast of North Vietnam were under attack. This was especially unsettling news, as an attack had occurred only two days prior. It seemed that the North Vietnamese had ignored Johnson's warning that an unprovoked attack on U.S. ships would have serious consequences. Johnson and his advisers set to work in a series of meetings that would last most of the afternoon and into the evening.

Johnson had a difficult decision to make on this day. For the United States, it seemed that the situation in Vietnam had reached a crisis point. Johnson had inherited the growing problem in Vietnam from Kennedy. Though the United States wanted to contain communism in Southeast Asia, Kennedy did not want to send U.S. troops overseas to help the South Vietnamese fight an insurgency supported by communist North Vietnam. Kennedy had sent weapons, equipment, technicians, and advisers, but the South Vietnamese were still losing. Johnson had increased U.S. support by authorizing covert attacks on radar stations along North Vietnam's coast. U.S. Navy warships located the stations, but the South Vietnamese carried out the attacks. Johnson had hoped to disrupt the flow of military aid into South Vietnam from North Vietnam. On August 2, the North Vietnamese had fired machine guns and torpedoes at a U.S. destroyer in the Gulf of Tonkin. Now, just two days later, reports indicated that a second attack had occurred.

Johnson decided to retaliate by ordering air strikes against naval bases in North Vietnam. He asked Congress to grant him authorization for these air strikes as well as the power to deal with any future attacks. At 11:34 P.M.—only 12 hours after first hearing about the attack—Johnson addressed the nation with news of the Gulf of Tonkin attack. It was later discovered that a second attack had never actually taken place.

Appointments in President Johnson's Daily Diary

Location
THE WHITE HOUSE
WASHINGTON, D.C

Date AUGUST 4, 1964
Day SUNDAY

TIME	ACTIVITY
10:34 a.m.	The President met with S. K. Patil, the Indian Railway Minister, and his translator.
10:40 a.m.	The President met with Congressman George Mahon to discuss the status of his proposed legislation.
11:06 a.m.	The President took a call from Secretary of Defense Robert McNamara. The Secretary reported that U.S. ships in the Gulf of Tonkin had been attacked by the North Vietnamese.
12:35 p.m.	The President went to the Cabinet Room for a National Security Council meeting to discuss the situation in North Vietnam.
2:35 p.m.	The President joined Mrs. Johnson's tea group. He stayed for eight minutes and shook hands with the group.
2:43 p.m.	The President sent flowers with a card to Senator Daniel Brewster in Bethesda Naval Hospital and to Senator Vance Hartke's daughter at George Washington University Hospital.
3:17 p.m.	The President sent two judicial nominations to the Senate.
6:16 p.m.	The President went to the Cabinet Room for a National Security Council meeting to discuss the situation in North Vietnam.
8:01 p.m.	The President took a call from FBI Assistant Director Cartha D. DeLoach. DeLoach delivered news of the finding of the bodies of three Mississippi civil rights workers.
11:34 p.m.	The President appeared before live television cameras to make a media statement about the action in Vietnam.
11:59 p.m.	The President spoke with Ambassador Averell Harriman about the President's upcoming visit to Syracuse to help the campaigns of Democratic candidates.

Source: Lyndon Baines Johnson Library.

President Johnson Document 1

```
                        Status of Bills
                       August 4, 1964

Poverty bill - Passed Senate -- On House floor for Wednesday. Open rule,
        6 hours debate

Wilderness bill - Expected to go to conference shortly

Food Stamp bill - In Rules Committee for House to recede and concur on
        Senate amendments - possibility of Rules Committee action
        on Thursday

Housing bill - Passed Senate - House Committee to consider tomorrow --
        possibility of floor action sometime next week

Nurses training bill - Passed House - Senate Labor Subcommittee will
        schedule as soon as Senator Hill completes HEW appropriation

Immigration legislation - Still in Committee

Food for Peace - House Subcommittee has marked-up bill - Full Committee
        may consider on Friday - to Rules early next week -- Senator
        Ellender hopes to consider week of August 10

Foreign aid bill - Passed House -- On Senate floor for debate

International Coffee Agreement - Passed both Houses - Question, to
        concur in Dirksen amendment or conference

Water pollution control bill - Passed Senate - House Committee expected
        to report Senate passed bill this week

Land conservation fund - Passed House - Senate Committee expected to
        report out today

Social Security amendments of '64 - Passed House - Senate Committee to
        meet today to discuss hearings procedure
```

Source: Lyndon Baines Johnson Library.

President Johnson Document 2

Summary Notes of the 538th National Security Meeting

~~TOP SECRET~~/SENSITIVE   FOR THE PRESIDENT ONLY
August 4, 1964   6:15 to 6:40 p.m.

Secretary of Defense McNamara: The North Vietnamese PT boats have continued their attacks on the two U.S. destroyers in international waters in the Gulf of Tonkin. No enemy aircraft was involved...

Secretary of State Rusk: An immediate and direct reaction by us is necessary. The unprovoked attack on the high seas is an act of war for all practical purposes... We are informing NATO, SEATO, and the UN... This second attack was a more serious decision for the North Vietnamese than...the first attack.

McNamara: We have agreed to air strikes on two bases in the north of North Vietnam and two base complexes in the south of North Vietnam...

CIA Director McCone: The proposed U.S. reprisals will result in a sharp North Vietnamese military reaction, but such actions would not represent a deliberate decision to provoke or accept a major escalation of the Vietnamese war...

President: Do they want a war by attacking our ships in...the Gulf of Tonkin?

McCone: No. The North Vietnamese are reacting defensively to our attacks on their off-shore islands. They are responding out of pride and on the basis of defense considerations. The attack is a signal to us that the North Vietnamese have the will and determination to continue the war...

President: Are we going to react to their shooting at our ships over 40 miles from their shores? If yes, we should do more than merely return the fire of the attacking ships...

USIA Director Rowan: Do we know for a fact that the North Vietnamese provocation took place? Can we nail down exactly what happened? We must be prepared to be accused of fabricating the incident.

McNamara: We will know definitely in the morning. As of now, only highly classified information nails down the incident. This information we cannot use and must rely on other reports we will be receiving.

Rusk: We should ask the Congressional leaders whether we should seek a Congressional resolution...

McNamara: In addition to the air strikes, we plan to send major U.S. reinforcements into the area. These include ships, men and planes...

A draft statement for the President was revised. It is to be made public by the President as soon as the U.S. attack planes are over target.

Source: Lyndon Baines Johnson Library.

Transcript of President Johnson Audio Clip

Telephone Conversation with FBI Assistant Director Cartha DeLoach

August 4, 1964   8:01 P.M.

President Johnson is meeting about attacks in the Gulf of Tonkin at the time of the call.

DeLoach: Mr. President?

Johnson: Yeah.

DeLoach: Mr. [J. Edgar] Hoover wanted me to call you, sir, immediately and tell you that the FBI has found three bodies six miles southwest of Philadelphia, Mississippi, the six miles west of where the civil rights workers were last seen on the night of June 21st. A search party of agents turned up the bodies just about 15 minutes ago while they were digging in the woods and underbrush several hundred yards off Route 21 in that area. We're going to get a coroner there right away, sir, and we're going to move these bodies into Jackson, Mississippi, where we hope they can be identified. We have not identified them as yet as the three missing men. But we have every reason to believe that they are the three missing men. They were under a—they were at the site of a dam that had been constructed near Philadelphia, Mississippi. Wanted to let you know right away, sir.

Johnson: When you gonna make the announcement?

DeLoach: Within ten minutes, sir, if it's all right with you.

Johnson: Well, how are you going to make it? Where? From there? From—?

DeLoach: I plan to make it from Washington here, sir.

Johnson: All right, all right.

DeLoach: Just indicate that the FBI has found three bodies, but not identified them.

Johnson: [sigh] Okay. If you can hold it about fifteen minutes, I think we ought to notify these families.

DeLoach: Well, Mr. President, the only thing I—suggestion—I'd have there is do you wish to do that prior to the time that they are identified? We think they're the ones, but—

Johnson: Well, I think we could tell them that we, we don't know, but we found 'em and that, that'd kinda ease it a little bit.

DeLoach: Yes, sir. All right, sir. Shall I wait until I hear—?

Johnson: Yeah. I'll get right back to you.

DeLoach: Very good, sir.

Source: Lyndon Baines Johnson Library.

President Richard Nixon

A Day in the Life of President Richard Nixon

In July 1971, President Richard Nixon made an announcement that would dramatically change U.S. relations with China. In a national address, Nixon accepted an invitation to visit the People's Republic of China the next year. When Nixon took office in 1969, the United States did not have diplomatic relations with China. Nor did it officially recognize the communist government that had ruled mainland China since 1949. After years of isolating China, Nixon believed it was in the best interests of the United States to improve its relations with the communist country.

On February 21, 1972, President Nixon made his historic trip to China. He left that morning from Guam International Airport, arriving in Shanghai, China, at 9 A.M. He was accompanied by Secretary of State William Rogers and top advisers H. R. Haldeman and Henry Kissinger, along with his wife and his press secretary. Upon deplaning, the presidential party was greeted by an official Chinese delegation. From there, the presidential party flew to Peking (Beijing), where they were welcomed by Premier Chou En-lai (Zhou Enlai) and other government officials. After a televised arrival ceremony and a tea ceremony, Nixon and his wife were escorted to their guest house.

Nixon participated in several meetings throughout the afternoon with various high-ranking officials in the Chinese government. He met with Chairman Mao Tse-tung (Mao Zedong), the leader of the People's Republic of China. Nixon was also honored at a special banquet that evening. At many of these events, the press and a White House photographer documented this diplomatic milestone. While in China, Nixon pledged to established diplomatic relations between the United States and China.

Nixon spent a week in China. In additional to diplomatic meetings with Chinese government officials, Nixon attended the ballet, a sports exhibition, and banquets. He toured the Great Wall, the Ming dynasty tombs, and the Forbidden City.

Appointments in President Nixon's Daily Diary

Location
PUGH RESIDENCE
AGANA, GUAM

Date FEBRUARY 21, 1972
Day MONDAY

TIME	ACTIVITY
6:45 a.m. (Guam time)	The President and the First Lady motored from the Pugh residence to Guam International Airport.
7:11 a.m.	The President and the First Lady flew to Hung Chiao Airport, Shanghai, People's Republic of China (PRC). The President met with his assistants, H. R. Haldeman and Henry Kissinger.
9:00 a.m. (China time)	The President and First Lady deplaned. They were accompanied by the Secretary of State, Mr. Haldeman, Mr. Kissinger, and the Press Secretary. The Presidential party was greeted by an official delegation of the PRC. The party had tea and toured the airport terminal with the Chinese delegation.
9:51 a.m.	The Presidential party flew to Capital Airport, Peking, PRC.
11:30 a.m.	The Presidential party was greeted by Chou En-lai, Premier of the State Council of the PRC and other PRC officials. The party participated in an arrival ceremony.
11:44 a.m.	The President, the First Lady and Premier Chou motored from Capital Airport to the Peking guest house. They had tea with U.S. and Chinese officials.
2:42 p.m.	The President and Premier Chou motored to the residence of Mao Tse-tung, Chairman of the Politburo of the PRC. The President met with Chairman Mao.
5:42 p.m.	The President motored to the Great Hall of the People. The President and Premier Chou met with U.S. and Chinese officials. Members of the press were in attendance.
7:42 p.m.	The Presidential party attended a welcoming banquet hosted by Premier Chou.
10:27 p.m.	The President signed Senate Joint Resolution 197, an arbitration settlement procedure for the West Coast dock strike.

Source: Nixon Presidential Library and Museum.

President Nixon Document 1

MEMORANDUM

THE WHITE HOUSE
WASHINGTON

February 4, 1972
6:30 p.m.

MEMORANDUM FOR: MEMBERS OF THE PRESIDENT'S PARTY

FROM: DWIGHT L. CHAPIN

SUBJECT: China -- 1972

Throughout China you will find sayings from Chairman Mao. Many of the Chairman's sayings center around "practice".

Borrowing from the Chairman the old "Practice makes perfect", I suggest you become acquainted with using the enclosed chopsticks.

Source: Nixon Presidential Library and Museum.

President Nixon Document 2

Statement on Signing a Bill to Arbitrate Settlement of the West Coast Dock Strike
February 21, 1972

THE SECRETARY of Labor has informed me today that an agreement has now been reached in the west coast dock strike and the workers have returned to their jobs.

While this contract will still be subject to approval... the entire Nation can be gratified by the willingness of the parties to settle their differences voluntarily. For thousands of Americans whose livelihoods have been threatened, this strike has been a painful experience and its end is most welcome.

For several days, I have delayed action on S.J. Res. [Senate Joint Resolution] 197, a bill to end the strike by arbitration [negotiation by a third party], in the hope that the pending legislation would encourage the parties to reach a voluntary accord. Today, as this legislation takes effect with my signature, I am pleased to note that the arbitration machinery will no longer be needed...

Repeatedly over the past 2 years I have urged the Congress to act on a comprehensive measure to avoid future strikes of this kind, and yet the Crippling Strikes Prevention Act still awaits action. The Congress did approve special legislation for this west coast strike, and I appreciate the significance of that action. The other shoe must now drop, however, or the Nation can only hobble into the future.

Source: The American Presidency Project.

Transcript of President Nixon Audio Clip

Oval Office Meeting
January 26, 1972

In attendance are Richard Nixon, Barend Biesheuvel, Alexander Haig, and J. William Middendorf.

Nixon: Uh, we do believe that by starting the long process of some sort of contact, there will—I will say, obviously, it will not come to recognition on our part—

Biesheuvel: No.

Nixon: —because it cannot, since we still recognize Taiwan and will continue to honor our treaty commitments. They know this will not come out. What may come out of it will be, uh, however, uh, uh, some method of communication in the future, uh, some contact in the future, uh, and perhaps reducing the chance in the immediate future of a confrontation between the United States and the PRC in Asia, such as we had in Korea, and such as we had indirectly in Vietnam. And looking further in the future, uh, when they become a super power, a nuclear super power, uh, to be in a position that at that time, uh, we will have such relations with them that, uh, we, uh, can discuss differences and, and not inevitably have a clash. Now, also, no one can look at Asia, uh, and take 750 million Chinese out of it and say you can have any policy in the Pacific that will succeed in preventing war without having the Chinese a part of it. It's just as cold-blooded as that.

Source: Nixon Presidential Library and Museum.

President George H. W. Bush

A Day in the Life of President George H. W. Bush

President George H. W. Bush had a busy plan for early November 1989. In addition to his daily routine of attending intelligence and national security briefings, he was scheduled to receive President Corazon Aquino of the Philippines. Bush welcomed the president with an official ceremony that included a review of troops and a photo session. U.S. and Philippine officials met in the Oval Office and the Cabinet Room for an hour. Later that evening, Bush hosted an official state dinner to honor President Aquino and her delegation. The four-hour affair included toasts, dinner, and dancing.

But November 9, 1989, was no ordinary day for the president and the world. After years of physical separation between East and West Berlin (Germany), the gates of the Berlin Wall were opened. Built by the East Germans, the wall was by far the most well-known symbol of the Cold War. Twelve feet tall and over 100 miles long, it divided the city and encircled West Berlin. Its 14,000 guards, aided by more than 6,000 tracking dogs, were under orders to shoot anyone who tried to escape to the West. As the news spread, hundreds of thousands of people rushed to the wall. Strangers hugged and kissed, while others cheered, danced, and set off fireworks. Then the crowd began to dismantle the wall by hand. This momentous event was televised all over the world.

Bush met with his press secretary, who suggested they call an impromptu press conference in the Oval Office. In the crowded room, Bush participated in a question-and-answer session about the events taking place in Berlin. He knew how important his responses would be, and he knew he needed to be diplomatic. He wanted to celebrate the historic moment, knowing what this meant to the people participating and watching this event. He also remained cautious to avoid provoking a Soviet response.

Bush worked with the Germans in the weeks that followed to support their effort to reunify not just Berlin, but also East and West Germany as one country.

Appointments in President Bush's Daily Diary

Location
THE WHITE HOUSE
WASHINGTON, D.C.

Date NOVEMBER 9, 1989
Day THURSDAY

TIME	ACTIVITY
6:00 a.m.	The President and the First Lady had breakfast.
8:26 a.m.	The President met for a national security briefing.
10:01 a.m.	The President and the First Lady participated in an arrival ceremony in honor of the President of the Republic of the Philippines Corazon C. Aquino.
11:00 a.m.	The President met with U.S. and Philippine officials.
11:39 a.m.	The President went to the horseshoe pitching court and pitched horseshoes.
1:15 p.m.	The President participated in a photo opportunity with members of the country music group "Alabama."
3:22 p.m.	The President participated in a question and answer session with members of the press on the opening of the borders between East and West Berlin.
3:52 p.m.	The President participated in a message taping session for the Macy's Thanksgiving Day Parade, the United Negro College Fund, congratulations for Sammy Davis, Jr., and the Port of Houston 75th Anniversary.
4:17 p.m.	The President met with his Chief of Staff to issue executive nominations and appointments.
6:28 p.m.	The President was telephoned by his Assistant for Legislative Affairs.
7:02 p.m.	The President and the First Lady hosted a State Dinner in honor of President Aquino. The evening included a receiving line, an exchange of toasts, dinner, a performance from opera singer Simon Estes, and dancing.
11:02 p.m.	The President and the First Lady returned to the second floor Residence.

Source: George Bush Presidential Library and Museum.

President Bush Document 1

```
          Nomination of Susan J. Crawford to Be
   Inspector General of the Department of Defense
                  November 9, 1989
```

The President today announced his intention to nominate Susan J. Crawford to be Inspector General of the Department of Defense. She would succeed June Gibbs Brown.

Since 1983 Mrs. Crawford has served as the General Counsel of the Department of the Army. Prior to this, she served as Principal Deputy General Counsel of the Department of the Army at the Pentagon, 1981 - 1983; partner with a law firm in Oakland, MD, 1979 - 1981; and an associate with the same firm, 1977 - 1979.

Mrs. Crawford graduated from Bucknell University (B.S., 1969) and received a law degree from the New England School of Law in 1977. She was born April 22, 1947, in Pittsburgh, PA. Mrs. Crawford is married, has one child, and resides in Falls Church, VA.

Source: The American Presidency Project.

President Bush Document 2

THE WHITE HOUSE
WASHINGTON

MEMORANDUM OF TELEPHONE CONVERSATION

SUBJECT: Telephone Conversation with Helmut Kohl, Chancellor, Federal Republic of Germany

PARTICIPANTS: The President
             Chancellor Helmut Kohl
             Notetaker: Robert M. Gates

DATE, TIME   November 10, 1989, 3:29 - 3:47 PM
AND PLACE: The Oval Office

<u>The President</u>: I'm very interested in the GDR [East Germany].

<u>Chancellor Kohl</u>: I've just arrived from Berlin. It is like witnessing an enormous fair. It has the atmosphere of a festival. The frontiers are absolutely open. At certain points they are literally taking down the wall and building new checkpoints. At Checkpoint Charlie, thousands of people are crossing both ways. There are many young people who are coming over for a visit enjoying our open way of life. I expect they will go home tonight. I would cautiously tell you that it appears that the opening has not led to a dramatic increase in the movement of refugees... This is a dramatic thing; an historic hour... The overall spirit was optimistic and friendly. When I thanked the Americans for their role in all of this, there was much applause. Without the US this day would not have been possible...

<u>The President</u>: First, let me say how great is our respect for the way the FRG [West Germany] had handled all of this... I want to tell the US press of our talk, that you gave me a thorough briefing, and that you did publicly acknowledge the role of the US, and that you and I agreed to talk later next week.

<u>Kohl</u>: Excellent.

<u>The President</u>: Take care, good luck. I'm proud of the way you're handling an extraordinarily difficult problem.

<u>Kohl</u>: Thank you. Give my best to Barbara [First Lady Barbara Bush]...

Source: George Bush Presidential Library and Museum.

Transcript of President Bush Audio Clip

Remarks to the National Association of Realtors
Dallas, Texas

November 10, 1989

Before going into my main remarks, let me just say a word about the momentous events in East Germany. I was moved, as you all were, by the pictures of Berliners from East and West standing atop the, the wall with chisels and hammers celebrating the opening of the most vivid symbol of the Iron Curtain. And then today, just on the plane coming down, I read a report where 18 new border crossings would be made in the wall in the, in the near future.

And to be honest with you, I doubted that this would happen in the very first year of this administration. Twenty-eight years after the desperate days of 1961, when tanks faced off at Checkpoint Charlie and that terrible barrier was built, now the East German government has responded to the wishes of its people. And while no one . . . [applause] And while no one really accurately predicted the speed of the changes underway in Eastern Europe—and certainly I didn't—but last May, right here in Texas, over at Texas A&M, I noted hopeful, indeed, remarkable signs of a Soviet break with the cycles of the past. And I called upon the Soviet Union to support self-determination for the nations of Eastern and Central Europe and to tear down the Iron Curtain. And now we're seeing it happen. And when I visited Poland and Hungary in July, I sensed that historically important events there held the seeds for even more dramatic change.

And this played a big part in the decision last July made, really, at the G-7 meeting in Paris, and on the way back, I proposed a face-to-face meeting with President Gorbachev [of the Soviet Union] before the next spring's summit. And the Malta meeting, given recent events, takes on, I think, even more importance than when I conceived the idea three and a half months ago.

The changes in recent months make clear that the process of reform initiated by the Eastern Europeans and supported by Mr. Gorbachev and by America and by our allies is real, offers us all much hope, and deserves our continued encouragement. We're living in fascinating times, and we will seize every opportunity to contribute to lasting peace and to extend democracy. And in doing so, I will conduct the foreign policy of this great country with the prudence that these fascinating times, times of change, demand—and with the imagination. The 1980s has been the decade of American renewal. And I believe that around the world, the 1990s will inevitably be the decade of democracy.

Source: The American Presidency Project.

Creating an Exhibit for a Presidential Library and Museum

You will work with your group to create an interactive exhibit of the day in the life of a modern president for one of four presidential libraries and museums. Your exhibit should use artifacts—documents, audio clip, photographs, and objects—to illustrate the various presidential roles that your president performed on this day. Visitors will tour your exhibit to guess these presidential roles.

Step 1: Assign roles for the exhibit.

☐ Review the roles below, and divide them among the members of your group. Make sure everyone understands his or her responsibilities. Everyone will participate as a museum docent when visitors tour your exhibit.

Historical Archivist You will lead the group during Step 2. You will make sure group members learn the key information about your assigned president. You will begin the tour by giving an introductory speech and will conclude the tour at the appropriate time.

Document Archivist You will lead the group as it analyzes the documents in Step 3. You will help visitors understand and connect these artifacts to the president's daily diary during the tour.

Audiovisual Archivist You will lead the group as it analyzes the audio clip and photographs in Step 3. You will help visitors understand and connect these artifacts to the president's daily diary during the tour.

Archaeological Archivist You will lead the group as it brainstorms additional objects to add to the exhibit in Step 3. You will help visitors understand and connect these artifacts to the president's daily diary during the tour.

Step 2: Learn about your assigned president.

☐ Take turns reading aloud from the handout about the day in the life of your president. Examine the daily diary of the president on this day. Afterward, have the Historical Archivist lead a discussion of the following questions. Use information from your Reading Notes and the handout in the discussion.

- What important crisis or event did the president deal with on this day?

- What presidential roles did he perform in dealing with this crisis or event? In what ways did he demonstrate these roles?

- What presidential roles did the president perform in dealing with his other responsibilities? In what ways did he demonstrate these roles?

Step 3: Design your exhibit.

☐ Examine each of the artifacts—documents, audio clip, and photographs—that you have received for your exhibit. Not every item is from the exact date of your exhibit, but they are all related to the day in some way.

☐ Complete *Student Handout 13F: Touring Exhibits in Presidential Libraries and Museums* for each of these artifacts.

☐ Brainstorm ideas for three or more objects to add to your exhibit to make it more interesting and informative. Add notes for these objects to Student Handout 13F.

Step 4: Create your exhibit.

☐ Write an introductory speech for the exhibit that includes information about your assigned president and this specific day.

☐ Find or make the objects that you are adding to the exhibit.

☐ Identify clues in the artifacts—documents, audio clip, photographs, and objects—that you can give visitors to help them connect the items to the daily diary and to identify the various roles demonstrated by the president.

Step 5: Rehearse your exhibit tour.

To set up and conduct your exhibit tour, follow these steps:

☐ Create your museum exhibit by carefully placing each artifact on a table or a group of desks. You may want to make your exhibit look like the president's desk or office or like a typical museum exhibit.

☐ Display the president's daily diary of appointments near the artifacts.

☐ The Historical Archivist begins the tour by welcoming visitors and giving the introductory speech.

☐ The other archivists help visitors examine the artifacts and complete Student Handout 13F. As museum docents, they offer clues to the visitors only if the visitors are having trouble or are making incorrect guesses.

☐ The Historical Archivist ends the tour by checking to see that the visitors have correctly filled in Student Handout 13F.

Touring Exhibits in Presidential Libraries and Museums

Complete this table for each exhibit about a day in the life of a modern president.

President: _____   Date: _____

Artifact	What time(s) does this artifact connect to on the daily diary?	Which presidential role or roles does this artifact demonstrate, and how does it demonstrate them?

Mastering the Content

1. Who initiated the tradition of addressing the president as "Mr. President"?
   A. Andrew Jackson
   B. Abraham Lincoln
   C. Theodore Roosevelt
   D. George Washington

2. The position of a lieutenant governor in a state is comparable to that of which position in the federal government?
   A. attorney general
   B. chief of staff
   C. secretary of defense
   D. vice president

3. The president's speechwriters, administrative assistants, and press secretary all work as part of which group?
   A. White House staff
   B. White House press corps
   C. Executive Office of the President
   D. Office of Management and Budget

4. Which of these is **not** a qualification for seeking the presidency?
   A. college graduate
   B. natural-born citizen
   C. at least 35 years old
   D. lived in United States at least 14 years

5. Which factor most influences whether a president might choose to use a pocket veto?
   A. who in Congress voted for the bill
   B. how close Congress is to adjournment
   C. whether the bill has broad public support
   D. the impact that signing will have on the budget

6. What did Andrew Jackson do that led his critics to call him "King Andrew"?
   A. He called Congress into special session.
   B. He suspended the right of habeas corpus.
   C. He used the presidency as a "bully pulpit."
   D. He expanded the use of the presidential veto.

7. Which of these processes allows voters in many states to remove an elected official from office?
   A. impeachment
   B. initiative
   C. recall
   D. referendum

8. What does the list below show?

   > *Vice President*
   > *Speaker of the House of*
   >   *Representatives*
   > *President Pro Tempore of the Senate*
   > *Secretary of State*
   > *Secretary of the Treasury*
   > *Secretary of Defense*
   > *Attorney General*
   > *Secretary of the Interior*
   > *Secretary of Agriculture*
   > *Secretary of Commerce*
   >   .
   >   .
   >   .
   > *Secretary of Homeland Security*

   A. the line of presidential succession
   B. the makeup of the president's cabinet
   C. the organization of the executive branch
   D. the leadership of the federal bureaucracy

9. All of the following are examples of independent agencies **except** the
   A. Peace Corps.
   B. Department of Justice.
   C. National Endowment for the Arts.
   D. Environmental Protection Agency.

10. What does a whistle-blower do?
    A. expose wrongdoing
    B. enforce party loyalty
    C. criticize civil servants
    D. schedule appointments

Exploring the Essential Question

What qualities do modern presidents need to fulfill their many roles?

Article II of the U.S. Constitution defines the formal qualifications and powers of the president. Read the parts quoted below and answer the questions that follow.

Article II of the U.S. Constitution

Section 1. The executive Power shall be vested in a President . . . *(Section 1 goes on to describe how presidents are elected, qualifications, succession, payment, and oath of office.)*

Section 2. The President shall be Commander in Chief of the Army and Navy of the United States, and of the Militia of the several States, when called into the actual Service of the United States; he may require the Opinion, in writing, of the principal Officer in each of the executive Departments, upon any Subject relating to the Duties of their respective Offices, and he shall have Power to grant Reprieves and Pardons for Offenses against the United States, except in Cases of Impeachment.

He shall have Power, by and with Advice and Consent of the Senate, to make Treaties, provided two thirds of the Senators present concur; and he shall nominate, and by and with the Advice and Consent of the Senate, shall appoint Ambassadors, other public Ministers and Consuls, Judges of the supreme Court, and all other Officers of the United States, whose Appointments are not herein otherwise provided for, and which shall be established by Law . . .

Section 3. He shall from time to time give to the Congress Information of the State of the Union, and recommend to their Consideration such Measures as he shall judge necessary and expedient; he may, on extraordinary Occasions, convene both Houses, or either of them . . . he shall receive Ambassadors and other public Ministers; he shall take care that the Laws be faithfully executed, and shall Commission all the Officers of the United States.

Section 4. The President, Vice President and all civil Officers of the United States, shall be removed from Office on Impeachment for, and Conviction of, Treason, Bribery, or other high Crimes and Misdemeanors.

---

1. List five powers granted expressly to the president by the Constitution.
2. Discuss the powers given to the president by the Take Care Clause in Article II, Section 3. In what way is this clause similar to the Necessary and Proper Clause in Article 1, Section 8?
3. Compare the president's powers relating to foreign policy in times of war and peace to those given to Congress. Based on your analysis, which branch of government do you think has primary responsibility for conducting foreign policy?
4. Identify one quality that you feel would help a modern president fill one or more of the roles defined in the Constitution. Explain your answer.

The Federal Budget

Does the federal government budget and spend your tax dollars wisely?

Speaking of Politics

As you complete the Reading Notes, use these terms in your answers:

balanced budget	progressive tax
budget surplus	regressive tax
federal deficit	entitlement
national debt	earmarks

PREVIEW

Examine the list of typical monthly living expenses for a young adult. Then answer these questions:

1. Are all of these expenses absolutely necessary? Why or why not?

2. If your monthly income did not cover all of these expenses, you would have certain options, such as borrowing money, working more, or eliminating expenses. What are the benefits and consequences of these options?

3. If you chose to eliminate expenses, how would you decide which expenses to keep and which to eliminate?

4. How might these personal budget challenges be similar to and different from those of the federal government?

**Typical Monthly Expenses
for a Young Adult**

housing (rent and utilities)

health insurance

cable television: basic service, premium channels

Internet

cell phone: basic service, fees for calls and text messaging

clothing

groceries

restaurants and takeout

transportation

education

entertainment

As you read each section, complete the given tasks.

Section 14.2

1. Create a timeline with the following three time periods along it.

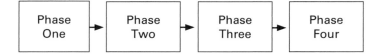

| 1789–1921 | 1921–1974 | 1974–present |

For each time period, identify which branch or branches of government controlled the federal budget process. Draw a simple illustration for each. Also explain how the budget process worked during each time period.

2. Based on your reading and the timeline you created, answer this question: *In what ways might these historical changes have contributed to the growth of the national debt?*

Section 14.3

Complete a flowchart like the one below by briefly describing what happens in each phase of the budget process.

```
Phase     Phase     Phase     Phase
One   →   Two   →   Three →   Four
```

Section 14.4

1. Create a diagram to summarize the main sources of federal revenue. Label and briefly describe each source.

2. What is the difference between a progressive tax and a regressive tax? Why do you think the government uses both types of taxes to raise revenue?

3. Create a diagram to summarize the differences between mandatory and discretionary spending. Briefly describe each type of spending, and provide examples.

Section 14.5

Compare the state and local budget process with the federal budget process by completing a Venn diagram like the one below. On the left, identify characteristics unique to the state and local budget process. On the right, identify characteristics unique to the federal budget process. In the center, identify characteristics that are shared by both.

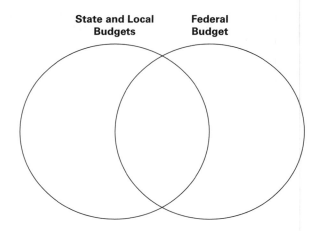

State and Local Budgets   Federal Budget

In two or more well-written paragraphs, respond to this question: *Does the federal government budget and spend your tax dollars wisely?* Include specific evidence—such as facts, data, quotations, and examples—to support your answer. Also provide advice on how the government can maintain or improve its current policies and decision-making process.

Department of Health and Human Services

The Department of Health and Human Services is the U.S. government's principal agency for protecting the health of Americans. The department provides essential human services, especially for those who are least able to help themselves. More than 300 programs cover a spectrum of activities. These activities include

- health and social science research.

- preventing disease, including immunization services.

- assuring food and drug safety.

- Medicare (health insurance for elderly and disabled Americans) and Medicaid (health insurance for low-income people).

- Head Start (preschool education and services).

- preventing child abuse and domestic violence.

- substance-abuse treatment and prevention.

- medical preparedness for emergencies, including potential terrorism.

PROPOSED BUDGET

Mandatory Expenditures

These are the department's projected mandatory expenditures for the next fiscal year.

Expenditure	Cost (in millions)
Medicare	$367,000
Medicaid	$198,000
Other	$46,000

Discretionary Expenditures

The department is requesting a 5% increase in discretionary spending for the next fiscal year. Here are the department's three budget proposals for discretionary spending.

Expenditure	Budget with Proposed Increase (in millions)	Budget with No Increase (in millions)	Budget with 5% Decrease (in millions)
Operating expenses	$55,000 This figure maintains current staff and programs with a cost-of-living increase.	$52,500 This figure maintains current programs with no cost-of-living increase and reduces staff by 1,000.	$50,000 This figure cuts 2% of current programs and reduces staff by 1,500.
Preparedness for influenza pandemic and bioterror attacks	$11,000 This figure funds 10 research facilities and builds 3 new manufacturing facilities to make and store vaccines.	$10,500 This figure funds 10 research facilities and builds no new manufacturing facilities.	$10,000 This figure funds 8 research facilities and builds no new manufacturing facilities.
State grants for health insurance to children of low-income families	$22,000 This figure funds 100% of projected need (4 million children).	$21,000 This figure funds 90% of projected need (3.6 million children).	$20,000 This figure funds 80% of projected need (3.2 million children).

Note: Budget proposals are hypothetical.

Department of Homeland Security

The National Strategy for Homeland Security and the Homeland Security Act of 2002 mobilized our nation to protect it from terrorist attacks. To be successful, this complex mission requires a focused effort. The Department of Homeland Security was established to unify the network of organizations and institutions helping to guard our nation. The main goals of the department are to

- identify and understand potential threats to our nation.

- distribute timely information about security threats to our partners and the American public.

- detect, deter, and mitigate attacks on our homeland.

- safeguard our people along with the critical infrastructure, property, and economy of our nation from acts of terrorism, natural disasters, and other emergencies.

- lead, manage, and coordinate the national response to acts of terrorism, natural disasters, and other emergencies.

- lead national, state, local, and private-sector efforts to restore services and rebuild communities after acts of terrorism, natural disasters, and other emergencies.

- facilitate lawful trade, travel, and immigration.

PROPOSED BUDGET

Mandatory Expenditures

These are the department's projected mandatory expenditures for the next fiscal year.

Expenditure	Cost (in millions)
Federal Emergency Management Agency	$3,000
Citizenship and Immigration Services	$2,000
U.S. Secret Service	$200
U.S. Coast Guard	$1,300

Discretionary Expenditures

The department is requesting an 8% increase in discretionary spending for the next fiscal year. Here are the department's three budget proposals for discretionary spending.

Expenditure	Budget with Proposed Increase (in millions)	Budget with No Increase (in millions)	Budget with 5% Decrease (in millions)
Operating expenses	$28,000 This figure adds 2,000 additional staff.	$26,000 This figure maintains current staff level.	$25,000 This figure reduces staff by 1,000.
No-interest loans to victims of natural disasters (hurricanes, floods, tornados)	$3,400 This figure funds 100% of projected need.	$3,100 This figure funds 75% of projected need.	$3,000 This figure funds 60% of projected need.
Scanners for containers entering U.S. seaports (to detect nuclear and chemical weapons)	$5,600 This figure provides scanners for 22 of the busiest seaports in the country.	$5,200 This figure provides scanners for 15 of the busiest seaports in the country.	$5,000 This figure provides scanners for 10 of the busiest seaports in the country.

Note: Budget proposals are hypothetical.

Department of State and Other International Programs

The State Department manages U.S. relations with foreign governments, international organizations, and the people of other countries. It aims to provide a freer, more prosperous, and more secure world. Through diplomacy, the State Department formulates, implements, and helps explain the president's foreign policy goals. The State Department protects our nation, its people, and our prosperity by helping to

- prevent terrorist attacks and strengthen international alliances to combat global terrorism.
- ensure homeland security by promoting policies to keep travel, trade, and infrastructure safe.
- provide guidelines to manage the entry of visitors to the United States.
- promote stability in all regions of the world.
- prevent enemies from threatening the United States or our allies with weapons of mass destruction.
- reduce the impact of international crime and illegal drugs on Americans.
- protect and assist U.S. citizens who travel, conduct business, and live abroad.

PROPOSED BUDGET

Mandatory Expenditures

The department has no mandatory expenditures for the next fiscal year.

Discretionary Expenditures

The department is requesting a 5% increase in discretionary spending for the next fiscal year. Here are the department's three budget proposals for discretionary spending.

Expenditure	Budget with Proposed Increase (in millions)	Budget with No Increase (in millions)	Budget with 5% Decrease (in millions)
Operating expenses	$7,700 This figure maintains current staff and programs with a cost-of-living increase.	$7,300 This figure maintains current programs with no cost-of-living increase and reduces staff by 100.	$7,000 This figure cuts 1% of current programs or reduces staff by 200.
Diplomatic and consular expenses	$5,500 This figure provides expenses for all U.S. embassies and for building maintenance and upgrades.	$5,200 This figure provides expenses for all U.S. embassies, but not building maintenance and upgrades.	$5,000 This figure closes 5 small U.S. embassies or 1 mid-size U.S. embassy.
International peace-keeping missions	$4,400 This figure provides civil support personnel for 100% of current commitments to peacekeeping missions.	$4,200 This figure provides civil support personnel for 90% of current commitments to peacekeeping missions.	$4,000 This figure provides civil support personnel for 80% of current commitments to peacekeeping missions.

Note: Budget proposals are hypothetical.

Department of the Treasury

The Department of the Treasury is the primary federal agency responsible for the economic and financial prosperity and security of the United States. This includes advising the president on economic and financial issues and promoting the president's growth agenda. The department works with other federal agencies, governments of other nations, and international financial institutions for several purposes. These include encouraging economic growth, raising living standards, and predicting and preventing, to the extent possible, economic crises. The basic functions of the department include

- managing federal finances.
- collecting taxes, duties, and other monies due to the United States.
- paying all bills of the United States.
- producing postage stamps and currency.
- managing government accounts and the public debt.
- supervising national banks.
- enforcing federal finance and tax laws.
- investigating and prosecuting tax evaders, counterfeiters, and forgers.

PROPOSED BUDGET

Mandatory Expenditures

These are the department's projected mandatory expenditures for the next fiscal year.

Expenditure	Cost (in millions)
Interest on the national debt	$464,000
Payments owed to taxpayers after filing taxes	$40,000

Discretionary Expenditures

The department is requesting a 10% increase in discretionary spending for the next fiscal year. Here are the department's three budget proposals for discretionary spending.

Expenditure	Budget with Proposed Increase (in millions)	Budget with No Increase (in millions)	Budget with 5% Decrease (in millions)
Operating expenses	$11,500 This figure restores 2,000 staff members to the Internal Revenue Service and U.S. Mint. Staff was lost in budget cuts over the past 5 years.	$11,000 This figure maintains current programs and staff with no cost-of-living increase.	$10,500 This figure reduces staff by 1,000.
Technology: hardware and software upgrades to monitor terrorist activities and to prevent fraud	$3,400 This figure adds 100 new computers and upgrades the security software on all department computers.	$3,100 This figure maintains the current level of hardware and software on all department computers.	$3,000 This figure downgrades the security software on all department computers.
Legal fees for criminal cases against major tax evaders (those who owe more than $1 million)	$6,200 This figure funds legal fees to pursue 95% of major tax evaders.	$5,700 This figure funds legal fees to pursue 90% of major tax evaders.	$5,500 This figure funds legal fees to pursue 85% of major tax evaders.

Note: Budget proposals are hypothetical.

Environmental Protection Agency

In July 1970, the White House and Congress established the Environmental Protection Agency in response to the growing public demand for cleaner water, air, and land. The agency leads the nation's environmental science, research, education, and assessment efforts by

- developing and enforcing regulations that implement environmental laws enacted by Congress.

- setting national standards for environmental programs.

- offering financial assistance to state environmental programs.

- performing environmental research to identify and solve current and future environmental problems.

- providing leadership in addressing emerging environmental issues.

- sponsoring voluntary pollution-prevention programs and energy-conservation efforts.

- educating to develop an environmentally conscious and responsible public and to inspire personal responsibility in caring for the environment.

PROPOSED BUDGET

Mandatory Expenditures

The agency has no mandatory expenditures for the next fiscal year.

Discretionary Expenditures

The agency is requesting a 5% increase in discretionary spending for the next fiscal year. Here are the agency's three budget proposals for discretionary spending.

Expenditure	Budget with Proposed Increase (in millions)	Budget with No Increase (in millions)	Budget with 5% Decrease (in millions)
Operating expenses	$4,400 This figure maintains current programs and staff with a cost-of-living increase.	$4,200 This figure maintains current programs and staff without a cost-of-living increase.	$4,000 This figure cuts current programs by 2% or reduces staff by 100.
State grants under Clean Air and Water Acts	$1,150 This figure funds 80% of proposed state grants for pollution cleanup, education and training programs, and legal fees to pursue major polluters.	$1,050 This figure funds 65% of proposed state grants for pollution cleanup, education and training programs, and legal fees to pursue major polluters.	$1,000 This figure funds 55% of proposed state grants for pollution cleanup, education and training programs, and legal fees to pursue major polluters.
Superfund expenses: cleanup of toxic waste sites identified by the EPA	$2,200 This figure funds cleanup of an additional 200 toxic waste sites from the Superfund waiting list.	$2,100 This figure accelerates the level of cleanup at the 1,200 Superfund sites across the country, reducing cleanup time by several months.	$2,000 This figure maintains the level of cleanup at the 1,200 Superfund sites across the country.

Note: Budget proposals are hypothetical.

Social Security Administration

The mission of the Social Security Administration is to advance the economic security of the nation's people through compassionate and vigilant leadership in shaping and managing Social Security programs. The administration is headquartered in Baltimore, Maryland, and has 10 regional offices and 1,300 local offices nationwide. The administration touches the lives of nearly everyone in America by

- issuing Social Security numbers.
- providing financial support for older Americans and Americans with disabilities, and their dependents.
- managing the Old-Age, Survivors, and Disability Insurance programs, universally known as Social Security.
- running the Supplemental Security Insurance program for low-income aged and disabled persons.

PROPOSED BUDGET

Mandatory Expenditures

These are the administration's projected mandatory expenditures for the next fiscal year.

Expenditure	Cost (in millions)
Old-Age, Survivors, and Disability Insurance	$604,000
Supplemental Security Insurance	$42,000

Discretionary Expenditures

The administration is requesting a 7% increase in discretionary spending for the next fiscal year. Here is the administration's budget proposal for discretionary spending.

Expenditure	Budget with Proposed Increase (in millions)	Budget with No Increase (in millions)	Budget with 5% Decrease (in millions)
Operating expenses	$9,000 This figure adds 800 staff to local and regional offices across the country.	$8,400 This figure maintains current level of staff without a cost-of-living increase.	$8,000 This figure reduces staff by 500.

Note: Budget proposals are hypothetical.

Executive Memorandum

EXECUTIVE OFFICE OF THE PRESIDENT
THE WHITE HOUSE
WASHINGTON D.C.

MEMORANDUM FOR THE OFFICE OF MANAGEMENT AND BUDGET

To create a spending plan, you will examine the budgets for six departments and agencies. The President requires each department or agency to identify mandatory and discretionary expenditures separately. For discretionary expenditures, each will propose three budgets:

- The cost (in millions of dollars) for a budget with a proposed increase
- The cost (in millions of dollars) for a budget with no increase
- The cost (in millions of dollars) for a budget with a 5% decrease

Your spending plan should reflect the priorities of the administration. The President has ranked these priorities in order of importance.

Priority 1: Ensure the security of the nation, including anti-crime and anti-terrorism efforts.

Priority 2: Protect the long-term health of the Medicaid, Medicare, and Social Security programs.

Priority 3: Support working families in addressing the challenges of finding affordable childcare, housing, and health insurance.

Priority 4: Create a world-class system of education and training for Americans of all ages.

Priority 5: Reduce pollution and protect the environment.

Priority 6: Increase department and agency efficiency by eliminating unnecessary jobs and investing in technology.

Above all, the President's main concern is that you try to balance the budget. Try to spend no more than $1,935,000 million among the six departments and agencies.

The President requests that you submit your spending plan and a brief report supporting your plan no later than the date specified on the White House calendar.

Proposed Spending Plan

Part 1 Complete the matrix below for each of the six departments or agencies.

- Identify the primary responsibilities for this department or agency.
- Rate (1 = very well, 5 = not well) how well these responsibilities address the president's priorities.
- Record the mandatory expenditures.
- Record how much you propose the government should spend for each discretionary expenditure.
- Total the mandatory and discretionary expenditures.

Balanced Budget = $1,935,000 million

	Primary Responsibilities	Rating	Mandatory Expenditures (in millions)	**+** Discretionary Expenditures (in millions)	**=** Total Expenditures (in millions)
Department of Health and Human Services				Operating expenses:	
				Preparedness:	
				State grants:	
Department of Homeland Security				Operating expenses:	
				No-interest loans:	
				Scanners:	

	Primary Responsibilities	Rating	Mandatory Expenditures (in millions)	+ Discretionary Expenditures (in millions)	= Total Expenditures (in millions)
Department of State and Other International Programs				Operating expenses: Diplomatic and consular: Peacekeeping missions:	
Department of the Treasury				Operating expenses: Technology: Legal fees:	
Environmental Protection Agency				Operating expenses: State grants: Superfund:	
Social Security Administration				Operating expenses:	

Part 2 Calculate your overall budget for all six departments and agencies. If this figure is unsatisfactory, you may revisit any of the stations to change your spending decisions.

Overall budget: _____

(Add the figures in the last column.)

Mastering the Content

1. Which of these is the largest source of federal revenue?
   A. corporate income taxes
   B. excise taxes
   C. individual income taxes
   D. payroll taxes

2. What is the largest category of federal discretionary spending?
   A. defense
   B. education
   C. health
   D. welfare

3. Property taxes are the main source of revenue for many local governments. What is the main disadvantage of this type of tax?
   A. It is a difficult tax to collect.
   B. It is a highly progressive tax.
   C. It may discourage people from saving.
   D. It may not reflect people's ability to pay.

4. A government with revenues of $52 million and expenditures of $49 million in the same year has which of the following?
   A. a budget deficit
   B. a budget surplus
   C. a balanced budget
   D. a proposed budget

5. Which of these is an entitlement?
   A. a low-income family's food stamps
   B. a federally funded highway program
   C. a manufacturer's government contract
   D. a federal grant to fund medical research

6. On which date does the federal fiscal year begin?
   A. January 1
   B. April 1
   C. July 1
   D. October 1

7. What is the purpose of a continuing resolution?
   A. to combine 13 appropriation bills into one budget
   B. to keep the government working without a budget
   C. to set guidelines for congressional budget making
   D. to close congressional debate on appropriation bills

8. Richard Nixon angered Congress by abusing the presidential power of impoundment. This power allows a president to refuse to
   A. sign spending bills.
   B. spend appropriated funds.
   C. prepare a budget proposal.
   D. honor negotiated agreements.

9. Which of these events happens first in the budget cycle?
   A. Congress adopts a budget resolution.
   B. Federal bureaucrats prepare budget requests.
   C. Legislators insert earmarks into appropriation bills.
   D. House and Senate budget committees hold hearings.

10. Which of these taxes is **most** likely to be regressive?
    A. a corporate income tax
    B. an estate tax
    C. an individual income tax
    D. a sales tax

Exploring the Essential Question

Does the federal government budget and spend your tax dollars wisely?

Politicians are constantly reminded that voters want government services but do not like to pay for them. The two graphs below show where the federal government raised revenue in fiscal year 2006 and how that money was spent. Examine the graphs, and then answer the questions below.

Federal Revenue, Fiscal Year 2006

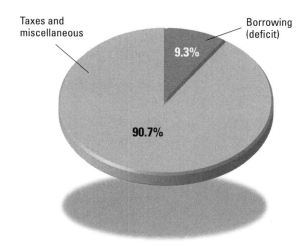

Federal Spending, Fiscal Year 2006

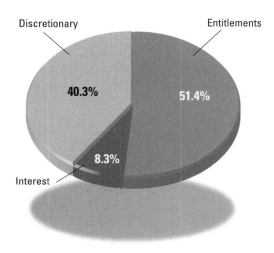

1. Using the information shown in the graph on the right, define mandatory spending.

2. Using data from both graphs, explain why the United States has a national debt and how it affects the federal budget and government services.

3. Suppose you are on the staff of a member of Congress who is dedicated to balancing the federal budget. Outline a brief proposal for how this could be accomplished.

Courts, Judges, and the Law

How is the U.S. judicial system organized to ensure justice?

Speaking of Politics

As you complete the Reading Notes, use these terms in your answers:

criminal law	prosecution
civil law	plaintiff
burden of proof	writ of certiorari
defendant	legal brief

PREVIEW

Examine the collage of photographs on the first page of Chapter 15. Then answer these questions:

1. What do all of these images relate to?

2. Have you had a personal experience with the court system? If so, what was it like? If not, what are your impressions of the court system from film, television, newspapers, magazines, and books?

3. What is the overall goal of the judicial system?

4. A primary purpose of the U.S. court system is to ensure justice. Do you think it does that?

READING NOTES

Follow these directions to complete your Reading Notes for this chapter.

1. Read the question on Card 1. Locate the answer to the question in Sections 15.3 to 15.7.

2. Find the box numbered 1 on Notebook Handout 15. Label the diagram as directed on Card 1.

3. Repeat the procedure for Cards 2 through 16, completing them in order.

4. Tape the completed diagrams into your notebook. Then answer these questions:

   - What did you learn about the judicial branch that you did not know before?

   - What are some characteristics of the U.S. court system that help ensure justice?

PROCESSING

You have learned about the structure and operation of the judicial branch. Now read the following postings from the fictional Web site "Pursuing Justice." Then write your own comment in response to one or both of the postings. Include the following in your response:

- your online name
- the date and time of your response
- your position on the topic being discussed
- support for your argument, including two specific courts that you have read about and how their structure or function adds to or detracts from justice being served

---

http://www.pursuingjustice.blogspt.com/

America's Court System: Two Thumbs Up

From: courtwatcher, 2:34pm, 09.31.08

It's become all too common to hear people grumbling about our judicial system. "Too many cases, too complicated, too political, too biased." Many Americans have become disenchanted with our courts and those who run them.

I couldn't disagree more. In today's society, our courts provide an open forum for raising grievances, asserting one's rights, and resolving conflicts. And they do it in a more efficient way than any other nation on this planet.

Our court system ensures that every citizen will receive justice. From the defendant accused of a crime to the employee suing for breach of contract, all have an avenue to seek justice. No system is perfect, but our system of courts does indeed ensure justice for those seeking it.

On 10.03.08, gavel_pounder says:

Two thumbs up? I'd like to know if courtwatcher has ever been inside a courtroom! A survey conducted for the American Bar Association revealed that 78% of Americans believe "it takes too long for courts to do their jobs" while 77% believe "it costs too much to go to court." Our legal system today is a mess. Judges are overwhelmed with crowded dockets, cases are appealed far too often, and frivolous lawsuits take judicial attention away from serious cases. Ensure justice? Not likely.

The U.S. Court System

For each card, find the corresponding number on one of the three court diagrams.
Label or annotate the diagram as directed on the card.

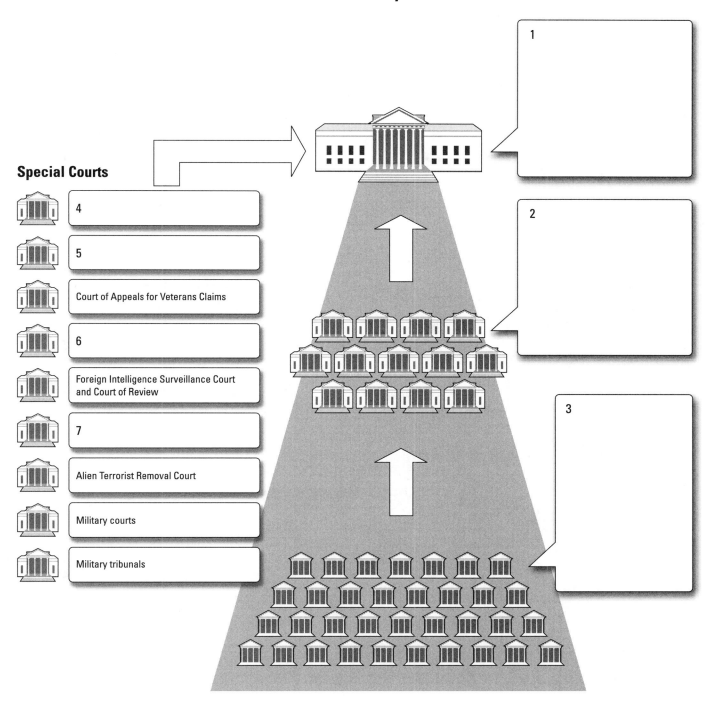

Federal Court System

Special Courts

4

5

Court of Appeals for Veterans Claims

6

Foreign Intelligence Surveillance Court and Court of Review

7

Alien Terrorist Removal Court

Military courts

Military tribunals

1

2

3

State Court System

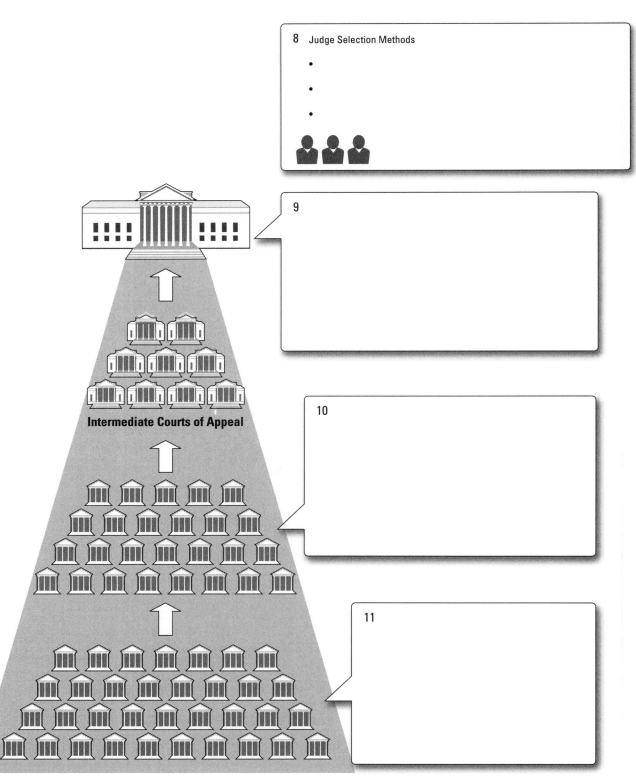

8   Judge Selection Methods

-
-
-

9

Intermediate Courts of Appeal

10

11

Supreme Court

Federal Judge Selection Process

12	13
	Judges are nominated by _____
	and confirmed by _____.

Stages of a Supreme Court Case

14

Legal and amicus curiae briefs are filed.

Oral arguments are presented to the Court.

Justices meet in private conferences and decide to uphold or to overrule a previous decision.

15   Opinions are written.

-
-
-

Schools of Thought About Judicial Review

16

Judicial Branch Card Sort

Card 1

Which court in the federal system is the court of last resort?

Label this court on the diagram. Then describe its function and draw in the number of justices who hear each case.

Card 2

Which courts in the federal system use three-judge panels to review cases?

Label these courts on the diagram. Then describe their function and draw in the number of justices who hear each case.

Card 3

Which courts in the federal system have original jurisdiction within their regions?

Label these courts on the diagram and describe their function.

Card 4

Which court hears cases that involve customs or other trade issues?

Label this court on the diagram.

Card 5

Which court hears cases in which claims for damages have been made against the United States?

Label this court on the diagram.

Card 6

Which court resolves disputes between taxpayers and the Internal Revenue Service?

Label this court on the diagram.

Card 7

Which court in the federal system reviews the convictions of military personnel who have violated military law?

Label this court on the diagram.

Card 8

What three methods are used to select state judges?

Write these methods on the diagram.

Card 9

Which courts in the state system have jurisdiction over all matters of state law and are the last avenue of appeal for most cases?

Label these courts on the diagram.

Card 10

Which courts in the state system handle most serious criminal cases and major civil disputes?

Label these courts on the diagram and describe their function.

Card 11

Which courts in the state system specialize in minor criminal or civil cases and usually involve informal hearings without juries?

Label these courts on the diagram and describe their function.

Card 12

Which practice in the selection process for federal judges allows senators to block nominations to federal courts in their home states?

Write this term and its definition on the diagram.

Card 13

Who nominates Supreme Court justices? Who confirms these nominations?

Write this information on the diagram.

Card 14

What is a legal document that the Supreme Court sends to a lower court ordering it to send up a complete record of a case?

Write this term and its definition on the diagram.

Card 15

What are three kinds of opinions that may be written by the Supreme Court after a case is decided?

Write this information on the diagram, and describe each kind of opinion.

Card 16

What are the two schools of thought surrounding the Supreme Court's power of judicial review?

List and describe each school of thought in the correct locations on the diagram.

Analyzing Court Materials

You will work in your group to determine which court is represented in each of six sets of information. Follow these steps:

Step 1 Carefully examine the information for each court. Identify as many clues as you can that might tell you which court in the judicial system is represented. Look for clues like these:

- the number of judges or justices involved in the case
- the topic of the case or cases being heard
- the plaintiff and the defendant in the case
- the specific manner in which the case is argued
- features of the court that might be unique
- references to geographic or other jurisdiction

Step 2 Use your Reading Notes and your book to determine which court is represented by the information. Then, on two pages of your notebook, draw a matrix like the one below. Leave lots of space for listing the evidence you find. Complete the matrix for the court you are examining.

	Court (2 points if correct)	**Evidence Supporting This Choice** (1 or 2 points each)	**What This Information Reveals About the Judicial System**
Court 1			
Court 2			
Court 3			
Court 4			
Court 5			
Court 6			

Scoring: For each court you identify correctly, your group will receive 2 points. For each piece of correct evidence you list, you will receive 1 point. If you list a correct piece of evidence that no other team has found, you will receive 2 points.

Court 1

Examine the information below, which relates to Court 1.

An Opinion from This Court, 2006

ZOLTEK CORPORATION,

Plaintiff-Cross Appellant,

v.

UNITED STATES,

Defendant-Appellant.

DECIDED: March 31, 2006

Before GAJARSA, Circuit Judge, PLAGER, Senior Circuit Judge, and DYK, Circuit Judge.

PER CURIAM. Concurring opinion filed by Circuit Judge GAJARSA. Separate concurring opinion filed by Circuit Judge DYK. Dissenting opinion filed by Senior Circuit Judge PLAGER.

The United States appeals the order of the Court of Federal Claims holding that it could assert jurisdiction over Zoltek Corporation's ("Zoltek")'s patent infringement allegations by treating the action as a Fifth Amendment taking under the Tucker Act. Zoltek cross-appeals the trial court's ruling that 28 U.S.C. § 1498(c) bars this action as arising in a foreign country. The Court of Federal Claims certified the rulings under 28 U.S.C. § 1292(d)(2), and this court accepted jurisdiction. See Zoltek Corp v. United States, No. 96-166 C (Fed. Cl. Feb. 20, 2004) (certification); see generally Zoltek Corp. v. United States, 58 Fed. Cl. 688 (2003), Zoltek Corp. v. United States, 51 Fed. Cl. 829 (2002).

We conclude that under § 1498, the United States is liable for the use of a method patent only when it practices every step of the claimed method in the United States. The court therefore affirms the trial court's conclusion that § 1498 bars Zoltek's claims. However, we reverse the trial court's determination that it had jurisdiction under the Tucker Act based on a violation of the Fifth Amendment.

Appeals Filed and Reversed, Oct. 1, 2005, to Sep. 30, 2006

Source of Appeals	Filed	Reversed
U.S. Court of International Trade	58	25%
U.S. Court of Federal Claims	154	19%
U.S. Court of Appeals for Veterans Claims	384	12%
U.S. District Courts	522	13%
Department of Veterans Affairs	3	0%
International Trade Commission	9	40%

Court 2

Examine the information below, which relates to Court 2.

"Do you ever have one of those days when everything seems unconstitutional?"

Transcript of a Case Heard by This Court, 2007

Bruce Edward Brendlin (Petitioner) v California
Washington, D.C., Monday, April 23, 2007
The above-entitled matter came on for oral argument
before [this court] at 11:03 a.m.

PROCEEDINGS

JUSTICE 1: We'll hear argument next in 06-8120, Brendlin versus California. Ms. Campbell.

ORAL ARGUMENT OF ELIZABETH M. CAMPBELL, ESQ. ON BEHALF OF THE PETITIONER

MS. CAMPBELL: May it please the Court:
When an officer makes a traffic stop, activates his flashing lights, he seizes not only the driver of the car but also the car and every person and everything in that car. This unremarkable conclusion is what Petitioner asks this Court to rule on, rule today. This simple rule is not only firmly rooted in this Court's precedence, it also protects police officers and the liberty interests of everyone traveling on a public State highway.

JUSTICE 1: Well, it wouldn't apply in a taxicab, right? I mean, the cab is driving erratically, the officer pulls it over. If I'm a passenger in the cab, I think I can get out and catch another cab, right?

MS. CAMPBELL: Whether or not you can get out and catch another cab is sort of a separate issue, but at the moment that the car comes to a stop you've been stopped by government means intentionally applied, and I believe you are seized at that point. After that it may become a factual question with the totality of the circumstances and it may be significantly different from that, from the question we face in a case like this where it's a passenger in a private car.

JUSTICE 2: And would that apply if a bus was pulled over?

MS. CAMPBELL: If a bus—

JUSTICE 2: Everybody on the bus is seized?

MS. CAMPBELL: Once again, a forward motion stopped by government means intentionally applied is a seizure under this Court's holding in Brower . . .

Court 3

Examine the information below, which relates to Court 3.

Inside the courtroom in Guantánamo, Cuba

Transcript of a Case Heard by This Court, 2007

OPENING

REPORTER: We are on the record.

RECORDER: All rise.

PRESIDENT: This hearing shall come to order. Please be seated.

RECORDER: This Tribunal is being conducted at 1355 on 9 March 2007 on board U.S. Naval Base Guantanamo Bay, Cuba. The following personnel are present [names have been removed]: Colonel, U.S. Air Force. President Commander, U.S. Navy. Member Lieutenant Colonel, U.S. Air Force. Member Major, U.S. Air Force. Personal Representative Sergeant First Class, U.S. Army, Reporter. Major, U.S. Air Force. Recorder. Lieutenant Colonel is the Judge Advocate member of the Tribunal.

OATH SESSION 1

RECORDER: All rise.

PRESIDENT: The Recorder will be sworn. Do you, Major, swear or affirm that you will faithfully perform the duties as Recorder assigned in this Tribunal so help you God?

RECORDER: I do.

PRESIDENT: The Reporter will now be sworn. The Recorder will administer the oath.

RECORDER: Do you, Sergeant First Class, swear that you will faithfully discharge your duties as Reporter assigned in this Tribunal so help you God?

REPORTER: I do.

CONVENING AUTHORITY

PRESIDENT: This hearing will come to order. You may be seated.

PRESIDENT: This Tribunal is convened by order of the Director, Combatant Status Review Tribunals under the provisions of his Order of 12 February 2007. This Tribunal will determine whether ABU FARAJ AL LIBI meets the criteria to be designated as an enemy combatant against the United States or its coalition partners or otherwise meets the criteria to be designated as an enemy combatant.

Court 4

Examine the information below, which relates to Court 4.

Court Statistics, 2006

Number of Courts	Number of Cases Filed	Number of Judges	Average Judge's Salary
94	335,868	678	$165,200

Partial Witness List for a Case Heard by This Court, 2005

UNITED STATES OF AMERICA

vs.   Case No. 8:03-CR-77-T-30TBM

GHASSAN ZAYED BALLUT

_____

DEFENDANT GHASSAN BALLUT'S WITNESS LIST

The Defendant, GHASSAN ZAYED BALLUT, by and through his undersigned counsel, pursuant to Local Rule 3.07 and the directions in the May Trial Calendar (Dkt. 964), hereby submits his Witness List for the jury trial in this cause:

Main Abdallah

Bassam Abdullah

Fatima Abu Eid

Ali Abunimah

Maher Affeneh

Abdel bari Al Akhrass

Abdel Ghafer Al Arouri

Kiser Al Deen

Khaled Al Disi

Sheik Mohammed Aleman

Badi Ali

Court 5

Examine the information below, which relates to Court 5.

Practice and Procedures from This Court's Web Site

http://www.court.com

The judicial power of [this court] in any particular case is exercised by a single judge to whom the case is assigned by the chief judge. When a case involves the constitutionality of an act of Congress, a Presidential proclamation, or an Executive order, or otherwise has broad and significant implications, the chief judge may assign the case to a three-judge panel . . .

Since the geographical jurisdiction of the court extends throughout the United States, the procedures are designed to accommodate the needs of parties not located in New York City.

Most significantly, judges of the court are assigned by the chief judge, as needed, to preside at trials at any place within the United States. These trials are held in the United States Courthouses. The court is equipped with conference telephones to hear oral arguments and conduct conferences with parties at other places.

Opinion from a Case Heard by This Court, 2007

PARKDALE INTERNATIONAL, LTD.,
RIVERVIEW STEEL CO., LTD., and
SAMUEL, SON & CO., LTD., :

          Plaintiffs,

   and

RUSSEL METALS EXPORT,

        Plaintiff-Intervenor,

   v.

UNITED STATES,

        Defendant.

Before: Jane A. Restani, Chief Judge

Court No. 06-00289,

OPINION

Plaintiffs are importers and exporter-resellers of certain corrosion-resistant carbon steel flat products from Canada that are covered by an antidumping duty order. See Certain Corrosion-Resistant Carbon Steel Flat Prods. & Certain Cut-to-Length Carbon Steel Plate from Canada, 58 Fed. Reg. 44,162, 44,162 (Dep't Commerce Aug. 19, 1993) (antidumping duty order). Plaintiffs seek liquidation or reliquidation of entries from a two-year period commencing on August 1, 2003, and ending on July 31, 2005. Plaintiffs claim they are entitled to liquidation at their producer's deposit rate under the "automatic liquidation rule," 19 C.F.R. § 351.212(c)(1),2 because the entries at issue were not the subject of periodic administrative review proceedings and, therefore, did not receive specific resller rates.

The Government challenges jurisdiction. It notes that plaintiffs did not participate in the applicable administrative reviews leading to the Final Results, which stated, in boilerplate language, that pursuant to the Reseller Policy the "all others" rate would apply to unreviewed resellers whose products were reviewed.

Court 6

Examine the information below, which relates to Court 6.

Diagram of This Courtroom

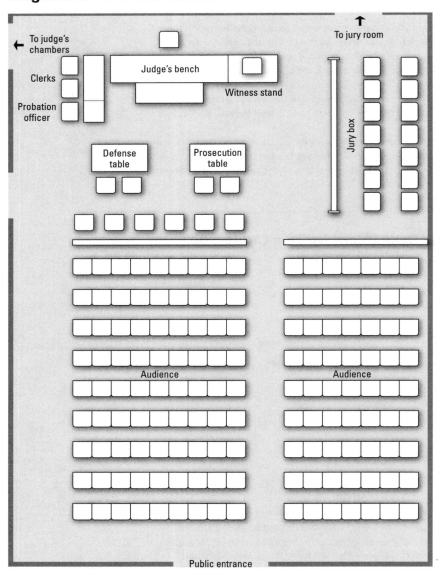

"Jury of my peers? That's a laugh.
How many of you ever kill a guy?"

Guide to the Courts

Court (2 points if correct)	Evidence Supporting This Choice (1 or 2 points each)	What This Information Reveals About the Judicial System
Court 1 — U.S. appeals court	• Case is heard by three judges. • The case involved is an appeal, so this must be an appellate court. • One party in the case is the U.S. • Table shows that the cases being heard come from lower courts within the federal system or from U.S. district courts.	• Federal courts hear cases in which the U.S. is the defendant. • Cases must make their way from lower to higher courts in the system of appeals.
Court 2 — Supreme Court	• Court is held in the nation's capital, Washington, D.C. • The respondent is the state of California. • Two justices interrupt the attorney during her oral argument. • The attorney references the Court's precedents. • Cartoon shows three judges sitting in front of the U.S. flag and the justices are referring to the constitutionality of cases.	• The Supreme Court looks only at the constitutionality of a case, not the specific facts of the case. • Decisions by the Court are often based on previous decisions, or precedents.
Court 3 — Military tribunal	• Transcript shows that only military personnel are present. • The defendant is accused of committing a crime against the U.S. • The trial is conducted at a naval base. • Flags of military branches are in the photograph.	• Specialized courts are created and structured to handle specific cases, such as those related to the military and military crimes. • Congress has the constitutional power to create these courts.
Court 4 — U.S. district court	• There are 94 of these courts. • A witness list indicates that this court is not appellate but has original jurisdiction. • Jurors are used to decide some of the cases. • The U.S. is a party in the case, indicating a federal court.	• Witness lists must be submitted before a trial. • District judges have large case-loads. • Some courts use juries and some do not.
Court 5 — U.S. Court of International Trade	• This court has jurisdiction over the entire U.S. • The opinion involves trade-related issues. • One of the parties is the U.S. • The plaintiffs are corporations. • Trials are held in U.S. courthouses.	• Certain courts have jurisdiction over the entire U.S. • Specialized courts handle specific cases, such as those related to trade issues.
Court 6 — Trial court of general jurisdiction	• Diagram shows a jury, a probation officer, a single judge, and a place for witnesses to testify. • Cartoon shows a single judge. • Cartoon indicates a criminal, not civil, action.	• The judicial system is designed to have impartial, qualified jury members deciding cases in the lower courts. • People within a courtroom serve different purposes, all designed to make a trial run smoothly.

Mastering the Content

1. Which of these does a prosecuting attorney represent?
   A. the injured party in a lawsuit
   B. the officials in the courtroom
   C. the person accused of a crime
   D. the government and the people

2. What is an order by the Supreme Court directing a lower court to send it the records of a case called?
   A. a writ of certiorari
   B. a writ of habeas corpus
   C. a writ of mandamus
   D. a writ of stare decisis

3. What is the job of an appellate court when it takes a case on appeal?
   A. to look for errors of law
   B. to conduct a new jury trial
   C. to weigh all the trial evidence
   D. to determine the proper verdict

4. How does someone become a judge in the federal court system?
   A. by a popular election
   B. by a retention election
   C. by presidential appointment
   D. by passing a civil service test

5. Which of these established the present system of federal district and circuit courts?
   A. Judiciary Act of 1789
   B. Senate Judiciary Committee
   C. Northwest Ordinance of 1787
   D. Article III of the Constitution

6. What is meant by the term *burden of proof*?
   A. the need to examine the reliability of witnesses
   B. the challenge of finding a fair and impartial jury
   C. the duty to prove alleged facts in a case with solid evidence
   D. the obligation to consider a person innocent until proven guilty

7. Which of the following is most likely to write an amicus curiae brief?
   A. an appellate judge
   B. a defense attorney
   C. an interest group
   D. a special prosecutor

8. Which term refers to the person who files a lawsuit in a civil case?
   A. bailiff
   B. plaintiff
   C. defendant
   D. friend of the court

9. Use this quotation to answer the question below.

   > *Judges are like umpires. Umpires don't make the rules, they apply them.*

   The quotation supports which of the following approaches to making judicial decisions?
   A. loose construction
   B. judicial activism
   C. judicial restraint
   D. interpretivism

10. What determines which appeals the Supreme Court will hear?
    A. The attorney general assigns cases.
    B. The justices choose their own cases.
    C. The circuit courts recommend cases.
    D. The special federal courts refer cases.

Exploring the Essential Question

How is the U.S. judicial system organized to ensure justice?

This chronology shows the path of one case through the U.S. judicial system. Use it to answer the questions below.

Chronology of the Sam Sheppard Case

1954: When Marilyn Sheppard is murdered in her Ohio home, the police suspect her husband Sam. The case receives extensive newspaper coverage, with such headlines as "Why Isn't Sam Sheppard in Jail?" and "Getting Away with Murder." Sheppard is charged with murder. His trial in the Common Pleas Court of Cuyahoga County becomes a media circus. The jury finds Sheppard guilty, and he is sentenced to life in prison.

1955–1963: Sheppard appeals his conviction to the court of appeals for Cuyahoga County and then the Ohio Supreme Court. His lawyer argues that the publicity surrounding his case denied Sheppard his due process right to a fair trial. The state appeals courts uphold his conviction.

1964–1965: Sheppard appeals his case in U.S. district court. The judge describes the 1954 trial as "a mockery of justice" and overturns Sheppard's conviction. Cuyahoga County prosecutors appeal to the U.S. Court of Appeals for the Sixth Circuit. The appellate court reverses the lower court decision.

1966: The Supreme Court hears *Sheppard v. Maxwell*. The justices conclude that the publicity surrounding Sheppard's trial prejudiced his right to a trial by an impartial jury. His conviction is once again overturned.

1966: Cuyahoga County prosecutors retry Sheppard for murder. At the end of the second trial, the jury finds him not guilty. Four years later, Sheppard dies at home at the age of 46.

1995–2000: Sam Reese Sheppard, Sam Sheppard's son, files a civil suit against Cuyahoga County, claiming that his father was wrongly imprisoned by county officials. During the civil trial, the jury hears evidence both for and against Sam Sheppard. At the end of the trial, the jurors side with the county. Six of the eight jurors say in interviews that they were convinced of Sheppard's guilt.

---

1. How many levels of state courts dealt with the Sheppard case? Which one had original jurisdiction?

2. How many levels of federal courts dealt with the Sheppard case? Which was the court of last resort?

3. What burden of proof did Cuyahoga Country prosecutors have to meet in their two criminal trials? What burden of proof did Sam Reese Sheppard have to meet in his civil trial?

4. Did the judicial system ensure justice in the Sam Sheppard case? Explain your answer.

The Criminal Justice System

From doing the crime to doing time: How just is our criminal justice system?

Speaking of Politics

As you complete the Reading Notes, use these terms in your answers:

misdemeanor	arraignment
felony	plea bargain
grand jury	restitution
indictment	incarceration

PREVIEW

Put yourself in this scenario. Two students in your class have been accused of a crime. Your teacher asks them to gather their belongings and proceed immediately to the principal's office. You later learn that the students have been taken into police custody. What rights do you think these students should have? Make a list of all the rights you believe a student accused of a crime should have.

READING NOTES

Section 16.2

After reading the section, answer these questions:

1. What elements categorize a certain behavior as a crime?

2. What is the difference between a misdemeanor and a felony? What determines whether a crime is classified as one or the other?

3. What does the constitutional protection of due process mean? What is the difference between procedural and substantive due process?

4. Do you think juveniles should be tried as adults in the justice system? Why or why not?

Sections 16.3 to 16.8

Complete the following for each of these sections.

1. List at least three rights of the accused or any criminal justice procedures that protect the accused.

2. Summarize one landmark Supreme Court case related to the stage described in the section.

3. Create a simple flowchart, with illustrations, outlining the basic steps in this criminal justice stage. Use the steps listed below for each section. (The steps for each section are not in order.)

Section 16.3: Police seize evidence and talk to witnesses. Police present evidence of probable cause to a judge. Police conduct a search. Police present evidence to a prosecutor. The judge issues a search warrant.

Section 16.4: The judge issues an arrest warrant. The suspect is read the Miranda rights. Police present evidence of probable cause to a judge. The suspect is booked. The suspect is arrested.

Section 16.5: The suspect is released on bail. The suspect makes an initial appearance in court. The suspect accepts a plea bargain. The suspect is arraigned. The grand jury hears the case.

Section 16.6: Jurors are selected randomly and are sent a jury summons. The prosecution and defense present evidence and call witnesses. Lawyers issue peremptory challenges. Jurors deliberate. Jurors are challenged "for cause." The jury foreman announces the verdict.

Section 16.7: The judge chooses to apply an indeterminate sentence. The judge requests a presentence report. The appeals court denies appeal. The defendant requests an appeal.

Section 16.8: The parole board hears testimony and examines evidence. The prisoner is sent to a minimum-security prison. The prisoner is released. The prisoner applies for parole.

---

4. Answer this question for the stage described in the section: *How just is this stage of the criminal justice system?*

Write a letter to the editor of a local newspaper taking a position on this question: *From doing the crime to doing time: How just is our criminal justice system?* Your letter must contain

- the name and address of the newspaper.

- a clear position statement.

- at least three arguments that incorporate examples, court cases, quotations, or statistics from the reading.

- references to two constitutional articles or amendments.

- a strong conclusion that reiterates your position statement.

The Prosecution's Theory of Guilt

Following is the prosecution's theory of how Dexter Dwight killed Floyd Babb.

- Dwight Dexter and Floyd Babb lived in Eaton, Michigan, and worked together at McDonald's. The two ran into each other on July 17, 1982, after a dance at a community center.

- Dexter hitched a ride from the community center with Babb and his girlfriend Deborah Sneed. After dropping Deborah off at her home, they bought some beer and drove to a nearby park.

- At 4 A.M., Dexter shot Babb two times, stole his car, and drove to Detroit, 80 miles away.

- At 8:30 A.M., Dexter drove up to the house of Randolph Stone in the stolen car and asked Stone for help in finding a place to stay. Stone offered to let Dexter stay with him. Dexter stayed for the weekend.

- During the weekend, Dexter bragged about killing a boy in Eaton and asked Stone to dispose of the murder weapon. Stone sold the gun to his neighbor for $25.

- Babb's body was found on Monday, July 19.

- Stone later retrieved the gun from his neighbor's house and gave it to the police. Ballistics evidence matched the gun to the bullets in Babb's body.

- Sneed identified Dexter as the last person with Babb on the night of the murder.

- Forensics experts estimated the time of death to be around 4 A.M. Dexter has no alibi until 8:30 A.M.

Individuals involved in events relating to the murder of Floyd Babb:

Dwight Dexter: murderer

Floyd Babb: victim

Deborah Sneed: girlfriend of victim

Randolph Stone: friend to whom Dwight Dexter confessed and who disposed of the murder weapon

---

Documents Relating to the Case of Dwight Dexter

Exhibit A, Document 1

The Investigation into the Murder of Floyd Babb

Notes from Sheriff Dodd: July 20 – July 30, 1982, Eaton, Michigan

July 20   I approached Morgan Livingston, an informant that we have used in the past, and told him I would pay him $200 to help us find the murder weapon. I told Livingston that we were fairly confident that Dwight Dexter deposited the murder weapon at the Detroit home of his friend Randolph Stone. Livingston assured us he could get the .25 caliber pistol used in the crime.

July 23   11 P.M.: Morgan Livingston called to tell me that Dexter agreed to drive Livingston to Detroit to buy a gun from his friend Randolph Stone.

July 24   1 A.M.: I followed Morgan Livingston's car to Detroit and watched Dexter enter a house. After Dexter returned to his car, I pulled the car over and searched it (I didn't have time to get a search warrant). I found a .22 caliber pistol in the car, but not the .25 caliber gun used in the murder. I then sent Dexter back to the station with another officer.

3 A.M.: We returned to Randolph Stone's house and spoke with him. I told Stone that if he didn't come up with the murder weapon, I would see to it that he was imprisoned for the rest of his life. Stone finally went next door and returned with a .25 caliber gun. We then took Stone down to the police station in Detroit, where he made this statement:

I, Randolph Stone, met Dwight Dexter for the first time on Sunday, July 18, at 8:30 A.M. Dwight Dexter pulled up in a blue Chevy and asked for help. He ended up staying the weekend at my house. During that time, he told me that he killed a white boy in Eaton and that he still had the gun. On Monday, Dwight Dexter returned to Eaton by bus but left the gun and car with me. I ended up selling the gun to a neighbor and abandoning the car in south Detroit.

We now have what we need to charge Dwight Dexter in the murder of Floyd Babb.

July 30   I have a ballistics expert who will testify that the gun Randolph Stone retrieved on 7/24 was the same gun used in the murder of Floyd Babb. I also advised the prosecutor to begin coaching Randolph Stone and Morgan Livingston for the upcoming trial.

Discuss these questions in your team:

- How did Morgan Livingston help in the investigation?
- Did police abide by the Fourth Amendment when they stopped Dexter's car? Why or why not?
- What did Randolph Stone say that Dwight Dexter had confessed to?
- What did the ballistics expert say about the gun that Randolph Stone had retrieved?

Create a large T-chart in your notebook with the column headings "Evidence That Dexter's Rights Were Upheld" and "Evidence That Dexter's Rights Were Not Upheld." Then add evidence to your T-chart based on the investigation.

Exhibit A, Document 2

Police Booking Report of Dwight Dexter

ARREST NUMBER		RECORD OF ARREST		COUNTY	STATE
011266				MACON	MICHIGAN

LAST NAME		FIRST NAME		MIDDLE NAME	
DEXTER		DWIGHT		JAKE	

RACE/ETHNICITY	GENDER	AGE	DATE OF BIRTH	PLACE OF BIRTH
AFRICAN AMERICAN	MALE	21	JUNE 7, 1961	DETROIT, MI

HEIGHT	WEIGHT	EYES	HAIR	SOCIAL SECURITY NUMBER
5'6"	150	BROWN	BROWN	111-22-3333

ADDRESS	CITY	STATE	ZIPCODE
1893 WOODSON DR.	EATON	MI	48775

OCCUPATION	SCARS, MARKS, AND TATTOOS
CASHIER AT MCDONALDS	NONE

TIME OF ARREST	DATE OF ARREST	ARRESTING OFFICER	PLACE OF ARREST	DATE OF OFFENCE
1:45 AM	JULY 24, 1982	SHERIFF LAMOND DODD	DETROIT, MI	JULY 18, 1982

BOOKING CHARGE

CAPITAL MURDER

SUMMARY OF ARREST

Dexter was arrested on 7/24/82 and charged with the murder of Floyd Babb, who was shot twice in the head in Eaton, MI. Upon arrest, Dexter was read his Miranda rights and told the reason for his arrest. He was booked in the Eaton jailhouse and stripped of his personal belongings. He made two phone calls. He awaits trial.

Discuss these questions in your team:

- What additional information did you learn about Dwight Dexter from the police booking report?
- Did police abide by the Fifth Amendment when they arrested and booked Dexter? Why or why not?

Add evidence to your T-chart based on the arrest.

Be prepared to answer this question: *Were the rights of Dwight Dexter upheld during the investigation and arrest? Why or why not?*

Exhibit B, Document 1

Jury Selection in the Trial of Dwight Dexter

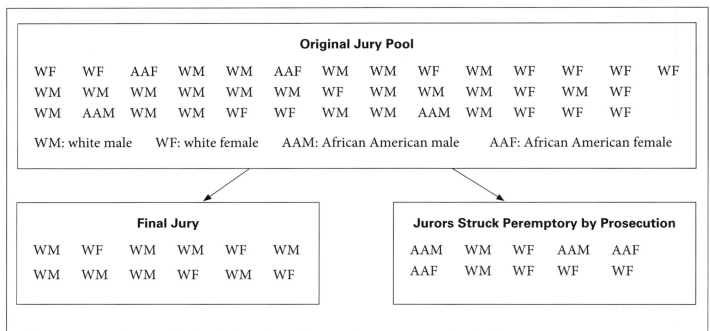

Objections raised in 2001 by the defense about the use of peremptory strikes by the prosecution:

- The prosecution had a history of using peremptory strikes to eliminate African Americans from the jury pool.
- In 1981–1982, 14 of the 16 juries were all white or contained only one black juror.
- In 1981–1982, 75 out of 83 black jurors were struck peremptory.

Reasons the prosecution gave for striking African Americans from the jury pool:

- AAF: taught victim in grade school
- AAF: not strong on death penalty
- AAM: answered in a defiant way
- AAM: hesitant to impose death penalty

Discuss these questions in your team:

- During which stage of the jury selection were all blacks struck from the jury pool?
- According to the defense, was the striking of blacks from the jury pool uncommon in Eaton in 1982?
- According to the prosecution, how did it abide by the Sixth Amendment's guarantee of an impartial jury?

Add evidence to your T-chart based on the jury selection.

Exhibit B, Document 2

The Trial of Dwight Dexter

Reporter's Notes Taken During the Trial of Dwight Dexter
Macon County District Court: Eaton, Michigan: Sep. 6 – Sep. 12, 1982

PRETRIAL

9/6: Defense attorney tells judge that he has not been to the crime scene, or viewed the crime scene photographs, or seen the ballistics report. He also states that he has not viewed the prosecution's witness list. Judge responds that all of these materials have been available to the defense for several weeks.

TRIAL

9/7: Prosecution and defense make opening statements.

9/8–9/10: Prosecution calls witnesses:

- Deborah Sneed testifies that Floyd Babb and Dwight Dexter drove her home on the night of Babb's murder. Sneed identifies Dexter as the last person with Babb on Saturday evening, July 17.

- Randolph Stone testifies that on the morning of July 18, Dexter arrived at his home in a blue Chevy and asked for a place to stay. Dexter claimed he had killed "a white boy" and asked Stone to dispose of the murder weapon and car. Stone sold the gun to a neighbor and abandoned the car in south Detroit. *On cross-examination, defense asks Stone if the prosecution had ever coached him. Stone replies no.*

- Ballistics expert testifies that bullets from the gun retrieved by Stone matched the bullets in Babb's body.

Defense calls no witnesses.

9/11: Prosecution and defense make closing statements. Jury deliberates for 6 hours. Guilty verdict is delivered at 11 P.M.

SENTENCING

9/12: Prosecution calls witnesses who claim that Dexter is a threat to society and should be sentenced to death:

- Damon Trace testifies that Dexter is a violent man who beat him with a pistol the week before the murder.

- Morgan Livingston testifies that on the day of his arrest, Dexter drove to Detroit to get a gun so he could commit armed robbery and kill anyone in his way. *On cross-examination, Livingston is asked if he is a paid informant for the state. Livingston answers no.*

Defense calls Dexter, Dexter's parents, and two of Dexter's friends. All attest to Dexter's good moral character. Defense attorney admits that he has not prepared any of the witnesses to testify.

Jury deliberates for 1 hour. Death sentence is delivered at 6 P.M.

Discuss these questions in your team:

- Did the defense provide adequate counsel as guaranteed by the Sixth Amendment? Why or why not?
- What evidence did the prosecution suppress during the trial and sentencing phases?

Add evidence to your T-chart based on the trial.

Be prepared to answer this question: *Were the rights of Dwight Dexter upheld during the jury selection and trial? Why or why not?*

Exhibit C, Document 1

The Appeals Process in the Case of Dwight Dexter

State Court System

3   **Michigan State Supreme Court**
Lansing, MI

The court rejected an appeal in 2000.

2   **Michigan State**
Criminal Court of Appeals
Detroit, MI

The court rejected an appeal in 1983 but accepted another appeal in 1999.

Verdict: Dexter's death sentence is upheld on appeal.

1   **Macon County District Court**
Eaton, MI

Dexter's trial was held in September 1982.

Verdict: Dexter is convicted and sentenced to death.

Federal Court System

6   **U.S. Supreme Court**
Washington, DC

The Supreme Court accepted the appeal.

Verdict: Pending.

5   **U.S. Court of Appeals for**
the Sixth Circuit
Detroit, MI

The court accepted an appeal in 2001.

Verdict: Dexter's death sentence is reinstated.

4   **U.S. Federal District Court**
Detroit, MI

The court accepted an appeal in 2000.

Verdict: Dexter's death sentence is overturned.

Discuss these questions in your team:
- In how many courts was the Dexter case heard?
- Which court(s) overturned Dexter's death sentence?

Add evidence to your T-chart based on the appeals process.

Exhibit C, Document 2

The Supreme Court Agrees to Hear the Case of Dwight Dexter

High Court to Hear Dexter Case

Washington Press

District of Columbia At 11:50 p.m. last night, Dwight Dexter was strapped into the electric chair awaiting execution. At the last minute, the Supreme Court issued him a stay of execution and a last chance to appeal his case. Dexter has been scheduled to die 12 times over the past two decades.

Supreme Court justices will review Dexter's case and consider whether his constitutional rights were upheld at each stage of the criminal justice system. Additionally, they will consider whether recent admissions of perjury by two key witnesses necessitate a retrial.

One of the witnesses, Randolph Stone, admitted in 1999 that he falsely testified at Dexter's trial.

The Supreme Court Building

Stone stated that while Dexter had shown up at his house on July 18, 1982, he was on foot and without a weapon; furthermore, Dexter did not confess to any crime. Defense lawyers have since recovered a lengthy transcript of a pretrial rehearsal meeting with Stone,

during which Stone was repeatedly coached. The prosecution had suppressed the transcript and allowed Stone to lie about it during the trial.

The second key witness, Morgan Livingston, admitted in 1999 that he was a paid informant by the state and had lured Dexter to Detroit in an attempt to frame him. He also testified that he lied during the sentencing phase about Mr. Dexter's intention to commit other crimes.

The Supreme Court has heard cases dealing with the rights of the accused before. Lawyers for both sides undoubtedly will refer to the following Court precedents when they argue their case: *Brady v. Maryland, Strickland v. Washington,* and *Batson v. Kentucky.*

Discuss these questions in your team:

- What did Randolph Stone and Morgan Livingston admit in 1999?

- What evidence did the prosecution suppress in the Dexter trial?

- How might lawyers from both sides use the following Supreme Court precedents in their oral arguments: *Brady v. Maryland, Strickland v. Washington,* and *Batson v. Kentucky?* (These precedents are described in Chapter 16.)

Add evidence to your T-chart based on the new evidence and Supreme Court precedents.

Be prepared to answer these questions: *According to the Supreme Court precedents mentioned above, were the rights of Dwight Dexter upheld in the criminal justice process? Why or why not?*

Writing an Amicus Brief

The Criminal Bar Association has asked you to submit an amicus brief to the Supreme Court in the case of *Dexter v. Michigan State Prosecutor*. Your brief should include the following items:

- This heading:

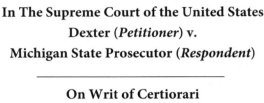

  In The Supreme Court of the United States
  Dexter (*Petitioner*) v.
  Michigan State Prosecutor (*Respondent*)

  _____

  On Writ of Certiorari
  To the Supreme Court of the United States

  _____

  BRIEF *AMICUS CURIAE* OF THE
  Criminal Bar Association
  In Support of _____ [respondent or petitioner]

- A position statement of at least three sentences in which you take a stance on this question: *Were the rights of Dwight Dexter upheld in the criminal justice system?*

- Three one-paragraph arguments that support your position statement. Each paragraph should begin with a clear topic sentence and incorporate evidence—facts, examples, or quotations—that support your topic sentence.

- References to at least two constitutional articles or amendments that support your position.

- Reference to at least one Supreme Court precedent that supports your position.

- A conclusion of at least three sentences in which you restate your position and reiterate your most important points.

- A signature line that reads,

  Respectfully submitted,

  _____ (your name)

  Attorney at Law, Criminal Bar Association

Mastering the Content

1. In our judicial system, for which of these is the jury responsible?
   A. the burden of proof
   B. the arrest warrant
   C. the arraignment
   D. the verdict

2. What is the purpose of setting bail?
   A. to guarantee that the accused will return for trial
   B. to punish a minor offense without going to court
   C. to cover the costs of time a criminal spends in jail
   D. to enable the judge to dispose of a case more quickly

3. A crime is defined as a wrongful act that
   A. damages property.
   B. is done with intent.
   C. violates federal law.
   D. does harm to others.

4. Which of these is typically a felony?
   A. armed assault
   B. disturbing the peace
   C. petty theft
   D. traffic violation

5. What is the role of the jury foreman during a trial?
   A. to break a tie vote by the jury
   B. to chair the jury's deliberations
   C. to takes notes for the jury's use later
   D. to protect the jury from outside pressure

6. Law enforcement officials must present evidence to a judge in order to do which of the following?
   A. obtain a search warrant
   B. question a suspect in a case
   C. book someone after an arrest
   D. chase a suspect fleeing a crime

7. What does a grand jury decide?
   A. whether a plea bargain is fair to the accused
   B. whether the rights of the accused were violated
   C. whether an accused person should be brought to trial
   D. whether evidence against the accused was legally obtained

8. How does restitution differ from other forms of punishment?
   A. It allows prisoners to seek early parole.
   B. It rehabilitates criminals through job training.
   C. It requires defendants to do community service.
   D. It compensates the victims of crimes for their losses.

9. What is the principal advantage to the criminal justice system of allowing plea bargains?
   A. It protects innocent suspects from pressure.
   B. It ensures that the punishment will fit the crime.
   C. It reduces the number of trials courts must hold.
   D. It gets criminals off the streets for a longer time.

10. The exclusionary rule excludes which of these from use in trials?
    A. confessions made after an arrest
    B. evidence gained by illegal means
    C. circumstantial or indirect evidence
    D. testimony from unreliable witnesses

Exploring the Essential Question

From doing the crime to doing time: How just is our criminal justice system?

Several protections guaranteed by the Bill of Rights are listed below. The flowchart on the right provides a basic outline of the workings of the criminal justice system.

Excerpts from the Bill of Rights

Fourth Amendment

- "secure in their persons, houses, papers, and effects, against unreasonable searches and seizures"
- "no Warrants . . . but upon probable cause . . . describing the place to be searched, and the persons or things to be seized"

Fifth Amendment

- "nor shall any person be subject for the same offense to be twice put in jeopardy"
- "nor shall be compelled in any criminal case to be a witness against himself"

Sixth Amendment

- "right to a speedy and public trial, by an impartial jury"
- "to be informed of the nature and cause of the accusation"
- "to be confronted with the witnesses against him"
- "to have the Assistance of Counsel for his defence"

Eighth Amendment

- "excessive bail shall not be required"
- "nor cruel and unusual punishments inflicted"

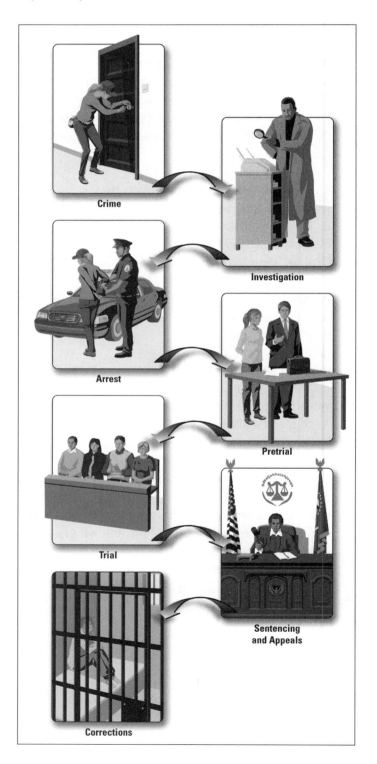

Crime

Investigation

Arrest

Pretrial

Trial

Sentencing and Appeals

Corrections

1. List the seven stages of the criminal justice process. Beside each stage, list the amendments that affect what happens at this point in the process.

2. Discuss what happens during these three steps in the pretrial phase: the initial appearance, the preliminary hearing, and the arraignment.

3. Choose one of the rights listed above. Write a paragraph explaining how that right contributes to making the criminal justice system just.

Creating American Foreign Policy

How should the United States conduct foreign policy?

Speaking of Politics

As you complete the Reading Notes, use these terms in your answers:

foreign policy

globalization

diplomacy

ambassador

diplomatic immunity

diplomatic recognition

summit

sanction

PREVIEW

Review the list of foreign policy goals. Then answer the questions.

1. Which two goals do you think are the most important for the United States to pursue? Why?

2. Which two goals do you think are the least important for the United States to pursue? Why?

Foreign Policy Goals

Promote freedom and democracy abroad.

Respond to international environmental disasters.

Establish good trade relations with other countries.

Protect our national borders.

Maintain positive relations with allies.

Ensure the safety of Americans abroad.

Eliminate world dictators.

Combat terrorism.

Send humanitarian aid to impoverished nations.

Mediate civil wars in other nations.

READING NOTES

Section 17.2

Create a table in your notebook as shown below. As you read, add at least two examples in each column. Then place the foreign policy goals listed in the Preview in the appropriate columns.

Security Goals	Peacekeep- ing Goals	Economic Goals	Humanitarian Goals

Sections 17.3 and 17.4

Copy the spoke diagram below across two pages of your notebook. For each of the six "soft power" and six "hard power" tools you read about, add a spoke to the corresponding circle. Then, to each new spoke, add the following:

- an illustration to represent that foreign policy tool
- a definition of that tool
- an explanation of why that tool is used

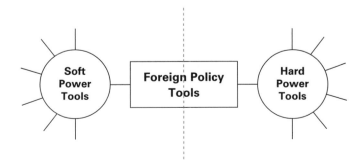

Section 17.5

Create a T-chart like the one below. As you read, add at least three items to each side. Then answer this question: *Why did Edward Corwin describe this division of power as "an invitation to struggle"?*

Presidential Foreign Powers	Congressional Foreign Powers

Find and read a current news article about U.S. involvement in a foreign event. Tape the article into your notebook. Then answer these questions:

1. What foreign policy goal or goals does the United States seem to be pursuing in this event?

2. What foreign policy tools are being used in this event?

3. Do you agree with how the United States is conducting foreign policy with respect to this event? Why or why not?

Section 17.6

Create a simple illustration to represent each worldview described in the section. Then choose the worldview that you most agree with, and write a paragraph describing your choice.

National Security Briefing A

To: National Security Council

From: Assistant Secretary of Defense, Department of Defense

Re: Seizure of suspected nuclear weapons material

Current Situation

Three hours ago, Italian authorities, acting on intelligence supplied by our government, stormed a freighter in the Mediterranean Sea heading toward Libya. The freighter contains thousands of centrifuges. These machine parts were bought by Libya to enrich uranium. Italian authorities have seized the freighter and await further direction from the United States.

As you well know, enriched uranium is a critical component in nuclear power generation. It is also used in the manufacture of nuclear weapons. The secret transport of nuclear components is illegal under international law and a direct affront to the United States and the international community.

Libya's leader, Colonel Muammar al-Gaddafi, has not publicly responded to the seizure of the freighter. Neither has he responded to allegations that these centrifuges were purchased to produce nuclear weapons. In the past, Gaddafi has defended his country's right to enrich uranium to fuel Libya's nuclear energy plants, which provide power to Libya's citizens.

CIA Country Profile: Libya

Population: 5,680,000

Ethnicity: Berber and Arab 97%, other 3%

Religion: Sunni Muslim 97%, other 3%

Government: military dictatorship

Chief of State: Muammar al-Gaddafi

Legal system: Islamic law

GDP per capita: $7,600

Unemployment: 30%

Main exports: crude oil, refined petroleum products, natural gas, chemicals

Government history: In 1969, a small group of military officers, led by Gaddafi, seized power from the Libyan monarchy through a coup d'état. Gaddafi declared Libya an "Islamic socialist state" and promised to bring equality and freedom to its people. In practice, the regime is dictatorial and dissidents are punished.

Source: *The World Factbook,* Central Intelligence Agency.

Suspected Nuclear and Chemical Weapons Sites

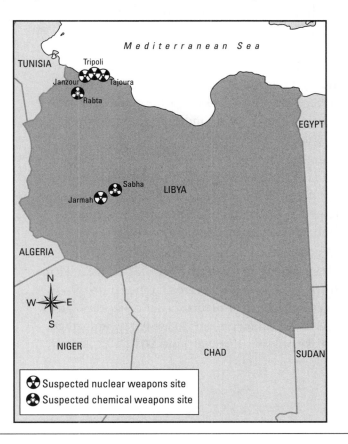

Suspected nuclear weapons site
Suspected chemical weapons site

National Security Briefing A (continued)

Libya's Nuclear Weapons Program

Intelligence suggests that Libya is developing a nuclear weapons program. Over the past two decades, Libya has purchased nuclear reactors from Russia. It has bought centrifuges from companies in as many as 10 countries. These include Pakistan, Singapore, South Korea, Turkey, and Switzerland.

Recent satellite images show several suspected nuclear facilities in Libya. These facilities are being used for everything from rocket testing to uranium conversion to centrifuge manufacture. These images also reveal suspected chemical weapons sites.

Terrorist Involvement

Nuclear weapons in the hands of a rogue nation like Libya concern us for several reasons. Gaddafi supports international terrorist organizations by supplying training, weapons, and a safe haven for its leaders. In addition, Libya has been implicated in several terrorist attacks. These include the 1986 bombing of a German disco (frequented by U.S. servicemen) and the 1988 bombing of a commercial airplane over Scotland (containing many American passengers). Furthermore, Libya denounces the country of Israel (an important U.S. ally) and supports all efforts to bring about its demise.

Tensions between the United States and Libya have been high for several decades. This is especially true since the United States conducted air strikes on Libya and imposed economic sanctions on the country. These sanctions were lifted only recently.

As we meet today, our forces are deployed in nearby Iraq and Afghanistan, both of which have links to terrorism. Libya is well aware that the United States knows it is a sponsor of terrorism. It also knows that we have the military means to launch an immediate air strike or lead a direct ground assault.

Possible U.S. Responses

The Department of Defense has outlined five possible options. The president has asked that you devise a policy recommendation to present at the upcoming NSC meeting by choosing one or more of these options or by creating alternative options. After crafting your recommendation, prepare a spokesperson to defend it at the upcoming meeting.

Option 1: Gather additional covert intelligence about Libya's nuclear weapons program.

Option 2: Host a summit with leaders from the United States and Libya, and encourage Libya to end its nuclear weapons program.

Option 3: Impose economic sanctions on Libya and on all countries from which Libya purchased centrifuges.

Option 4: Launch a military air strike, and bomb suspected nuclear and chemical weapons sites.

Option 5: Invade Libya, depose Libya's leader Muammar al-Gaddafi, and pave the way for democratic elections.

National Security Briefing B

To: National Security Council
From: Special Envoy to Sudan, Department of State
Re: Ethnic cleansing in Darfur, Sudan

Overview

For the past several years, the region of Darfur in northwest Sudan has been the scene of ethnic cleansing. This is the systematic elimination of an ethnic group. The situation is now so dire that some analysts have labeled it the worst humanitarian crisis in the world today.

Background on Darfur

Darfur is one of the poorest regions in Sudan. Its terrain is rugged and dry, making farming difficult and transportation slow. Most inhabitants live in small villages. They lack such basic services as running water and electricity.

Muslims dominate the population of Sudan. However, they divide themselves along ethnic lines, namely black African and ethnic Arab. These two Muslim groups harbor a deep-seated resentment of each other stemming from age-old tensions over land use.

Darfur is predominantly made up of black Africans. Ethnic Arabs control the government. The government has virtually neglected Darfur for decades, evidenced by the lack of expenditures in the region.

Current Situation

In 2003, rebel groups from Darfur, made up of black Africans, began attacking government targets. They demanded more autonomy and a greater share of the country's resources for its people. The government responded by arming local militias called the Janjaweed and supporting their attacks on communities linked to the rebels.

CIA Country Profile: Sudan

Geography: At 2.5 million sq. miles, Sudan is the largest country in Africa.

Capital: Khartoum

Total Population: 39,379,360

Life Expectancy: 49.1 years

Ethnic Groups: black African 52%, ethnic Arab 39%, other 9%

Religion: Sunni Muslim 70%, Christian 5%, indigenous beliefs 25%

GDP per capita: $2,400

Key industries: oil, cotton ginning, textiles, cement

Key export partners: Japan 49.6%, China 32.0%, Saudi Arabia 3.1%

Source: *The World Factbook,* Central Intelligence Agency.

Sudan and Darfur

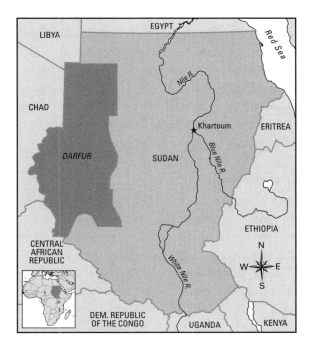

National Security Briefing B (continued)

In a typical raid, the Janjaweed enter a village on horseback, kill the men, rape the women, and pillage and burn the village. Government air strikes often follow, resulting in total obliteration of the village. Since the onset of fighting, hundreds of villages have been destroyed and more than 400,000 people have died.

In addition, up to 2.5 million Darfur residents have been displaced. They now live in camps located on the border with Chad. With limited food and water and no waste-disposal system, disease and malnutrition are rampant. Many countries, including ours, have sent foreign aid. However, it is nowhere near enough to address the needs of the displaced. Additionally, the Janjaweed occasionally raid the camps, leading to heightened insecurity and desperation. No one in the region is safe, not even foreign aid workers, some of whom have been murdered by the Janjaweed.

International Peace Efforts

In 2006, one of the Darfur rebel groups and the Sudanese government signed the Darfur Peace Agreement. It called for an immediate ceasefire. The Sudanese government agreed to oversee the dismantling of the Janjaweed and ensure the safe return of Darfur residents to their villages. To this end, it agreed to allow peacekeeping troops from the African Union—made up of Africans from throughout the continent—into Darfur. The agreement also laid out a democratic process by which Darfur residents could elect their own regional leaders and be represented in the Sudanese government.

Despite this agreement, raids by the Janjaweed continue and the number of displaced persons increases. The African Union has received little support from the Sudanese government. It has been unable to quell the violence alone. Still, the Sudanese government refuses to allow the United Nations to send additional peacekeeping forces. Many suspect that the government continues to provide military and financial support to the Janjaweed.

Possible U.S. Responses

The Department of State has outlined five possible options. The president has asked that you devise a policy recommendation to present at the upcoming NSC meeting by choosing one or more of these options or by creating alternative options. After crafting your recommendation, prepare a spokesperson to defend it at the upcoming meeting.

Option 1: Stay out of the conflict, and let Sudan resolve its own internal issues.

Option 2: Provide additional aid to the camps for the displaced, and send military arms to the African Union.

Option 3: Have the president and secretary of state speak with the Sudanese president and insist that his government enforce the Darfur Peace Agreement.

Option 4: Impose economic sanctions on Sudan until the nation enforces the Darfur Peace Agreement and allows UN peacekeepers into the country. Encourage other countries to participate in the sanctions.

Option 5: Lead a full-scale U.S. military assault into Sudan, and monitor the safe return of displaced persons to their villages. Maintain a military presence in the region until the government holds new, democratic elections.

National Security Briefing C

To: National Security Council

From: Assistant Secretary of Commerce, Department of Commerce

Re: Counterfeiting and piracy of U.S. goods

Overview

Over the past decade, the counterfeiting and piracy of U.S. goods has skyrocketed worldwide. These illegal activities pose a significant threat to the U.S. economy and to consumer health and safety. While the production and purchase of counterfeit and pirated goods occurs here in the United States on a small scale, it is rampant in other areas of the world, particularly Asian countries like China and Vietnam. The governments in these countries turn a blind eye to U.S. copyright and patent laws. This allows for the unregulated duplication of U.S. goods, from DVDs and electronic devices to designer jeans, golf clubs, and car parts.

Economic Impact

Economists estimate that annual losses to U.S. companies from counterfeiting and piracy average $250 billion a year. These losses are incurred by many industries, such as the motion picture, music, software, and pharmaceutical industries. Losses in revenue have resulted in widespread job losses, estimated at 750,000 jobs a year.

Health and Safety

Counterfeit goods are not subject to safety and reliability testing. This means the potential dangers to U.S. consumers could be catastrophic. Such counterfeit goods as airplane and car parts—which have been confiscated by U.S. Customs—could result in deadly accidents. Counterfeit prescription drugs could lead to severe illness and death. Although U.S. Customs officials have attempted to stop counterfeit goods from entering the country, they are able to seize only a fraction of these goods. Such items are often sold on the streets of these countries only hours after their release in the United States.

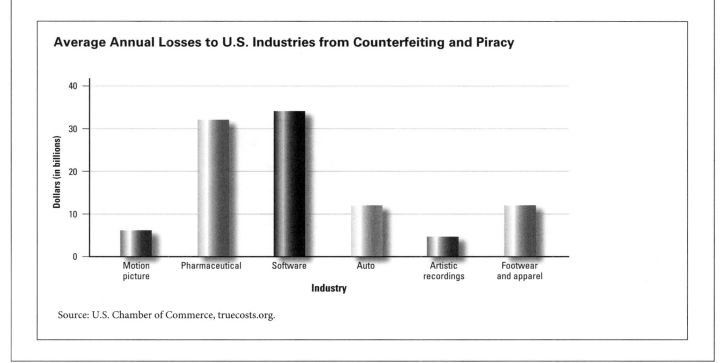

Average Annual Losses to U.S. Industries from Counterfeiting and Piracy

Source: U.S. Chamber of Commerce, truecosts.org.

National Security Briefing C (continued)

Attempts to Combat International Counterfeiting and Piracy

Over the past decade, the United States has pressured countries with high rates of counterfeiting and piracy to crack down on these illegal operations. Diplomats regularly address the issue at meetings with foreign officials. However, counterfeiting and piracy operations continue to flourish worldwide.

Some U.S. industries are attempting to take action on their own. The Motion Picture Association of America has launched a nationwide campaign to educate Americans about the detrimental impact of piracy on the U.S. economy. Musical artists are urging their fans to stop buying pirated CDs.

Possible U.S. Responses

What remains is a major dilemma for our administration: *Just how far should we go to protect U.S. industries and consumers from counterfeit and pirated goods?* Coming down too hard on foreign governments could have severe political consequences. However, not doing anything will result in continued losses to U.S. businesses and jobs. It may also jeopardize the health and safety of Americans.

The Department of Commerce has outlined five possible options. The president has asked that you devise a policy recommendation to present at the upcoming NSC meeting by choosing one or more of these options or by creating alternative options. After crafting your recommendation, prepare a spokesperson to defend it at the upcoming meeting.

Option 1: Do nothing. Let the global market monitor and regulate itself.

Option 2: Fund an international advertising campaign to teach consumers around the world not to buy counterfeit or pirated goods.

Option 3: Send diplomats to meet with government representatives of countries with high counterfeiting and piracy rates. Pressure government officials to crack down on illegal activities, and threaten to rescind trade agreements.

Option 4: Rescind all trade agreements from countries with high counterfeit and piracy rates. In addition, raise tariffs on imports from these countries.

Option 5: Send military troops to assist governments in conducting raids on counterfeit operations.

Conducting an NSC Meeting

Step 1: Prepare the room for a National Security Council meeting.

- Arrange the room according to the diagram below.
- The spokesperson from each group will sit at the conference table (center desks). All other NSC members will sit in the desks behind their spokesperson.

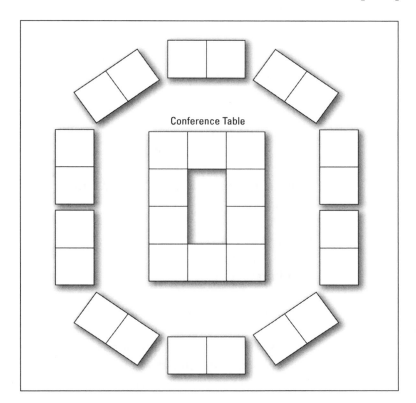

Conference Table

Step 2: Present policy recommendations to the president and the National Security Council.

- When called upon, the spokesperson shares the group's recommendation to the president. He or she begins by saying, "Mr. President, we recommend . . ."
- After all policy recommendations have been presented, NSC members in the outer circle comment on the recommendations. They begin by saying, "Mr. President, I believe . . ."
- When the meeting is adjourned, everyone stands up and says, "Thank you, Mr. President."

Mastering the Content

1. Which of these officials serves as one country's highest-ranking, long-term representative to another country?
   A. ambassador
   B. chief of staff
   C. consul
   D. secretary of state

2. All of the following are basic goals of U.S. foreign policy except
   A. promoting prosperity.
   B. preserving world peace.
   C. preventing globalization.
   D. protecting national security.

3. Diplomacy is the art and practice of which of the following?
   A. competing for advantages in international trade
   B. imposing a powerful country's will upon weaker countries
   C. managing communication and relationships between nations
   D. negotiating agreements between the executive and legislative branches

4. Which of these foreign policy powers belongs primarily to Congress?
   A. negotiating trade agreements
   B. controlling military spending
   C. gathering foreign intelligence
   D. appointing foreign ambassadors

5. Sending food to disaster victims in another country is an example of which of the following?
   A. military assistance
   B. security assistance
   C. development assistance
   D. humanitarian assistance

6. Where is a most-favored-nation clause most likely to appear?
   A. in a multilateral peace treaty
   B. in a bilateral trade agreement
   C. in a cultural exchange contract
   D. in a diplomatic recognition statement

7. Issuing passports and visas is the responsibility of which of the following?
   A. Department of State
   B. Department of Defense
   C. National Security Council
   D. Central Intelligence Agency

8. Which of these is considered a "hard power" tool of foreign policy?
   A. foreign aid
   B. covert action
   C. trade agreements
   D. cultural exchanges

9. What is the main purpose of sanctions?
   A. to reward allies for policies of cooperation
   B. to expose other countries to foreign cultures
   C. to encourage the growth of international trade
   D. to pressure another country to change its policies

10. Which of these best describes the North Atlantic Treaty Organization (NATO)?
    A. a powerful economic trading bloc
    B. the world's largest military alliance
    C. a coalition of countries fighting terrorism
    D. the international agency for patent enforcement

Exploring the Essential Question

How should the United States conduct foreign policy?

Over more than two centuries, U.S. presidents have taken different approaches to foreign policy. Read the quotations below, and then answer the questions.

The great rule of conduct for us in regard to foreign nations is in extending our commercial relations, to have with them as little political connection as possible . . . It is our true policy to steer clear of permanent alliances with any portion of the foreign world.

—George Washington, 1796

The world must be made safe for democracy. Its peace must be planted upon the tested foundations of political liberty. We have no selfish ends to serve . . . We shall fight for the things which we have always carried nearest our hearts . . . [to] make the world itself at last free.

—Woodrow Wilson, 1917

The peoples of a number of countries of the world have recently had totalitarian regimes forced upon them against their will . . . It must be the policy of the United States to . . . assist free peoples to work out their own destinies in their own way.

—Harry S. Truman, 1947

Whether we bring our enemies to justice, or bring justice to our enemies, justice will be done . . . From this day forward, any nation that continues to harbor or support terrorism will be regarded by the United States as a hostile regime.

—George W. Bush, 2001

---

1. List the terms *isolationism, containment, human rights,* and *antiterrorism* on your paper. Beside each term, write the name of the president whose statement best expresses that foreign policy worldview.

2. Discuss what the quotations by Wilson and Truman have in common. Explain how a person who supports a foreign policy based on disengagement would be likely to view their statements.

3. Select the quotation that best fits your foreign policy worldview. Explain your selection.

Confronting Global Issues

How effectively do international organizations respond to global issues?

Speaking of Politics

As you complete the Reading Notes, use these terms in your answers:

intergovernmental organization (IGO)

nongovernmental organization (NGO)

global warming

collective security

sustainable development

convention

greenhouse effect

protocol

PREVIEW

In early 2007, the United Nation's Intergovernmental Panel on Climate Change (IPCC) published its latest findings on global climate change. Examine the excerpts from the report below. Also examine the graph, which shows the change in Earth's temperature from 1800 to the present. It also shows three predictions of global temperature change up to the year 2100. Then answer these questions:

1. How concerned are you about global climate change? Why?

2. Which of the following do you think can most effectively respond to an issue like global climate change: individuals, cities, national governments, or international organizations? Why? How might they respond?

3. What advantages might international organizations have in responding to global issues? What disadvantages might they have?

Projections from the 2007 IPCC Report Based on Current Warming Trends

Many millions more people are projected to be flooded every year.

Approximately 20-30% of plant and animal species . . . are likely to be at increased risk of extinction.

[Climate change is] likely to affect the health status of millions of people . . . through increases in malnutrition and . . . increased deaths, disease and injury due to heat waves, floods, storms, fires and droughts.

Coasts are projected to be exposed to increasing risks, including coastal erosion.

Disturbances from pests, diseases, and fire [in North America] are projected to have increasing impacts on forests, with an extended period of high fire risk and large increases in area burned.

Cities [in North America] that currently experience heat waves are expected to be further challenged by an increased number, intensity and duration of heat waves.

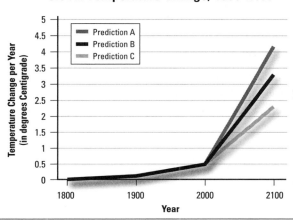

Global Temperature Change, 1800–2100

As you read each section, complete the given tasks.

Section 18.2

1. Create a simple illustration to represent each of the four goals outlined in the Preamble to the UN Charter. Label each goal.

2. Describe four of the main activities of the United Nations.

3. Create a T-chart with the headings "Strengths of the UN" and "Limitations of the UN." List at least three items on each side.

4. On a scale from 1 to 5, with 5 being the highest, rank how effectively you think the UN responds to global issues. Write at least two sentences defending your ranking.

Section 18.3

1. Choose three IGOs, and list their objectives.

2. Create a T-chart with the headings "Strengths of IGOs" and "Limitations of IGOs." List at least two items on each side.

3. On a scale from 1 to 5, with 5 being the highest, rank how effectively you think IGOs respond to global issues. Write at least two sentences defending your ranking.

Section 18.4

1. Describe four purposes of NGOs.

2. Choose one NGO and create an illustration to represent its mission.

3. Create a T-chart with the headings "Strengths of NGOs" and "Limitations of NGOs." List at least three items on each side.

4. On a scale from 1 to 5, with 5 being the highest, rank how effectively you think NGOs respond to global issues. Write at least two sentences defending your ranking.

Section 18.5

1. List the rights guaranteed under the Universal Declaration of Human Rights. Also list the rights guaranteed under the Convention on the Rights of the Child.

2. Do you agree that the right to own property and the right to work are human rights? Why or why not?

3. Describe how one NGO is responding to human rights violations.

Section 18.6

1. Complete a flowchart like the one below to show the causes and effects of global climate change.

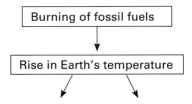

2. Why has the United States not signed the Kyoto Protocol? Do you think the United States should sign it? Why or why not?

3. Describe at least three ways that U.S. federal and state governments, as well as NGOs, are confronting climate change.

Choose a global issue that you are concerned about. Then identify an international organization, other than the United Nations, that is working to solve this issue. Find out the following information about the organization:

- where the organization is headquartered and the office nearest you

- three examples of how the organization is responding to the issue

- ways in which you could get involved in the organization

Then answer these questions in at least two paragraphs:

- Would you consider joining or working for this organization? Why or why not?

- How effectively does this organization respond to the global issue? Explain.

UN Draft Resolution

DRAFT RESOLUTION

Submitted to UN General Assembly by Member State ICELAND
Subject: Global Climate Change

ICELAND is deeply disturbed that the Kyoto Protocol does not adequately address the serious threat of global climate change to the nations of the world. Iceland thus requests that the General Assembly abandon the Kyoto Protocol and adopt the following resolution:

1. REQUIRE all countries that emit more than 50,000 metric tonnes of carbon dioxide (based on 2007 emissions as shown on the map) to reduce total emissions by the following percentages by 2025:
   - Over 3 million: 15%
   - 1 to 3 million: 10%
   - 100,000 to 1 million: 8%
   - 50,000 to 100,000: 6%
   - Under 50,000: none

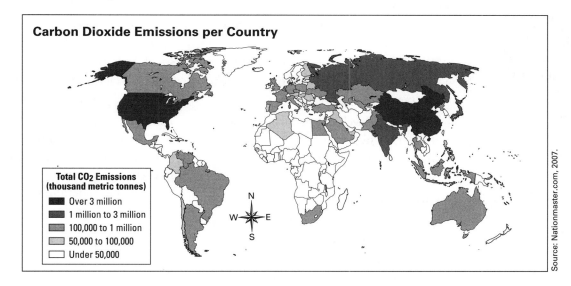

Carbon Dioxide Emissions per Country

Total CO$_2$ Emissions
(thousand metric tonnes)
- Over 3 million
- 1 million to 3 million
- 100,000 to 1 million
- 50,000 to 100,000
- Under 50,000

Source: Nationmaster.com, 2007.

2. After 2025, REQUIRE all countries to maintain their rates of emissions. Report annual emissions to the UN General Assembly.

3. After 2025, FINE $50 billion per year to any country that has not met its goal.

4. ESTABLISH a UN fund that provides financial aid to help countries develop clean-burning fuels.

Position Cards of UN Member States

⅄⅃∀ᴚ⊥S∩∀ ℲO H⊥⅂∀ƎMNOWWOƆ

Fold —————————————————————————————————————

**Commonwealth
of Australia**

Land area:
7,686,850 sq km

Population:
20,434,176

GDP per capita:
$33,300

Key export partners:
Japan 20%,
China 12%, US 6%,
India 5%

Key import partners:
US 14%, China 14%,
Japan 10%,
Germany 5%

Source: *The World Factbook,*
Central Intelligence Agency.

Position on Kyoto Protocol

Australia did not ratify the Kyoto Protocol for the following reasons:

- It claimed that the protocol would harm the Australian economy and lead to unemployment.
- It felt that developing countries, particularly China and India, should also have emissions restrictions.

Position on Resolution

- Australia is opposed to this resolution as written. It insists it cannot decrease emissions by this amount without shutting down its coal-fired power plants. These plants emit large amounts of greenhouse gases. The cost of converting these plants to nuclear power would force many companies out of business and result in widespread job loss.
- Australia will support this resolution only if it has a lower reduction target and a later target date.

Other Points to Consider

- Australia received widespread criticism for not ratifying the Kyoto Protocol. It does not want to be seen again as an obstacle to the worldwide effort to address global climate change.
- Australia may consider offering foreign aid packages to low greenhouse gas emitters, like Zambia and Bolivia, in exchange for their support of Australia in the General Assembly session.

Fold —————————————————————————————————————

CANADA

Fold

Canada

Land area:
9,984,670 sq km

Population:
33,390,141

GDP per capita:
$35,700

Key export partners:
US 82%, Japan 2%,
UK 2%

Key import partners:
US 55%, China 9%,
Mexico 4%

Source: *The World Factbook,*
Central Intelligence Agency.

Position on Kyoto Protocol

Canada ratified the Kyoto Protocol and agreed to lower emissions to 6% below 1990 levels. Since then, however, a new government was elected that opposes the protocol's high reduction rates. The government argues that they are impossible to meet. (Canada's greenhouse emissions have actually increased since the Kyoto Protocol was signed.)

Position on Resolution

- Canada is undecided about this resolution. Although its target reduction rate (8%) is similar to the Kyoto Protocol, it would have much longer to reduce its greenhouse gas emissions than under this resolution. In addition, it strongly supports the inclusion of developing nations in the resolution.

- On the other hand, Canada feels that the reduction rates are still too high. Meeting the reduction rate set out by this resolution would pose a serious economic hardship to Canada's industrial sector. This is because many of its factories operate on coal, a fossil fuel that emits large amounts of greenhouse gases.

Other Points to Consider

- Alberta, Canada's most industrial province, has threatened to ignore any emissions restrictions imposed by the government.

- Canada will sign this resolution only if the United States signs it. Otherwise, it worries that Canadian businesses will move to the United States to avoid emissions regulations that the Canadian government will have to impose.

Fold

PEOPLE'S REPUBLIC OF CHINA

Fold

People's Republic of China

Land area:
9,596,960 sq km

Population:
1,321,851,888

GDP per capita:
$7,800

Key export partners:
US 21%, Hong Kong 16%, Japan 10%, South Korea 5%, Germany 4%

Key import partners:
Japan 15%, South Korea 11%, Taiwan 11%, US 8%, Germany 5%

Source: *The World Factbook,* Central Intelligence Agency.

Position on Kyoto Protocol

China ratified the Kyoto Protocol. As a developing nation, China is exempt from lowering greenhouse gas emissions.

Position on Resolution

- China is adamantly opposed to this resolution. It insists that the prohibitive costs of imposing eco-friendly measures would be devastating to its economy. It believes it would force many industries out of business and result in massive unemployment.

- China asserts that the developed nations, who have been polluting for decades, should pay the brunt of addressing the global climate change issue. For that reason, China believes that developing nations should be exempt from lowering their greenhouse gas emissions.

Other Points to Consider

- Over the past decade, China has experienced an economic boom. It is one of the world's fastest-growing economies. However, the accompanying growth in automobile use, power generation (from coal), and industrial activity has resulted in massive greenhouse gas emissions. China recently surpassed the United States as the world's leading emitter of greenhouse gases.

- Many consider China—with its strong economy, massive military, and extensive trading network—to be an international superpower. China could use this status to pressure other countries not to sign this resolution.

FEDERAL REPUBLIC OF GERMANY

Fold

Federal Republic of Germany

Land area:
357,021 sq km

Population:
82,400,996

GDP per capita:
$31,900

Key export partners:
France 10%, US 9%,
UK 7%, Italy 7%,
Netherlands 6%

Key import partners:
Netherlands 12%,
France 9%, Belgium 8%,
Italy 6%, China 6%

Source: *The World Factbook*,
Central Intelligence Agency.

Position on Kyoto Protocol

Germany ratified the Kyoto Protocol and agreed to lower greenhouse gas emissions by 8%. Germany has already met its target under the Kyoto Protocol and plans to further lower its emissions.

Position on Resolution

- Germany supports this resolution. It believes that other nations should join the effort to address global climate change.

- Germany believes that developing nations should contribute to the worldwide effort to address global warming. However, it also recognizes that it is unrealistic to expect them to do so by 2025 and at such high reduction rates. For that reason, Germany would like to see an alternative set of reduction rates for developed and developing countries.

Other Points to Consider

- Germany is a member of the European Union. The EU has agreed that its member nations (such as the United Kingdom) will vote similarly on any UN resolution.

- Germany provides foreign aid to developing countries such as Bolivia, South Africa, and Zambia and may use this fact to pressure these countries.

Fold

UNITED KINGDOM of Great Britain and Northern Ireland

Fold ———

United Kingdom of Great Britain and Northern Ireland

Land area:
244,820 sq km

Population:
60,776,238

GDP per capita:
$31,800

Key export partners:
US 14%, Germany 11%, France 10%

Key import partners:
Germany 13%, US 9%, France 7%, Netherlands 7%, China 5%

Source: *The World Factbook,* Central Intelligence Agency.

Position on Kyoto Protocol

The United Kingdom ratified the Kyoto Protocol and agreed to lower greenhouse gas emissions by 8%. It recently pledged to cut greenhouse gas emissions by 60% by 2050 (compared with 1990 levels).

Position on Resolution

- Over the past decade, the United Kingdom has implemented eco-friendly measures in public transportation and industry. Meeting the requirements of this resolution will not negatively affect its economy.

- The United Kingdom realizes that without the support of key countries like the United States, China, and India, any worldwide effort to address climate change is futile.

- The United Kingdom believes that the target reductions in the resolution are too low to actually make a dent in global climate change. It would like to see an increase in the target reductions.

Other Points to Consider

- The United Kingdom is a member of the European Union. The EU has agreed that all EU nations (such as Germany) will vote similarly on any UN resolution.

- The United Kingdom provides foreign aid to developing countries like Bolivia, South Africa, and Zambia and may use this fact to pressure these countries to support its position on the resolution.

Fold ———

REPUBLIC OF INDIA

Fold

Republic of India

Land area:
3,287,590 sq km

Population:
1,129,866,154

GDP per capita:
$3,800

Key export partners:
US 17%, UAE 8%,
China 8%, UK 4%

Key import partners:
China 9%, US 6%,
Germany 5%,
Singapore 5%

Source: *The World Factbook,*
Central Intelligence Agency.

Position on Kyoto Protocol

India ratified the Kyoto Protocol. As a developing nation, India is exempt from lowering greenhouse gas emissions.

Position on Resolution

- India is strongly opposed to this resolution. It believes that developing nations should be exempt from lowering greenhouse gas emissions. India insists that the cost of imposing eco-friendly measures would be devastating to its economy, forcing many industries out of business and resulting in massive unemployment.

- India asserts that the developed nations, who have been polluting for decades, should pay the brunt of addressing the global climate change issue.

Other Points to Consider

- Over the past decade, India has experienced a huge economic boom. It is one of the world's fastest-growing economies. Economic growth has led to a large increase in energy demand. India relies heavily on coal-fired power plants, which are high greenhouse gas emitters. As a result of the country's rapid industrial growth, analysts expect India to be one of the world's top greenhouse gas emitters by 2025.

- China and the Philippines have similar positions on the resolution. They too have experienced rapid industrial growth over the past decade.

Fold

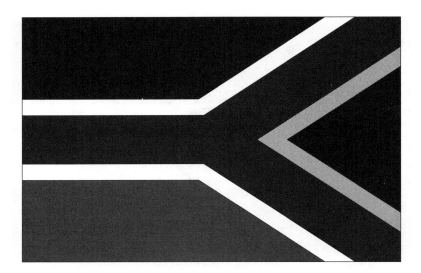

REPUBLIC OF SOUTH AFRICA

Fold

Republic of South Africa

Land area:
1,219,912 sq km

Population:
43,997,828

GDP per capita:
$13,300

Key export partners:
Japan 12%, US 12%, UK 9%, Germany 8%, Netherlands 5%

Key import partners:
Germany 13%, China 10%, US 8%, Japan 7%, Saudi Arabia 5%, UK 5%

Source: *The World Factbook,* Central Intelligence Agency.

Position on Kyoto Protocol

South Africa ratified the Kyoto Protocol. As a developing nation, South Africa is exempt from lowering its greenhouse gas emissions.

Position on the Resolution

- South Africa is strongly opposed to the resolution. It believes that developing countries should be exempt from lowering greenhouse gas emissions.

- Over the past decade, South Africa has experienced moderate growth, particularly in the mining and metalworking industries. South Africa's industries, as well as electricity for its citizens, are powered from burning coal. Coal is a fossil fuel that emits large amounts of greenhouse gases. Imposing limits on greenhouse gases would mean that South Africa would have to close down polluting industries and find alternative energy sources. This would result in massive layoffs and an economic slowdown.

Other Points to Consider

- The Philippines has a similar position on this resolution.

- South Africa is interested in securing foreign aid packages from developed countries like the United States, members of the European Union (such as the United Kingdom and Germany), Japan, and Australia.

Fold

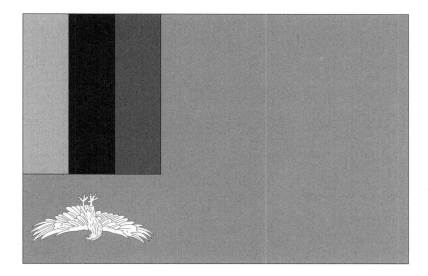

REPUBLIC OF ZAMBIA

Fold

Republic of Zambia

Land area:
752,614 sq km

Population:
11,477,447

GDP per capita:
$1,000

Key export partners:
Switzerland 38%,
South Africa 22%,
China, 10%, UK 8%,
Tanzania 6%

Key import partners:
South Africa 47%,
UAE 10%, Zimbabwe
6%, Norway 4%

Source: *The World Factbook,*
Central Intelligence Agency.

Position on Kyoto Protocol

Zambia ratified the Kyoto Protocol. As a developing nation, it is exempt from lowering greenhouse gas emissions.

Position on the Resolution

- Zambia is indifferent to the resolution. Since it is not an industrialized nation, Zambia emits low amounts of greenhouse gases. These are not projected to increase significantly in the near future.

- Zambia would like any subsidies in this resolution to be allocated solely to developing nations. Zambia's few power plants run on coal, which is a fossil fuel that emits high amounts of greenhouse gases. Zambia would use UN subsidies to make these plants more eco-friendly.

Other Points to Consider

- Zambia relies on foreign aid from the United States, members of the European Union (such as the United Kingdom and Germany), and Japan. For this reason, Zambia wants to make sure it does not alienate these countries during the General Assembly session.

- Zambia might be influenced to vote one way or the other in exchange for a beneficial foreign aid package from another nation.

Fold

JAPAN

Fold ——————————————————————————————————

Japan

Land area:
377,835 sq km

Population:
127,433,494

GDP per capita:
$33,100

Key export partners:
US 23%, China 13%,
South Korea 8%,
Taiwan 7%

Key import partners:
China 21%, US 12%,
Saudi Arabia 6%,
Australia 5%

Source: *The World Factbook,*
Central Intelligence Agency.

Position on Kyoto Protocol

Japan ratified the Kyoto Protocol and agreed to lower its greenhouse gas emissions by 6% by 2012. It is unlikely that Japan will meet its target reduction. Still, Japan continues to support the Kyoto Protocol, in part out of pride that it was signed in Japan.

Position on Resolution

- If pressured, Japan would support this resolution. However, it would prefer to see the target date extended to 2050.

- Japan still obtains some of its energy from coal-fired power plants. These plants emit high amounts of greenhouse gases. To meet the target reductions, Japan would need to convert these plants to nuclear power. It would like to use the UN funds in this resolution to do so.

- Japan agrees that developing nations should have to contribute to the worldwide effort to address global climate change.

Other Points to Consider

- Japan and China are economic and political rivals in Asia.

- Japan provides foreign aid to developing countries. It is the top provider of aid to the Philippines and may use this fact to pressure this country.

Fold ——————————————————————————————————

RUSSIAN FEDERATION

Fold

Russian Federation

Land area:
17,075,200 sq km

Population:
141,377,752

GDP per capita:
$12,200

Key export partners:
Netherlands 12%, Italy 9%, Germany 8%, China 5%, Ukraine 5%

Key import partners:
Germany 14%, China 10%, Ukraine 7%, Japan 6%, US 5%

Source: *The World Factbook,* Central Intelligence Agency.

Position on Kyoto Protocol

Russia ratified the Kyoto Protocol in 2004. Since Russia's emissions were calculated before the fall of the Soviet Union, when emissions were at their highest, Russia should have no problem meeting its reduction target.

Position on Resolution

- Russia is opposed to the resolution. It would prefer to stick with the Kyoto Protocol, as it would have a hard time lowering emissions based on the resolution's calculations.

- Russia still obtains much of its energy from coal-fired power plants. These plants emit high amounts of greenhouse gases. To meet the target reductions in this resolution, Russia would need to convert these plants to nuclear power. Russia insists that its economy is fragile and that it does not have the financial resources to meet these reductions without causing widespread factory closures and unemployment.

- Russia might consider signing this resolution if the target reduction rates were significantly lowered.

Other Points to Consider

- Over the past few years, Russia has forged a close political and economic relationship with China.

- Russia wants to remain in good standing with members of the European Union (such as the United Kingdom and Germany). This is because, in exchange for ratifying the Kyoto Protocol, the EU agreed to support Russia's admission into the World Trade Organization (WTO).

REPUBLIC OF ICELAND

Fold ───

Republic Of Iceland

Land area:
103,000 sq km

Population: 301,931

GDP per capita:
$38,000

Key export partners:
Netherlands 17%, UK 16%, Germany 15%, US 11%, Spain 6%

Key import partners:
US 13%, Germany 12%, Norway 7%, Sweden 7%, Denmark 6%, UK 5%, China 5%

Source: *The World Factbook,* Central Intelligence Agency.

Position on Kyoto Protocol

Iceland ratified the Kyoto Protocol. Although Iceland was actually allowed an increase of 10%, it has reduced its greenhouse gases by 4%.

Position on Resolution

- As the sponsor of this resolution, Iceland greatly supports all of its provisions. In particular, Iceland hopes that this resolution will force the world's largest greenhouse gas emitters—the United States, China, India, Japan, and Russia—to curb their emissions.

- Many Icelanders think that the target reduction rates in the resolution are too low. They have urged the government to increase the rates.

Other Points to Consider

- As an isolated island with a tiny population, Iceland is largely self-sufficient.

- Iceland is a leader in the effort to address global climate change. It obtains most of its energy from renewable geothermal and hydrogen sources.

- Iceland considers itself culturally aligned with Europe and tends to vote similarly with members of the European Union (such as the United Kingdom and Germany).

Fold ───

KINGDOM OF SAUDI ARABIA

Fold ——

Kingdom of Saudi Arabia

Land area:
2,149,690 sq km

Population:
27,601,038

GDP per capita:
$13,800

Key export partners:
Japan 18%, US 16%,
South Korea 10%,
China 7%, Taiwan 5%

Key import partners:
US 12%, Germany
9%, China 8%, Japan
7%, UK 5%, Italy 5%

Source: *The World Factbook,*
Central Intelligence Agency.

Position on Kyoto Protocol

- Saudi Arabia ratified the Kyoto Protocol. As a developing nation, it is exempt from lowering greenhouse gas emissions.

- Initially, Saudi Arabia was a vocal critic of the Kyoto Protocol. As one of the world's largest oil exporters, it stood to lose if developed countries reduced their dependence on oil. Saudi Arabia agreed to sign the Kyoto Protocol after being assured that fuel demand would remain high due to booming economies in nations like China and India.

Position on Resolution

- Saudi Arabia is strongly opposed to this resolution since it would no longer be exempt from reducing its own greenhouse gas emissions. Thus Saudi Arabia worries that this resolution would result in a dramatic decrease in world oil demand, causing the country's economy to plummet.

- Saudi Arabia would benefit from any amendment that would greatly reduce its own target rates as well as those of its key export partners.

Fold ——

REPUBLIC OF BOLIVIA

Fold

Republic of Bolivia

Land area:
1,098,580 sq km

Population:
9,119,152

GDP per capita:
$3,100

Key export partners:
Brazil 43%, US 12%,
Argentina 11%,
Colombia 8%,
Japan 6%, Peru 5%

Key import partners:
Brazil 25%, Argentina 19%, Chile 12%,
US 9%, Peru 7%

Source: *The World Factbook,*
Central Intelligence Agency.

Position on Kyoto Protocol

Bolivia ratified the Kyoto Protocol. As a developing nation, it is exempt from lowering greenhouse gas emissions.

Position on the Resolution

- Bolivia is undecided on the resolution. Since it is not an industrialized nation, Bolivia emits low amounts of greenhouse gasses. These are not projected to increase significantly in the near future.

- Bolivia would like any subsidies in this resolution to be allocated to developing nations only.

Other Points to Consider

- Bolivia relies on foreign aid from the United States, members of the European Union (such as the United Kingdom and Germany), and Japan. Bolivia will want to make sure not to alienate these countries during the General Assembly session.

- Bolivia might be influenced to vote one way or the other in exchange for a beneficial foreign aid package from any nation.

Fold

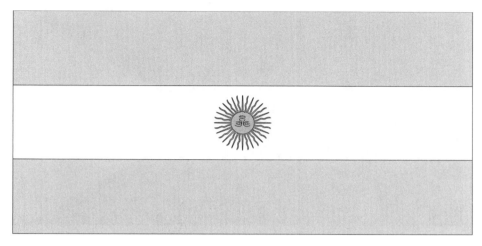

ARGENTINE REPUBLIC (ARGENTINA)

Fold

Argentine Republic (Argentina)

Land area:
2,766,890 sq km

Population:
40,301,927

GDP per capita:
$15,200

Key export partners:
Brazil 17%, Chile 9%, US 8%, China 7%

Key import partners:
Brazil 36%, US 15%, China 6%, Germany 5%

Source: *The World Factbook,* Central Intelligence Agency.

Position on Kyoto Protocol

Argentina ratified the Kyoto Protocol. As a developing nation, it is exempt from lowering greenhouse gas emissions. However, Argentina is a supporter of efforts to address global climate change. It has set voluntary reduction limits, which it plans to meet by 2012.

Position on Resolution

- Argentina is undecided about this resolution.

- On one hand, Argentina agrees that developing nations should contribute to a worldwide effort to reduce greenhouse gas emissions.

- On the other hand, Argentina feels it is unrealistic to expect developing nations to meet the target rates set out in the resolution. It would like to see a set of alternative target rates for developing nations, as well as a target date of at least 2050.

Other Points to Consider

Argentina is one of the wealthiest countries in South America. As such, it has significant influence on other South American countries.

Fold

REPUBLIC OF THE PHILIPPINES

Fold ———————————————————————————————————————

**Republic of
the Philippines**

Land area:
300,000 sq km

Population:
91,077,287

GDP per capita:
$5,000

Key export partners:
US 18%, Japan 17%,
Netherlands 10%,
China 10%,
Hong Kong 8%

Key import partners:
US 16%, Japan 14%,
Singapore 9%, Tai-
wan 8%, China 7%,
South Korea 6%

Source: *The World Factbook,*
Central Intelligence Agency.

Position on Kyoto Protocol

The Philippines ratified the Kyoto Protocol. As a developing nation, it is exempt
from lowering greenhouse gas emissions.

Position on the resolution

- The Philippines is strongly opposed
  to this resolution.

- The Philippines has experienced
  significant economic growth over
  the past decade, particularly in the
  electronics industry. However, the
  accompanying growth in automobile
  use, power generation (from coal), and
  industrial activity has resulted in an
  increase in greenhouse gas emissions.
  The country worries that reducing
  greenhouse gas emissions would
  lead to an economic slowdown and
  increased unemployment.

- The Philippines believes that it is the
  developed nations, who have been polluting for decades, who should pay the

brunt of addressing the global climate
change issue. For that reason, it believes that developing nations should
be exempt from this resolution.

Other Points to Consider

- Over the past decade, the Philippines
  has forged a close political and economic relationship with Japan.

- South Africa has a similar position on
  this resolution.

Fold ———————————————————————————————————————

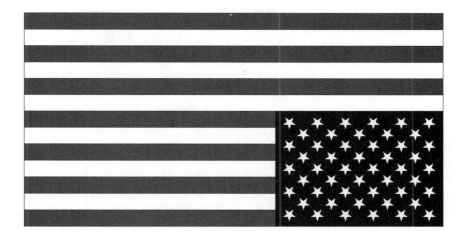

UNITED STATES OF AMERICA

Fold ——

**United States
of America**

Land area:
9,826,630 sq km

Population:
301,139,947

GDP per capita:
$43,500

Key export partners:
Canada 22%, Mexico 13%, Japan 6%, China 5%, UK 4%

Key import partners:
Canada 16%, China 16%, Mexico 10%, Japan 8%, Germany 5%

Source: *The World Factbook,*
Central Intelligence Agency.

Position on Kyoto Protocol

The United States did not ratify the Kyoto Protocol for these reasons:

- It felt that the emissions reduction targets were too high and would harm the U.S. economy.

- It felt that developing countries—particularly China and India—should have emissions restrictions as well.

Position on Resolution

- As currently written, the United States is opposed to this resolution. It believes that the target rates are too high and, if enforced, would pose a serious hardship to the U.S. economy and result in significant job loss.

- The United States could be convinced to sign the resolution if developing nations were held accountable for lowering emissions and target reduction rates were lowered.

Other Points to Consider

- The United States is one of the two largest emitters of carbon dioxide. For that reason, it received international criticism for not signing the Kyoto Protocol.

- The United States has been considered an international superpower for several decades due to its economic stability, strong military, and extensive trading network. The United States could use this status to pressure countries to support its stance.

Fold ——

Preparing for the General Assembly Session

Check off each step as you complete it.

☐ **Step 1: Review the documents.** Discuss the following questions with your partner. Record your answers in your notebook.

Draft Resolution

- How does the draft resolution differ from the Kyoto Protocol?

- According to the draft resolution, by what percentage would your country have to reduce emissions by 2025?

- Which countries will most likely support this resolution? Why? Which will most likely oppose this resolution? Why?

Position Card

- Did you sign the Kyoto Protocol? If not, why not?

- Are you a developed or a developing nation?

- Who are your key export and import partners? How might this affect your negotiations with these countries?

- What is your country's position on this resolution? Why?

☐ **Step 2: Write an amendment.** Write one amendment that will make the resolution more appealing to your country. An amendment can delete a clause, add words to an existing clause, or add a new clause. Write your amendment clearly and in 50 words or less. Some possible amendment topics:

- Reduce/increase the emissions reduction rates for all/some countries.

- Exempt some countries from reducing emissions.

- Set an earlier or later target date.

- Increase/decrease fines for noncompliance.

- Allocate UN financial aid to specific countries.

☐ **Step 3: Prepare your opening statement.**

- Your opening statement should be 1 minute or less.

- Your statement should include (1) the name of your country and whether you are a developed or a developing nation, (2) your overall position on the draft resolution, and (3) a description of your proposed amendment.

- Prepare a spokesperson to deliver the opening statement. He or she should refer to your country in the third person. For example, *China believes that this resolution is . . .*

☐ **Step 4: Set up a position table.** Create the table below in your notebook with rows for 16 countries. You will complete the table during the General Assembly session.

Country	Summarize this country's proposed amendment.	Do you agree with this country's proposed amendment?	Might this country support your amendment?

Conducting the General Assembly Session

☐ **Step 1: Participate in the opening ceremony.**

  a. Set up the General Assembly by arranging the desks in a large circle. Take a seat next to your partner.

  b. Create a placard by folding your position card so that your country name faces outward.

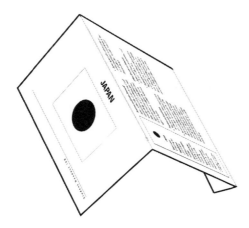

  c. The Chair will open the session by saying, *The United Nations General Assembly is now in session. We will begin with a roll call.* When called on, raise your placard and say, *Present.*

  d. The Chair will call on each country to deliver its opening statement. As other countries present their opening statements, complete your position table.

  e. After all countries have delivered their opening statements, the Chair will say, *We will now break to caucus.*

☐ **Step 2: Gain support for your amendment.**

  a. Review your position table to determine which countries you want to talk to.

  b. Walk around the room and meet with other countries to gain support for your amendment. In order for your amendment to be considered by the General Assembly, it must have a minimum of *four* signatories. In addition, your country may only sign *two* amendments (in addition to your own).

  c. Prepare arguments to support or oppose other countries' amendments.

  d. Submit all amendments to the Chair and be seated in the General Assembly.

☐ Step 3: Debate the resolution in the General Assembly.

    a. The Chair will read the first amendment aloud. Raise your placard if you want to comment on it. When recognized by the Chair, explain why your country supports or opposes the amendment.

    b. The Chair will call for a vote on the amendment by saying, *We will now vote on the amendment. All in favor, raise your placards. All opposed, raise your placards.*

    c. If the amendment passes (if two-thirds of countries vote in favor of it), insert the amendment into the appropriate part of your copy of the resolution.

    d. Continue this process for the remaining amendments or until the Chair announces that time for considering amendments has passed.

    e. The Chair will call for a 5-minute recess. Use this time to consult with your partner about your country's position on the resolution and to consult one last time with other countries.

    f. After the Chair reconvenes the meeting, raise your placard if you want to comment on the resolution as a whole. When recognized by the Chair, explain why your country supports or opposes the resolution. Continue debating until the Chair calls for a vote.

    g. The Chair will call for a vote on the resolution by saying, *We will now vote on the resolution. All in favor, raise your placards. All opposed, raise your placards.*

    h. The resolution passes if at least two-thirds of countries vote in favor of it.

Mastering the Content

1. Which of these human activities do scientists consider the main cause of recent global warming?
   A. burning fossil fuels
   B. cutting down forests
   C. building nuclear plants
   D. mining precious metals

2. In which of these UN organs or agencies does the United States hold veto power?
   A. World Bank
   B. Security Council
   C. General Assembly
   D. International Monetary Fund

3. *Sustainable development* is economic development that meets human needs without doing which of the following?
   A. using up resources needed in the future
   B. limiting the sovereignty of nation-states
   C. favoring wealthy nations over poor ones
   D. increasing extreme poverty in poor countries

4. In the phrase Geneva Conventions, the word *convention* refers to which of these?
   A. a traditional practice widely accepted around the world
   B. an amendment or addition to an international treaty
   C. a gathering of heads of state to discuss common issues
   D. an international agreement on matters of broad interest

5. The International Court of Justice handles which type of legal cases?
   A. disputes between one nation and another
   B. human rights violations such as child labor
   C. requests for military intervention in troubled areas
   D. charges against individuals for crimes against humanity

6. The Millennium Declaration was signed by leaders of 150 countries at a summit in 2000. What did this document do?
   A. defined the right to freedom of expression
   B. set specific goals to combat global poverty
   C. affirmed human equality regardless of race or religion
   D. agreed on sanctions against countries that threatened others

7. What did the nations that signed the Kyoto Protocol in 1997 agree to do?
   A. ensure the safety of ships at sea
   B. ban the use of chemical weapons
   C. reduce their greenhouse gas emissions
   D. provide troops for peacekeeping missions

8. Which organ of the United Nations has power to impose its decisions by force?
   A. Secretariat
   B. Security Council
   C. General Assembly
   D. Economic and Social Council

9. Which of these international organizations was formed on the basis of shared economic interests?
   A. International Criminal Court (ICC)
   B. International Atomic Energy Agency (IAEA)
   C. Association of Southeast Asian Nations (ASEAN)
   D. Organization of the Petroleum Exporting Countries (OPEC)

10. What is the purpose of the 1968 Nuclear Non-Proliferation Treaty?
    A. to stop the spread of nuclear weapons
    B. to solve the problem of storing nuclear waste
    C. to increase the safety of nuclear power plants
    D. to discourage the development of nuclear energy

Exploring the Essential Question

How effectively do international organizations respond to global issues?

Thousands of nongovernmental organizations (NGOs) are active in the world today. Four of them are listed in the table below. Use the information in the table to answer the questions that follow.

NGO	Goals/Concerns	Methods/Activities	Sample Action
Environmental Defense Fund	Use of science, law, and economics to solve environmental problems	• Work for the passage of environment-friendly laws • Bring lawsuits against polluters • Establish partnerships with businesses	Formed alliance with Pacific islanders to preserve coral reefs and fishing grounds
Human Rights Watch	Protection of human rights by exposing human rights violations	• Conduct fact-finding missions • Prepare research reports • Use diplomatic pressure to end human rights abuses	Conducted a campaign to cut off foreign aid to countries using children as soldiers
International Red Cross	Disaster response, disaster preparedness activities, and health care	• Provide emergency response to disasters • Help with long-term rebuilding efforts • Train volunteers	Brought food, shelter, and medical care to victims of a severe earthquake in Peru
Save the Children	Bringing about long-term improvement in the lives of children living in poverty	• Provide resources to poor families • Promote self-sufficiency • Support disaster victims	Built wells to provide clean drinking water for displaced families in Darfur, Sudan

1. Identify two NGOs in the table that pursue their goals through advocacy campaigns directed at governments. Discuss why that approach makes sense given each of the NGO's goals.

2. Identify the two NGOs in the table that focus on humanitarian work. Explain under what circumstances they might need to coordinate their efforts to be most effective.

3. Select the NGO in the table that you would most like to support. Explain your selection. Refer to both the organization's goals and its methods or activities in your explanation.

Chapter 3

27: Thucydides account of Pericles's "Funeral Oration Speech," at "Ancient History Sourcebook," Fordham Univ., www.fordham.edu. **28:** Cicero, *Des Officiis (On Duties),* translated by Walter Miller, at the Constitution Society, www.constitution.org. **29:** "Treasures in Full: Magna Carta Translation," at British Library, www.bl.uk. **30:** English Bill of Rights, 1689, at the British National Archives, www.nationalarchives.gov.uk. **31:** John Locke, *Two Treatises on Government,* at "Modern History Sourcebook," Fordham Univ., www.fordham.edu. **32:** Baron de Montesquieu, *The Spirit of the Laws,* 1748, at "Modern History Sourcebook," Fordham Univ. **33:** John Adams, "Thoughts on Government," 1776, at The Founders' Constitution, press-pubs.uchicago.edu/founders. **34:** Declaration of Independence, 1776.

Chapter 4

66: James Madison, *The Federalist* No. 64, Feb. 8, 1788, at Founding Fathers, www.foundingfathers.info/federalistpapers/.

Chapter 11

157, 159, 161, 163, 165, 167, 169, 171, 173: *Freshman Orientation,* Edward I. Sidlow, Washington, DC: CQ Press. Copyright © 2007 CQPress, a division of Congressional Quarterly Inc. Reprinted by permission.

Chapter 13

207: Franklin D. Roosevelt Presidential Library and Museum, www.fdrlibrary.marist.edu. **208:** Franklin D. Roosevelt, Mar. 5, 1933, at the National Archives, arcweb.archives.gov. **209:** Franklin D. Roosevelt Presidential Library. **210:** Franklin D. Roosevelt, "Proclamation No. 2038 Calling Congress into Extraordinary Session," Mar. 5, 1933, at the American Presidency Project, www.presidency.ucsb.edu. **211:** Franklin D. Roosevelt, "First Fireside Chat," Mar. 12, 1933, at the American Presidency Project. **212:** Franklin D. Roosevelt, Inaugural Address, Mar. 4, 1933, at the American Presidency Project. **214:** Lyndon Baines Johnson Library and Museum, National Archives and Records Administration, www.lbjlib.utexas.edu. **215:** Ibid. **216:** Ibid. **217:** Ibid. **219:** Nixon Presidential Library and Museum, nixon.archives.gov. **220:** Ibid. **221:** Richard M. Nixon, "Statement on Signing a Bill to Arbitrate Settlement of the West Coast Dock Strike," Feb. 21, 1972, at the American Presidency Project. **222:** Nixon Presidential Library and Museum. **224:** George Bush Presidential Library and Museum, bushlibrary.tamu.edu. **225:** American Presidency Project. **226:** George Bush Presidential Library. **227:** American Presidency Project.

Chapter 15

261: U.S. Court of Appeals for the Federal Circuit, at Georgetown Law Library, www.ll.georgetown.edu/federal/judicial/fed/. **262:** U.S. Supreme Court, at www.supremecourtus.gov. **263:** U.S. Department of Defense, at www.defenselink.mil. **264:** U.S. District Court, Middle District of Florida, Tampa Division, at TBO.com Special Reports, reports.tbo.com. **265:** U.S. Court of International Trade, at www.cit.uscourts.gov.

Chapter 17

293: George Washington, Farewell Address, 1796, at the Avalon Project, Yale Law School, www.yale.edu/lawweb/avalon/. Woodrow Wilson, Apr. 2, 1917, at History Matters, historymatters.gmu.edu. Harry S. Truman, Mar. 12, 1947, at Encyclopedia Britannica Online, www.britannica.com. George W. Bush, Sep. 20, 2001, at the White House, www.whitehouse.gov.

Chapter 18

295: Intergovernmental Panel on Climate Change, www.ipcc.ch.

Photographs

Cover: © Randy Santos/dcstockimages.com **i:** © Randy Santos/dcstockimages.com **95:** Jimmy Ellis/The Tennessean **153:** Getty Images **262:** © The New Yorker Collection 1974 Joseph Mirachi from cartoonbank.com. All Rights Reserved. **263:** AP Photo **266:** © Mike Baldwin, www.CartoonStock.com **279:** RF/TCI # 27

Art

7: QYA Design Studio **20:** QYA Design Studio **25:** QYA Design Studio **35:** Rosiland Solomon **36:** Rosiland Solomon **37:** Rosiland Solomon **38:** Rosiland Solomon **39:** Rosiland Solomon **40:** Rosiland Solomon **41:** Rosiland Solomon **42:** Rosiland Solomon **43:** Rosiland Solomon **44:** Rosiland Solomon **57:** QYA Design Studio **78:** QYA Design Studio **82:** QYA Design Studio **83:** QYA Design Studio **119:** QYA Design Studio **121:** QYA Design Studio **145:** QYA Design Studio **172:** Gary Undercuffler **175:** QYA Design Studio **179:** QYA Design Studio **181:** Phong Saechao **182:** Phong Saechao **183:** Phong Saechao **184:** Phong Saechao **185:** Phong Saechao **186:** Phong Saechao **188:** QYA Design Studio **199:** QYA Design Studio **235:** Gary Undercuffler **236:** Gary Undercuffler **237:** Gary Undercuffler **238:** Gary Undercuffler **239:** Gary Undercuffler **240:** Gary Undercuffler **241:** Gary Undercuffler **242:** Gary Undercuffler **243:** Gary Undercuffler **244:** Gary Undercuffler **245:** Gary Undercuffler **246:** Gary Undercuffler **247:** Gary Undercuffler **251:** QYA Design Studio **255:** QYA Design Studio **256:** QYA Design Studio **257:** QYA Design Studio **266:** QYA Design Studio **282:** QYA Design Studio **289:** QYA Design Studio **291:** QYA Design Studio **295:** QYA Design Studio